A Stanley Gibbons Thematic Catalogue

COLLECT SHIPS ON STAMPS

Peter Bolton

First Edition 1989

Stanley Gibbons Publications Ltd
London and Ringwood

By Appointment to Her Majesty The Queen
Stanley Gibbons Ltd., London
Philatelists

Published by **Stanley Gibbons Publications Ltd.**
Editorial, Sales Offices and Distribution Centre:
5 Parkside, Christchurch Road, Ringwood,
Hants BH24 3SH

First Edition – April 1989

© Stanley Gibbons Publications Ltd. 1989

ISBN: 0–85259–169–1

Item No. 2889 (89)

Printed in Great Britain by LR Printing Services, Crawley, West Sussex

Sea Fever

From earliest times mankind has had an urge to travel. The desire to see over the next hill was often thwarted by the intervening river, lake or sea and it was not very long before our ancestors were launching their rafts or dugout canoes to cross these obstacles.

Since that time water-borne transport has played an increasingly important part in the evolution of history. Once the focus of civilisation had shifted from the Middle East to the Mediterranean and then on to Western Europe the need for maritime travel became all-important. The galleys of Greece and Rome gave way to the Scandinavian longship and the rotund kogge. The caravels of Portugal and Spain, pushing the sea frontiers ever outwards, were subsequently challenged by the galleons of England, France and the Netherlands. Trade shaped the modern world; campaigns were fought to gain or protect it and colonial empires grew and were maintained in support of it. The absolute supremacy of the ship lasted for centuries and it is only in the last 50 years that it has given ground in the carriage of passengers and small valuable cargoes to the aeroplane.

Ships make a very early appearance in stamp designs. Virtually every type has been represented from dugout canoes to atomic submarines. It is possible through the stamp album to discover the New World with Columbus, break through the line at Trafalgar on H.M.S. *Victory,* race up Channel with a cargo of tea in the *Cutty Sark* or sail into San Carlos water on the *Canberra.*

It is no wonder that this is the largest theme so far covered in the Stanley Gibbons Thematic series. This first edition has been three years in preparation. Much additional work has been required to cope with its size, including an increase in format to A4. The final product has only been possible by the use of a Typecraft computer software system which, with the assistance of Pardy Printers of Ringwood, has enabled editorial and typesetting functions to be combined.

The use of this new system has been our own voyage of exploration and we hope that the result will be useful as a "chart" for collectors of ships on stamps.

David J. Aggersberg
Pam Basley

About This Book

This catalogue is a listing of stamps depicting ships and boats issued by countries throughout the world. It is based on the Stanley Gibbons *Stamps of the World Simplified Catalogue* published annually in two volumes (three volumes from 1990 edition). This first edition contains over 11,000 stamps which depict over 2,400 different named ships. It has been updated to include all ship and boat stamps that have appeared in *Gibbons Stamp Monthly* Catalogue Supplements up to and including the December 1988 issue.

What is Included

All issues, including overprints and surcharges, depicting ships and boats as listed in the *Stamps of the World Catalogue*. Miniature sheets are included where they contain designs different from those in the basic set.

What is Excluded

All stamp variations of watermark and perforation outside the scope of *Stamps of the World*. The list also omits designs showing symbolic or stylised ships or those where only a small part of the vessel is visible. Stamps listed as Appendix entries in *Stamps of the World* are treated in a similar manner in this catalogue.

Countries Section

This section lists in alphabetical order, with prices, the various countries and territories which have issued ship and boat stamps. Within each country the stamps are listed in chronological order with the year of issue and catalogue number taken from the *Stamps of the World Catalogue*.

Each vessel is identified by its name, if known, its type and, in appropriate instances, the name of a famous person connected with it.

For sailing ships the descriptions of naval vessels are based on their rate and those for merchantmen on the principal rig types:

Barque—three or more masts. Fore and aft sails on the mizzen-mast, square-rigged on the remainder.

Barquentine—three or more masts. Square-rigged on the foremast, fore and aft sails on the remainder.

Brig—two masts. Both square-rigged, but the mainmast also carries a fore-and-aft spanker sail.

Brigantine—two masts. Square-rigged on the foremast, fore and aft on the mainmast with square-rigged topsails above.

Full-rigged Ship—three or more masts. All square-rigged with the mizzen mast also carrying a fore and aft spanker sail.

Schooner—two or more masts. Rigged fore and aft. Some vessels of this type carried square-rigged topsails and are known as topsail schooners.

Index Section

This is divided into two parts with entries under name or by type. Each entry gives, in alphabetical order, country names and catalogue numbers of those stamps depicting that particular ship or type. Many ships have experienced changes of name or function, but the entries refer to the name and ship type depicted on the stamps concerned.

Acknowledgments

The compilation of this catalogue would have been made much more difficult without the help of the members of the Ship Stamp Society whose specialist knowledge has been invaluable.

To the many members at home and overseas who made available private checklists, loaned reference books and back numbers of *Log Book* or answered queries I owe a great deal and, of course, thanks are also due to David Aggersberg, Stanley Gibbons Catalogue Editor, and his staff who have transformed my listing into what we hope will be a useful reference book.

It is inevitable that in a work covering such a complex subject, spanning over 130 years of stamp issues, there will be omissions and controversial decisions as to ship identifications and categories. We would, of course, be grateful for any corrections or suggestions for a future edition.

Peter Bolton

Useful Books

There are many hundreds of books devoted to all aspects of shipping and it would be quite impossible to list all the different reference works, but the following have been of particular assistance in the editing of this catalogue.

British Warships and Auxiliaries (annual edition), M. Critchley. Maritime Books.

British Warships since 1945 (five volumes), M. Critchley or J. Worth (volume 4). Maritime Books.

Dictionary of Ship Types, A. Dudszus and E. Henriot. Conway Maritime Press.

Dreadnought, R. Hough. Michael Joseph.

Frigates, Sloops and Patrol Vessels of the Royal Navy 1900 to date, M. Cocker. Westmoreland Gazette.

Janes Merchant Ships. Janes Publishing.

Janes Fighting Ships. Janes Publishing.

Stamps and Ships, J. Watson. Faber.

Ships of the Royal Navy (revised edition), J. Colledge. Greenhill Books.

Ships on Stamps (various parts), E. Argyle. Picton Publishing.

The Last of the Windjammers (two volumes), B. Lubbock. Brown, Son & Fergusson.

The Author

Although having a general interest in all types of shipping Peter Bolton specialises in collecting stamps of the merchant sailing ships from the mid-19th century onwards with a particular interest in present day cadet ships, which are also a favourite subject for his other hobby of photography.

He lives near Preston and is employed by the National Institute of Agricultural Botany at their regional centre attached to the Lancashire College of Agriculture and Horticulture.

The Ship Stamp Society

The aims of the Society, which now has members in over twenty-three countries, are the advancement and study of ship stamps. The monthly illustrated magazine, *Log Book,* provides a medium for collectors to discuss their interests and to exchange and acquire material.

Local meetings are organised and a full week-end, at a venue of nautical interest, is held each Spring for the Annual General Meeting and a programme of visits and social events.

Membership details can be obtained from Mr T. Broadley, 33a Ridgeway Road, Timperley, Cheshire WA15 7HA.

Countings Section

Arrangement

The various countries and territories are listed in the same order as in *Stamps of the World*. Those few which are not in alphabetical order are covered by cross-references. Each entry includes the geographical location and details of the currencies used. The dates quoted against these currencies are those on which they were first used for stamps in this catalogue.

Illustrations

These are three-quarters of actual size. One design from each issue is depicted, but only those overprints and surcharges required for identification are included.

Listings

These are divided into years by dates and into individual issues by the illustrations.

For philatelic details the *Stamps of the World*, or the 22 volume standard catalogue, should be consulted.

A † against the catalogue number indicates an issue where unlisted stamps in the set depict designs other than ships.

Miniature sheets are indicated by a **MS** prefix.

Prices

Those in the left hand column are for unused stamps and those in the right hand column are for used.

Issues where all the designs depict ships are priced as sets only; single stamps and those from "broken" sets are priced individually.

Our prices are for stamps in fine average condition, and in issues where condition varies we may ask more for the superb and less for the sub-standard.

The prices of unused stamps are for lightly hinged examples for those issued before 1946, thereafter for unmounted mint.

Prices for used stamps refer to postally used examples, though for certain issues they may be for cancelled-to-order.

The minimum price quoted is 5p which represents a handling charge rather than a basis for valuing common stamps.

The prices quoted are generally for the cheapest variety of stamps but it is worth noting that differences of watermark, perforation, or other details, outside the scope of this catalogue, may often increase the value of the stamp.

All prices are subject to change without prior notice and we give no guarantee to supply all stamps priced. Prices quoted for albums, publications, etc. advertised in this catalogue are also subject to change without prior notice.

Guarantee

All stamps supplied by us are guaranteed originals in the following terms:

If not as described, and returned by the purchaser in the original transaction, we undertake to refund the price paid to us. If any stamp is certified as genuine by the Expert Committee of the Royal Philatelic Society, London, or by B.P.A. Expertising Ltd., the purchaser shall not be entitled to make any claim against us for any error, omission or mistake in such certificate.

Consumers' statutory rights are not affected by the above guarantee.

ABU DHABI

Arabian Peninsula
1000 fils = 1 dinar

1969

53†	60f Marine drilling platform	1.75	60
54†	125f Oil tanker	2.75	95

1971

77†	60f *Baniyas* (patrol boat)	1.40	40

ADEN

Arabian Peninsula
1937 16 annas = 1 rupee
1951 100 cents = 1 shilling

1937

1	½a Dhow		
2	9p Dhow		
3	1a Dhow		
4	2a Dhow		
5	2½a Dhow		
6	3a Dhow		
7	3½a Dhow		
8	8a Dhow		
9	1r Dhow		
10	2r Dhow		
11	5r Dhow		
12	10r Dhow		
	Set of 12	£225	£200

1939

18†	1a Liner at anchor	20	25
19†	1½a Dhow	50	75
21†	2½a Fishing boats, Mukalla	25	25
22†	3a H.M.S. *Volage* (frigate) and H.M.S. *Cruizer* (sloop) Aden, 1839	50	50
23†	8a Fishing boats, Mukalla	35	40
23a†	14a H.M.S. *Volage* and H.M.S. *Cruizer*, Aden, 1839	1.00	1.50
24†	1r Dhow	1.00	1.00
25†	2r Liner at anchor	3.75	1.75
27†	10r H.M.S. *Volage* and H.M.S. *Cruizer*, Aden, 1839	9.00	9.00

1949

As No. 115 of Antigua, but surch

33†	3a on 30c Paddle-steamer	75	90

1951

Nos. 18, 21/25 and 27 surch

36†	5c on 1a Liner at anchor	15	40
38†	15c on 2½a Fishing boats, Mukalla	20	75
39†	20c on 3a H.M.S. *Volage* and H.M.S. *Cruizer*, Aden, 1839	25	40
40†	30c on 8a Fishing boats, Mukalla	25	50
41†	50c on 8a Fishing boats, Mukalla	25	35
42†	70c on 14a H.M.S. *Volage* and H.M.S. *Cruizer*, Aden, 1839	45	65
43†	1s on 1r Dhow	45	45
44†	2s on 2r Liner at anchor	3.50	2.75
46†	10s on 10r H.M.S. *Volage* and H.M.S. *Cruizer*, Aden, 1839	11.00	7.50

1953

56†	35c Dhow	50	25
62†	1s Dhow building (brown and violet)	25	5
63†	1s Dhow building (black and violet)	25	5
71†	20s European ships, Aden, 1572 (brown and lilac)	7.50	14.00
72†	20s European ships, Aden, 1572 (black and lilac)	20.00	10.00

1954

As No. 62 but inscr "Royal Visit 1954"

73	1s Dhow building	25	25

ADEN PROTECTORATE STATES

Arabian Peninsula
1946 16 annas = 1 rupee
1955 100 cents = 1 shilling
1966 100 fils = 1 dinar

Kathiri State of Seiyun

1946

As No. 115 of Antigua, but surch

17†	3a on 30c Paddle-steamer	50	65

1966

92†	10f Fishing boat, Antibes	80	15

Qu'aiti State in Hadhramaut

1949

As No. 115 of Antigua, but surch

17	3a on 30c Paddle-steamer	60	80

1955

38†	2s Dhow building	80	80

1963

As No. 38 but with portrait of Sultan Awadh bin Saleh el Qu'aiti

50†	2s Dhow building	1.00	1.00

1966

*No. 50 surch **SOUTH ARABIA** in English and Arabic*

62†	100f on 2s Dhow building	45	75

AEGEAN ISLANDS

Mediterranean
100 centesimi = 1 lira

1929

18†	10c Galley of Knights of St. John	5	5

1930

*No. 18 optd **XXI Congresso Idrologico***

35†	10c Galley of Knights of St. John	45	1.50

1931
No. 18 optd **1931 CONGRESSO EUCARISTICO ITALIANO**
57† 10c Galley of Knights of St. John 20 75

1934
Nos. 436/7 of Italy optd **ISOLE ITALIANE DELL'EGEO**
169† 50c Naval launch..................... 8.00 15.00
170† 75c Naval launch..................... 8.00 15.00

1938
No. 513 of Italy optd **ISOLE ITALIANE DELL'EGEO**
193† 11i25 Roman galley 35 75

1943
No. 18 surch **CENT. 10 PRO ASSISTENZA**
215† 10c + 10c Galley of Knights of St. John 8 15

1944
No. 18 surch **L 3 PRO SINISTRATI DI GUERRA** and symbol
225† 10c + 3li Galley of Knights of St. John 12 30

AITUTAKI
South Pacific
100 cents = 1 dollar

1984

114† 1c H.M.S. *Bounty* and Bligh 20 15
115† 1c H.M.S. *Bounty*..................... 20 15
116† 5c H.M.S. *Bounty* and Bligh 40 20
118† 8c H.M.S. *Resolution* and Cook 50 25

Designs as Nos. 114/18, but inscr "AIR MAIL"
123† 10c H.M.S. *Bounty* and Bligh............ 60 20
124† 10c H.M.S. *Bounty* 60 20
125† 25c H.M.S. *Bounty* and Bligh............ 75 40
127† 30c H.M.S. *Resolution* and Cook 75 40

1976

191† 35c Sailing yachts 50 30

No. 191 optd **ROYAL VISIT JULY 1976**
196† 35c Sailing yachts 70 55

1977

225† 25c H.M.S. *Bounty* 85 55

1978

249† 50c Figurehead of H.M.S. *Resolution*
(Cook) 80 65

1979

267† 75c H.M.S. *Resolution* and H.M.S.
Adventure (Cook) 1.10 95

1984

504† 60c H.M.S. *Bounty* 50 55
505† 96c H.M.S. *Bounty* 80 85

AJMAN
Arabian Peninsula
1965 100 naye paise = 1 rupee
1967 100 dirhams = 1 riyal

1965

32† 1r Sailing yacht 45 30
35† 3r Sailing yacht 1.40 1.10

No. 35 optd **PAN ARAB GAMES CAIRO 1965**
49† 3r Sailing yacht 1.60 1.60

1967

139† 5d *Brasil* (liner)....................... 10 5
140† 15d *Yankee* (sail training and cruise
ship) 15 5
148† 10r *Brasil* (liner) 4.25 1.00

ALAND ISLANDS
Northern Europe
100 penni = 1 markka

1984

1† 10p Local fishing boat 5 5
2† 20p Local fishing boat 5 5
3† 50p Local fishing boat 5 5
5† 1m10 Local fishing boat 35 5
6† 1m20 Local fishing boat 35 5
7a† 1m30 Local fishing boat 50 5

16† 2m *Pommern* (barque) and modern car
ferries 2.00 2.00

1988

30 1m80 Mail sailing boat, Eckero 55 55

32 1m80 *Albanus* (Baltic galeass)
33 2m40 *Ingrid* (schooner)
34 11m *Pamir* (barque)
Set of 3 3.00 3.00

ALBANIA
South-east Europe
1957 leks
1965 100 qint = 1 lek

1957

600 2lek50 *Aurora* (Russian cruiser)
601 5lek *Aurora* (Russian cruiser)
602 8lek *Aurora* (Russian cruiser)
Set of 3 2.50 2.50

1964

848† 7lek Olympic yacht 75 40

1965

964 10q *Teuta* (freighter)
965 20q Punt
966 30q 19th-century sailing ship
967 40q 18th-century brig
968 50q *Vlore* (freighter)
969 1lek Illyrian galliots
Set of 6 5.50 1.75

1967

1126† 65q Fishing boat, Saranda 1.50 45

1968

1257† 25q Sailor and naval craft 55 12

1972

1533† 80q *Tirana* (freighter) 60 12

1975

1752† 15q Ferry carrying men and horse 10 5

1977

1875† 25q Fishing boat 15 5

1980

2059† 2lek40 *Tirana* (freighter) 1.40 85

ALDERNEY

See under Guernsey

ALGERIA

North Africa
1930 100 centimes = 1 franc
1964 100 centimes = 1 dinar

1930

106 10f *Provence* (sailing ship) in Bay of
Algiers 9.00 10.00

1939

159 20c *Extavia* (freighter)
160 40c *Extavia* (freighter)
161 90c *Extavia* (freighter)
162 1f25 *Extavia* (freighter)
163 2f25 *Extavia* (freighter)
Set of 5 6.50 2.50

1949

288 10f + 15f *Richelieu* (French battleship)
289 18f + 22f *Arromanches* (French aircraft
carrier)
Set of 2 6.00 7.50

1957

No. 1322 of France optd **ALGERIE**
371 12f + 3f 18th-century felucca 50 60

1970

550 30c Freighter 30 15

1981

807 60c 17th-century galley
808 1d60 17th-century xebec
Set of 2 95 55

ANGOLA

South-west Africa
1913 100 centavos = 1 escudo
1949 100 centavos = 1 angolar
1954 100 centavos = 1 escudo

1913

Surch **REPUBLICA ANGOLA** *and value in figures*
(a) On Nos. 1, 2, 5 and 7 of Portuguese Colonies
181† ¼c on 2½r Departure of Vasco da Gama's
fleet 40 30
182† ¼c on 5r Vasco da Gama's fleet at
Calicut 40 30
185† 5c on 50r *Sao Gabriel* (flagship) 40 30
187† 10c on 100r *Sao Gabriel* 75 50
(b) On Nos. 104, 105, 108 and 110 of Macao
189† ¼c on ½a Departure of Vasco da Gama's
fleet 70 60
190† ¼c on 1a Vasco da Gama's fleet at
Calicut 70 60
193† 5c on 8a *Sao Gabriel* (flagship).......... 50 45
195† 10c on 16a *Sao Gabriel* 95 60

(c) On Nos. 58, 59, 62 and 64 of Timor
197† ¼c on ½a Departure of Vasco da Gama's
fleet 70 60
198† ¼c on 1a Vasco da Gama's fleet at
Calicut 70 60
201† 5c on 8a *Sao Gabriel* (flagship).......... 50 45
203† 10c on 16a *Sao Gabriel* 90 60

1949

450 1a *Tentativa Feliz* (19th-century sailing
ship)
451 4a *Tentativa Feliz* (19th-century sailing
ship)
Set of 2 12.00 1.25

1967

658 1e *Don Carlos I* (Portuguese cruiser)
659 2e50 *Mindelo* (Portuguese sail/steam
corvette)
Set of 2 75 20

1968

676† 2e50 Cabral's fleet 50 10

1969

678 2e50 *Loge* (Portuguese gunboat) 45 12

1970

696† 1e50 Mailships *Infante Dom Henrique*
and *Principe Perfeito* 25 8

1972

704	1e 16th-century galleon	15	5

705	50c Sailing yachts	10	9

ANGUILLA

West Indies
100 cents = 1 dollar

1967

No. 138 *of St. Kitts-Nevis optd* **INDEPENDENT ANGUILLA** *and bar*

10†	20c Boat building	75.00	12.00

1968

32	10c Yachts
33	15c Boat on the beach
34	25c *Warspite* (schooner)
35	40c *Atlantic Star* (schooner)

Set of 4	1.40	75

1969

51†	40c Punt on salt pond	20	15

1970

84†	1c Boat building	5	10

1971

112	10c *Magnanime* and *Amiable* (ships of the line)

113	15c H.M.S. *Duke, Glorieux* and H.M.S. *Agamemnon* (ships of the line)	
114	25c H.M.S. *Formidable*, H.M.S. *Namur* and *Ville de Paris* (ships of the line)	
115	40c H.M.S. *Canada* (ship of the line)	
116	50c H.M.S. *St. Albans* and wreck of *Hector* (ships of the line)	

Set of 5	4.75	4.75

Nos. 112/16 were issued in horizontal *se-tenant* strips to form a composite design of a sea battle.

1972

133†	4c Ferry at Blowing Point	15	15
140†	40c Boat building	1.50	1.50

145	25c *Malcolm Miller* (cadet ship)
146	40c *Malcolm Miller* (cadet ship)

Set of 2	1.90	3.50

1973

159†	1c *Santa Maria* (Columbus)	5	5

1974

195†	1c Island rowing boat	5	5

1975

213†	$1 Boston Tea Party ships	40	40

1976

Nos. 133 *and* 140 *optd or surch* **NEW CONSTITUTION 1976**

226†	3c on 40c Boat building	15	20
227†	4c Ferry at Blowing Point	15	20
228†	5c on 40c Boat building	15	20
235†	40c Boat building	45	60

255	1c French ships approaching Anguilla, 1796
256	3c Sailing boat leaving Anguilla to fetch help, 1796
257	15c Capture of *Le Desius*, 1796,
258	25c *La Vaillante* aground, 1796
259	$1 H.M.S. *Lapwing* (frigate), 1796
260	$1.50 *Le Desius* burning, 1796

Set of 6	4.25	4.25

1977

269†	25c H.M.S. *Minerva* (frigate)	20	15
270†	40c Launch from Royal Yacht *Britannia* ..	25	20

283†	22c Lobster fishing boat...............	35	35
284†	35c Island dinghies................	40	35

Nos. 269/70 *optd* **ROYAL VISIT TO WEST INDIES**

298†	25c H.M.S. *Minerva* (frigate)	20	15
299†	40c Launch from Royal Yacht *Britannia* ..	25	25

1978

Nos. 283/4 *optd* **VALLEY SECONDARY SCHOOL 1953-1978**

325†	22c Lobster fishing boat...............	20	20
326†	35c Island dinghies................	30	30

1980

Nos. 283/4 *optd* **SEPARATION 1980**

432†	22c Lobster fishing boat...............	25	25
434†	35c Island dinghies................	30	30

1981

449	22c Ships in Nelson's Dockyard
450	35c Ships on which Nelson served
451	50c H.M.S. *Victory* (Nelson)
452	$3 Battle of Trafalgar

Set of 4	2.00	2.00

1982

486†	5c Ferries at Blowing Point.............	15	5
487†	10c Island dinghies................	15	5
489†	20c Launching boat, Sandy Point........	20	10

| 517† | 75c Scout yacht | 75 | 65 |

No. 487 *optd* **COMMONWEALTH GAMES 1982**
| 530† | 10c Island dinghies | 10 | 10 |

1983
No. 487 *optd* **150th ANNIVERSARY ABOLITION OF SLAVERY ACT**
| 573† | 10c Island dinghies | 5 | 8 |

1984
Nos. 486/7 *optd* **U.P.U. CONGRESS HAMBURG 1984** *or surch also*
| 625 | 5c Ferries at Blowing Point | 5 | 5 |
| 626 | 20c on 10c Island dinghies | 12 | 15 |

1985
No. 486 *optd* **GIRL GUIDES 75TH ANNIVERSARY 1910-1985**
| 676 | 5c Ferries at Blowing Point | 5 | 5 |

690	10c *Danmark* (cadet ship)		
691	20c *Eagle* (cadet ship)		
692	60c *Amerigo Vespucci* (cadet ship)		
693	75c *Sir Winston Churchill* (cadet ship)		
694	$2 *Nippon Maru* (cadet ship)		
695	$2.50 *Gorch Fock* (cadet ship)		
	Set of 6	4.25	4.25

No. 487 *optd* **80TH ANNIVERSARY ROTARY 1985**
| 697 | 10c Island dinghies | 5 | 5 |

1986

| 704† | $4 Mississippi riverboat | 2.25 | 2.25 |

734	10c Trading sloop		
735	45c *Lady Rodney* (cargo liner)		
736	80c *West Derby* (19th-century sailing ship)		
737	$3 *Warspite* (sloop)		
	Set of 4	2.25	2.25
MS738	$6 Island dinghies	3.75	4.00

| 741† | 35c *Santa Maria* (Columbus) | 30 | 30 |

COLLECT RAILWAYS ON STAMPS
A Stanley Gibbons thematic catalogue on this popular subject. Copies available at £7.50 (p. + p. £2) from: Stanley Gibbons Publications Ltd, 5 Parkside, Christchurch Road, Ringwood, Hants BH24 3SH.

1987

| 753† | 80c Previous sailing ferry and new motor ferry, Blowing Point | 35 | 40 |

1988

| 798† | 45c Sailboard | 20 | 25 |

ANTIGUA
West Indies
1932 12 pence = 1 shilling
20 shillings = 1 pound
1951 100 cents = 1 dollar

1932

87†	6d H.M.S. *Victory* (Nelson)	11.00	14.00
88†	1s H.M.S. *Victory* (Nelson)	14.00	22.00
89†	2s6d H.M.S. *Victory* (Nelson)	40.00	48.00
90†	5s Sir Thomas Warner's *Concepcion*, 1632	80.00	£110

1949

| 115† | 3d Paddle-steamer | 90 | 75 |

1962

142	3c *Solent* (paddle-steamer)		
143	10c *Solent* (paddle-steamer)		
144	12c *Solent* (paddle-steamer)		
145	50c *Solent* (paddle-steamer)		
	Set of 4	1.00	80

1967

| 208† | 4c 17th-century settlers' ship | 10 | 5 |
| 210† | 25c 17th-century settlers' ship | 15 | 15 |

1968

| 218† | 25c Yachts | 15 | 5 |

221	2c Ships in old harbour St. Johns, 1768		
222	15c Ships in old harbour St. Johns, 1829		
223	25c Freighter and chart of new harbour		
224	35c New harbour		
225	$1 Ships in old harbour, 1768		
	Set of 5	1.25	70

1969

| 230† | 4c Freighter | 5 | 5 |
| 231† | 15c Freighter | 12 | 10 |

1970

269	½c War canoe		
270	1c *Nina* (Columbus)		
271	2c Sir Thomas Warner's *Concepcion*		
325	3c Viscount Hood and H.M.S. *Barfleur* (ship of the line)		
326	4c Sir George Rodney and H.M.S. *Formidable* (ship of the line)		
274	5c Nelson and H.M.S. *Boreas* (frigate)		
275	6c William IV and H.M.S. *Pegasus* (frigate)		
329	10c Blackbeard and pirate ketch		
330	15c Collingwood and H.M.S. *Pelican* (sloop)		
278	20c Nelson and H.M.S. *Victory*		
279	25c *Solent* (paddle-steamer)		
280	35c George V and H.M.S. *Canada* (screw corvette)		
281	50c H.M.S. *Renown* (battle cruiser)		
282	75c *Federal Maple* (freighter)		
283	$1 *Sol Quest* (yacht)		
333	$2.50 H.M.S. *London* (destroyer)		
285	$5 *Pathfinder* (tug)		
	Set of 17	26.00	22.00

1972

| 345† | 35c Yachts | 20 | 10 |
| 346† | 50c Yachts | 35 | 30 |

1974

| 387† | 1c *Orinoco* (mail steamer) | 5 | 5 |
| 388† | 2c Hydrofoil | 5 | 5 |

1975

No. 282 surch

425† $10 on 75c *Federal Maple* (freighter) 7.50 11.00

427 5c Carib war canoe
428 15c Ship of the line, 1770
429 35c H.M.S. *Boreas* (frigate), 1787, and Nelson
430 50c Yachts
431 $1 Yachts
                    Set of 5   2.40   2.00

440† 20c Galleon, 1775 .... 20 10

1976

492† $1 *Montgomery* (privateer) 1.25 85
493† $5 *Ranger* (privateer sloop) 4.00 4.00

504† 1c Sailing dinghies 5 5
506† 20c Game-fishing boat 12 12

524† $2 *Freelance* (yacht) 2.25 2.25

1977

540† $2 Scout raft......................... 1.50 1.75

1978

576 10c Yacht regatta
577 50c Fishing and work boat race
578 90c Yacht race
579 $2 Power boat race
                    Set of 4   2.10   2.00
MS580 $2.50 Guadeloupe–Antigua yacht race........................... 1.90 2.50

1979

623† 50c H.M.S. *Endeavour* (Cook) 65 50
MS626† $2.50 H.M.S. *Resolution* (Cook) 1.90 2.25

1981

715† 90c Sailing dinghy 65 65

1984

830 45c *Booker Vanguard* (freighter)
831 50c *Canberra* (liner)
832 60c Sailing boats
833 $4 *Fairwind* (liner)
                    Set of 4   4.50   4.00
MS834 $5 18th-century English man-o-war 3.50 4.00

1985

911† $1 Statue of Liberty and cadet ship 60 60
MS913† $5 Liner and New York skyline........ 3.00 3.25

944† $3 Windsurfing......................... 1.60 1.75

967† $4 Royal Yacht *Britannia* 3.25 3.50

1986

1009 30c Tug
1010 60c Game-fishing boat
1011 $1 Yacht
1012 $4 Lugger
                    Set of 4   3.50   3.50
MS1013 $5 Boat building.................... 3.00 3.50

1987

1072 30c *Canada I* (yacht), 1981
1073 60c *Gretel II* (yacht), 1970
1074 $1 *Sceptre* (yacht), 1958
1075 $3 *Vigilant* (yacht), 1893
                    Set of 4   2.75   2.75
MS1076 $5 *Australia II* defeating *Liberty* (yachts), 1983 .... 2.75 3.00

1100† 10c *Spirit of Australia* (powerboat), 1978 .... 5 8
1102† 30c U.S.S. *Triton* (submarine), 1960 .... 12 15
1104† 60c U.S.S. *New Jersey* (battleship), 1942 .... 25 30
1106† 90c *United States* (liner), 1952 .... 40 45
1109† $3 *Queen Elizabeth 2* (liner), 1969 ...... 1.40 1.50

1988

1172† 10c Fleet of Columbus, 1493 .... 5 8
1173† 30c Fleet of Columbus off Indian village 12 15
1174† 45c *Santa Mariagalante* (Columbus), 1493 .... 20 25
1175† 60c Painos Indian canoe, 1493 .... 25 30
1177† $1 Fleet of Columbus and ship's boat, 1493 .... 45 50
1178† $3 Fleet of Columbus at anchor, 1493 .. 1.40 1.50
1179† $4 Fleet of Columbus at sea, 1493 ...... 1.75 1.90

1190 30c Two yachts rounding buoy
1191 60c Three yachts
1192 $1 British yacht under way
1193 $3 Three yachts
                    Set of 4   1.90   2.25
MS1194 $5 Two yachts 2.25 2.40

ARGENTINE REPUBLIC

South America
100 centavos = 1 peso

1892

219 2c Columbus's fleet
220 5c Columbus's fleet
                    Set of 2   20.00   8.50

1902

290   5c Ships in Port Rosario 5.50   2.00

1933

635   3c Harbour scene, La Plata   50   25

1939

670   5c *President Sarmiento* (cadet ship)   20   8

1944

735   5c Liner, warship and yacht   15   5

1947

791   5c Ship in the Antarctic
792   20c Ship in the Antarctic
                                    Set of 2   70   15

795   5c *President Sarmiento* (cadet ship)   15   5

1948

MS808a   85c Sailing ship, 1767
MS808b   1p20 Sailing ship, 1798
                        Price for 2 sheets   13.00   13.00
Nos. MS808a/b each contain three other designs.

1951

829†   25c *President Peron* (liner)   35   10

1953

855   50c *Uruguay* (sail/steam gunboat)   40   5

1954

868†   50c Tug and liner, Buenos Aires
            (33 × 22 *mm*)   25   5
869†   50c Tug and liner, Buenos Aires
            (32 × 21 *mm*)   30   5

1957

900†   40c *Hercules* (sail frigate)   15   5
902†   60c *Zefiro* and *Nancy* (sail warships) at
            Battle of Montevideo (air)   25   5

1958

916†   40c + 20c River ferry   45   20

933†   80c Paddle-steamer, Buenos Aires, 1858   25   5

1960

990   1p Galleon
991   5p Galleon
992   1p80 Galleon (air)
993   10p70 Galleon
                                    Set of 4   1.50   55

1961

1007   2p *America* at Battle of San Nicolas,
            1810   20   5

1963

1093   4p *La Argentina* (sail frigate)   30   5

1964

1116†   11p + 5p Sailing yacht   65   65

1965

1127†   4p *General San Martin* (ice-breaker)   70   25

1146   8p *Mimosa* (sail merchantman)   30   5

1966

1161†   8p River boats, San Fernando   35   8

1967

1200   20p *Invincible* (schooner)   85   5

1211   20p *General Brown* (cadet ship)   85   5

1968

1224   20p *Libertad* (cadet ship)   85   5

1226   68p *Legh II* (yacht) 50   20

1236   20p *Lynch* (coastguard cutter) 30   5

1969

1247   20p *Hercules* (sail frigate) 80   5

1970

1298   20c *Juliet* (naval schooner) 1.00   5

1344   26c San Martin and Liberation fleet,
        1820 90   5

1971

1364   25c *Carmen* (sloop) 1.50   5

1972

1397   25c *Libertad* (liner) 30   5

1400   25c *Santisima Trinidad* (brigantine), 1815   90   5

1404   25c *President Sarmiento* (cadet ship)   80   5

1973

1425   70c *La Argentina* (sail frigate)   65   5

1974

1449†   4p50 Freighter and barge, General
         Belgrano Bridge 2.75   30

1452   1p20 *Belgrano* (brigantine)   80   10

1975

1472†   2p *Luisito* (naval cutter) in the Antarctic   55   5

1479   6p *25 de Mayo* (sail frigate)   45   10

1976

1514   6p *Heroina* (sail frigate)   35   8

1521   12p *Rio de la Plata* (schooner)   40   5

1977

1562†   60p + 30p Old and modern ships 1.10   85

1565   30p *Sarandi* (schooner)   40   10

1978

1584†   100p Barges   45   8

1609   100p Push-pull tug
1610   200p *Legador* (tug)
1611   300p *Rio Parana Mini* (tug)
1612   400p *Ciudad de Parana* (river passenger
        ship)
                          Set of 4   2.40   70

1979

1640   250p *Uruguay* (sail/steam gunboat)......   45   15

1642   250p *Comodoro Rivadavia*
        (hydrographic survey ship)   45   15

1646   400p + 400p *Magdalena* (caravel)
1647   500p + 500p Three-masted sailing ship
1648   600p + 600p *Descubierta* (corvette)
1649   1500p + 1500p *Fortuna* (yacht)
                              Set of 4 27.00 22.00

1662   1000p Oil rig 2.75   55

MS1663   250p + 250p Paddle-steamer (on Buenos Aires stamp No. P4); 1000p + 1000p Columbus's fleet (on No. 220) 12.00   12.00
No. MS1663 also contains two other designs

1980

1675   500p *La Argentina* (sail frigate)   75   30

1676   500p *Villarino* (merchantman), 1880   75   30

1981

1702†   2000p *Almirante Irizar* (ice-breaker) 2.50   95

1719   1300p 15th-century caravel   35   20

No. 1719 *optd* **CURSO SUPERIOR DE ORGANIZACION DE SERVICIOS FILATELICOS–UPAE BUENOS AIRES–1981**
1724   1300p 15th-century caravel   35   20

1982

1770   3000p + 1500p Fishing boat   40   25

1984

1866†   5p + 2p50 *Nina* (Columbus)   70   15
1867†   5p + 2p50 *Pinta* (Columbus)   70   15
1868†   5p + 2p50 *Santa Maria* (Columbus)   70   15

1891†   20p *Parana* (sail/steam corvette)   40   25

1987

2075†   50c Yachts   20   15

OFFICIAL STAMP

1985
No. 868 optd **S. OFICIAL**
O879   50c Tug and liner, Buenos Aires   15   5

ASCENSION

South Atlantic
1924 12 pence = 1 shilling
20 shillings = 1 pound
1971 100 pence = 1 pound

1924

10   ½d *London* (East Indiaman)
11   1d *London* (East Indiaman)
12   1½d *London* (East Indiaman)
13   2d *London* (East Indiaman)
14   3d *London* (East Indiaman)
15   4d *London* (East Indiaman)
15d   5d *London* (East Indiaman)
16   6d *London* (East Indiaman)
17   8d *London* (East Indiaman)
18   1s *London* (East Indiaman)
19   2s *London* (East Indiaman)
20   3s *London* (East Indiaman)
                           Set of 12 £225 £300

1949
As No. 115 *of Antigua*
53   4d Paddle-steamer 3.00   1.40

1969

121   4s Crest of H.M.S. *Rattlesnake* (minesweeper)
122   9d Crest of H.M.S. *Weston* (sloop)
123   1s9d Crest of H.M.S. *Undaunted* (destroyer)
124   2s3d Crest of H.M.S. *Eagle* (aircraft carrier)
                             Set of 4 3.50 1.10

1970

130   4d Crest of H.M.S. *Penelope* (frigate)
131   9d Crest of H.M.S. *Carlisle* (cruiser)
132   1s6d Crest of H.M.S. *Amphion* (submarine)
133   2s6d Crest of H.M.S. *Magpie* (sloop)
                             Set of 4 5.00 3.25

1971

140†   3½p 18th-century ship and Harrison's chronometer   55   45

149   2p Crest of H.M.S. *Phoenix* (submarine)
150   4p Crest of H.M.S. *Milford* (sloop)
151   9p Crest of H.M.S. *Pelican* (sloop)
152   15p Crest of H.M.S. *Oberon* (submarine)
                             Set of 4 4.50 2.40

1972

154   1½p Crest of H.M.S. *Lowestoft* (frigate)
155   3p Crest of H.M.S. *Auckland* (sloop)
156   6p Crest of H.M.S. *Nigeria* (cruiser)
157   17½p Crest of H.M.S. *Bermuda* (cruiser)
                             Set of 4 3.75 4.50

160† 4p *Quest* (polar vessel) 1.10 90
161† 7½p *Quest* (polar vessel) 1.25 1.00

1973

166 2p Crest of H.M.S. *Birmingham* (destroyer)
167 4p Crest of H.M.S. *Cardiff* (destroyer)
168 9p Crest of H.M.S. *Penzance* (sloop)
169 13p Crest of H.M.S. *Rochester* (sloop)
         Set of 4 11.50 5.00

1975

195† 2p H.M.S. *Peruvian* and H.M.S. *Zenobia*, (sloops), 1815 . . . . 35 25

1976

217† 25p *Southampton Castle* (liner) 50 60

1979

242† 3p H.M.S. *Resolution* (Cook) 45 25

249† 3p Cable ship 12 12
250† 8p *Anglia* (cable ship) 25 25
252† 15p *Seine* (cable ship) 35 35

256† 12p *London* (East Indiaman) (on stamp No. 20) 25 30

1980

264 8p 17th-century sailing ship
265 12p 19th-century sailing ship
266 15p *Garthcastle II* (merchantman), 1863
267 50p *St. Helena* (mail ship), 1980
         Set of 4 1.75 1.75

274† 10p H.M.S. *Tortoise*, (storeship), 1830 . . 45 40

1982

317† 40p H.M.S. *Beagle* (survey ship) (Darwin) 1.10 95

1984

360† 15p *Southampton Castle* (liner) 35 35
362† 70p *The Dane* (mail ship) 1.50 1.50

1985

384† 70p Crest and gun from H.M.S. *Hood* (battle cruiser) 1.50 1.50

1986

403† 15p *St. Helena* (mail ship) (on No. 267) 30 35

409 1p H.M.S. *Ganymede* (frigate), c 1811
410 2p H.M.S. *Kangaroo* (sloop), c 1811
411 4p H.M.S. *Trinculo* (sloop), c 1811
412 5p H.M.S. *Daring* (brig), c 1811
413 9p H.M.S. *Thais* (sloop), c 1811
414 20p H.M.S. *Pheasant* (sloop), c 1819
415 15p H.M.S. *Myrmidon* (frigate), 1819

416 18p H.M.S. *Atholl* (frigate), 1825
417 18p H.M.S. *Medina* (frigate), 1830
418 25p H.M.S. *Saracen* (sloop), 1840
419 30p H.M.S. *Hydra* (paddle-sloop), c 1845
420 50p H.M.S. *Sealark* (brig), 1849
421 70p H.M.S. *Rattlesnake* (screw corvette), 1868
422 £1 H.M.S. *Penelope* (armoured corvette), 1889
423 £2 H.M.S. *Monarch* (battleship), 1897
         Set of 15 9.00 9.75

1987

431† £1 U.S.S. *Noa* (aircraft carrier), 1962 . . . . 2.00 2.10

1988

461 9p H.M.S. *Resolution* (ship of the line), 1667
462 18p H.M.S. *Resolution* (Cook), 1772
463 25p H.M.S. *Resolution* (battleship), 1892
464 65p H.M.S. *Resolution* (battleship), 1916
         Set of 4 2.10 2.25

Nos. 461/4 *optd* **SYDPEX 88 30.7.88–7.8.88**
465 9p H.M.S. *Resolution* (ship of the line), 1667
466 18p H.M.S. *Resolution* (Cook), 1772
467 25p H.M.S. *Resolution* (battleship), 1892
468 65p H.M.S. *Resolution* (battleship), 1916
         Set of 4 2.10 2.25

AUSTRALIA

Oceania
1932 12 pence = 1 shilling
20 shillings = 1 pound
1966 100 cents = 1 dollar

1932

141 2d *Orford* (liner)
142 3d *Orford* (liner)
143 5s *Orford* (liner)
         Set of 3 £350 £170

1953

270† 2s Ships at Hobart, 1804 . . . . 3.00 3.25

1963

355†	4s Tasman and *Heemskerk*	5.00	40
356†	5s Dampier and *Roebuck*	7.00	60
358†	10s Flinders and *Investigator*	40.00	4.50
359†	£1 Bass and whale boat	48.00	14.00
360†	£2 Admiral King and *Mermaid*	70.00	55.00

1966

398†	40c Tasman and *Heemskerk*............	15.00	20
399†	50c Dampier and *Roebuck*	18.00	10
401†	$1 Flinders and *Investigator*	4.25	10
402†	$2 Bass and whale boat	11.00	50
403†	$4 Admiral King and *Mermaid*	8.00	4.50

408	4c Dirk Hartog's *Eendracht*, 1616	15	5

1969

438	5c *Walumba* (tug)	20	10

1970

459†	5c H.M.S. *Endeavour* and Captain Cook	30	10
460†	5c H.M.S. *Endeavour* and sextant	30	10
461†	5c H.M.S. *Endeavour* at Botany Bay	30	10
463†	5c H.M.S. *Endeavour* and raising Union Flag	30	10
464†	30c H.M.S. *Endeavour*, Cook and sextant	1.75	3.50

1972

529†	80c *Gem* (paddle-steamer)	65	90

1979

704	20c *Canberra* (river paddle-steamer)	
705	35c *Lady Denman* (river vessel)	
706	50c *Murray River Queen* (river paddle-steamer)	
707	55c *Curl Curl* (hydrofoil)	

	Set of 4	2.00	2.50

1981

833	24c Ocean racing yacht	
834	35c "Sharpie" yacht	
835	55c 12 metre yacht	
836	60c "Sabot" yacht	

	Set of 4	2.40	2.25

1982

864	27c *Orford* (liner) (on stamp No. 143)	30	25

1983

879	27c H.M.S. *Sirius* (frigate), 1788		
880	27c H.M.S. *Supply* (brig), 1788		
	Set of 2	60	70

886	27c Royal Yacht *Britannia*	40	25

1984

911	30c *Cutty Sark* (clipper)		
912	45c *Orient* (clipper)		
913	75c *Sobraon* (clipper)		
914	85c *Thermopylae* (clipper)		
	Set of 4	3.00	3.00

1985

973†	33c Dirk Hartog's *Eendracht*, 1616	45	35

1986

1000†	33c H.M.S. *Buffalo* (storeship), 1836	50	55

1021†	33c Captain Arthur Phillip and ship of 1788	50	40

1036†	36c *Australia II* (yacht)	50	35

1987

1046	36c Aerial view of Americas Cup yacht	
1047	55c Two yachts tacking	
1048	90c Two yachts turning	
1049	$1 Two yachts under full sail	

	Set of 4	3.00	2.75

1059	36c H.M.S. *Sirius* (frigate), 1787		
1060	36c Ship's boat, 1787		
1061	36c Ship of the line on stocks, 1787		
1062	36c H.M.S. *Sirius* and *Supply* in River Thames		
1063	36c First Fleet in English Channel, 1787		
	Set of 5	1.60	1.60

1064	36c Ship's boat off Tenerife, 1787		
1065	36c Ship's boat off Tenerife, 1787		
1066	$1 First Fleet off Tenerife, 1787		
	Set of 3	1.50	1.50

1077†	37c First Fleet off Rio de Janeiro, 1787	35	35
1078†	37c Brazilian fishing boat, 1787	35	35
1081†	37c Brazilian fishing boats and First Fleet, 1782	35	35

1091†	37c First Fleet loading livestock, Cape of Good Hope, 1787	30	35
1092†	$1 Cape fishing boat and First Fleet	90	95

1988

1105†	37c Arrival of First Fleet, 1788	30	35
1106†	37c Aborigine canoe	30	35
1107†	37c First Fleet in cove	30	35
1108†	37c Ship's boat	30	35

1145†	37c Sailing clipper	30	35

OFFICIAL STAMPS

Nos. 142 *and* 144 *optd* **O.S.**

O16	2d *Orford* (liner)	10.00	4.00
O17	3d *Orford* (liner)	22.00	9.00

AUSTRALIAN ANTARCTIC TERRITORY

Antarctica
100 cents = 1 dollar

1966

10†	4c Ship and iceberg	70	50

1972

22†	35c H.M.S. *Resolution* (Cook)	7.50	6.00

1979

37	1c *Aurora*
38	2c *Penola* (Rymill)

39	5c *Thala Dan*		
40	10c H.M.S. *Challenger* (survey ship)		
41	15c *Morning* (bow view) (incorrectly inscribed "S.Y.Nimrod")		
42	15c *Nimrod* (stern view)		
43	20c *Discovery II*		
44	22c *Terra Nova*		
45	25c *Endurance* (Shackleton)		
46	30c *Fram*		
47	35c *Nella Dan*		
48	40c *Kista Dan*		
49	45c *L'Astrolabe* (D'Urville)		
50	50c *Norvegia*		
51	55c *Discovery* (Scott)		
52	$1 H.M.S. *Resolution* (Cook)		
	Set of 16	8.00	7.50

1988

79†	37c *Nella Dan* (supply ship)	30	35

AUSTRIA

Central Europe
1915 100 heller = 1 krone
1925 100 groschen = 1 schilling

1915

245†	20 + 3h *Viribus Unitas* (battleship)	35	1.25

1935

773†	1s Danube river steamer	20	70
777†	10s Yachts on Attersee	35.00	55.00

1937

805	12g *Maria Anna* (Danube paddle-steamer)		
806	24g *Helios* (Danube paddle-steamer)		
807	64g *Oesterreich* (Danube paddle-steamer)		
	Set of 3	1.40	95

1954

1267	1s + 25g 18th-century river boat	3.00	4.00

1957

1312†	2s50 Danube river steamer, Linz	35	5

1961

1364	3s Canal barge	70	40

1962

1381	1s50 Danube barge	30	20

1971

1625†	4s Danube barge, Linz	45	45

1973

1666	2s50 *Admiral Tegetthoff* (polar vessel)	40	15

1687†	10s Yachts on Neusiedlersee	80	5

1979

1831	1s50 *Franz I* (Danube paddle-steamer)		
1832	2s50 *Linz* (Danube pusher tug)		
1833	3s *Theodor Korner* (Danube cargo vessel)		
	Set of 3	70	55

1987

2133   4s Passenger ferry, Achensee 35   20

AZORES

Atlantic Ocean
1898 1000 reis = 1 milreis
1912 100 centavos = 1 escudo

1898

As Nos. 378/9 and 384 of Portugal, but inscr "ACORES"

171†	2½r Departure of Vasco da Gama's fleet	45	25
172†	5r Vasco da Gama's fleet at Calicut	70	30
175†	50r *Sao Gabriel* (flagship)	1.60	1.10
177†	100r *Sao Gabriel*	3.25	1.60

1911

Nos. 171/2, 175 and 177 optd **REPUBLICA** *or surch also*

218†	2½r Departure of Vasco da Gama's fleet	20	20
219†	15r on 5r Vasco da Gama's fleet at Calicut	20	20
221†	50r *Sao Gabriel* (flagship)	35	25
224†	100r *Sao Gabriel*	30	25

1985

466   40e Jeque (small sailing boat)
467   60e Bote (small sailing boat)
      Set of 2   1.10   70

BAHAMAS

West Indies
1948 12 pence = 1 shilling
20 shillings = 1 pound
1966 100 cents = 1 dollar

1948

183†	3d Fishing fleet	40	85
185†	6d Tuna fishing	70	1.00
188†	1s Racing yacht	60	50
190†	3s Boat building	5.00	7.50
191†	5s Liners at anchor	3.75	6.00

1949

As No. 115 of Antigua

197†	3d Paddle-steamer	80	1.25

1954

As Nos. 183, 185, 188 and 190/1 but with portrait of Queen Elizabeth II and without commemorative inscription

205†	3d Fishing fleet	20	25
208†	6d Liners at anchor	20	10
211†	1s Yacht racing	35	10
213†	2s6d Boat building	2.50	1.50
214†	5s Tuna fishing.....................	6.00	1.25

1964

Nos. 205, 208, 211 and 213/14 overprinted **NEW CONSTITUTION 1964**

232†	3d Fishing fleet	15	30
235†	6d Liners at anchor	20	30
238†	1s Yacht racing	30	25
240†	2s6d Boat building	2.00	2.50
241†	5s Tuna fishing.....................	3.50	3.75

No. 211 surcharged with Olympic rings and value

245	8d on 1s Yacht racing	10	10

1965

248†	1d Yacht regatta	15	5
252†	4d *Queen Elizabeth* (liner)	55	70
254†	8d Yachts	50	40
261†	£1 *Santa Maria* (Columbus)	7.00	4.50

No. 254 surcharged

264	9d on 8d Yachts........................	15	10

1966

Nos. 248, 252, 254 and 261 surcharged in decimal currency

274†	2c on 1d Yacht regatta	8	5
277†	5c on 4d *Queen Elizabeth* (liner)	15	12
279†	10c on 8d Yachts......................	25	25
287†	$3 on £1 *Santa Maria* (Columbus)	5.50	4.00

1967

296†	2c Yacht regatta	15	5
299†	5c *Oceanic* (liner)	60	20
301†	10c Yachts	30	15
309†	$3 *Santa Maria* (Columbus)	4.25	2.50

1968

316†	11c Yachts	60	30

319†	5c Racing yacht	25	15
322†	$1 Racing yacht	1.75	3.00

1969

333†	3c Game fishing boats	20	10
335†	12c "Sunfish" sailing boats	40	25

1970

349†	12c *Canberra* (liner)	70	50

1971

367†	10c Bahamian sponge boat	40	45
469†	40c Bahamian sponge boat	80	75

1972

385	18c Olympic yacht	60	80

393	11c Galleon		
394	18c Galleon		
	Set of 2	30	35

1976

480†	25c Racing yachts	35	50

1977

499†	21c Scout yacht	40	35

1979

543†	40c 19th-century mail boat	40	45

1980

557†	1c Columbus's fleet	15	10
563†	16c Wrecking in the 1800s.............	30	25
564†	18c Blockade running during American Civil War	40	30
570†	$2 *Queen Elizabeth 2* (liner)	3.00	2.75

1983

644†	$1 Liner at anchor	1.25	1.40

Nos. 563/4 surcharged

647†	35c on 16c Wrecking in the 1800s	60	60
648†	80c on 18c Blockade running during American Civil War	1.40	1.40

649†	31c Liner and customs officers	45	45

1984

675	5c *Trent* (sail/steam)		
676	31c *Orinoco* (mail ship)		
677	35c Cruise liners in Nassau harbour		
678	50c *Oropesa* (container ship)		
	Set of 4	1.90	2.10

1986

746†	5c Columbus's fleet and blockade running during American Civil War (on stamps Nos. 557 and 564)	5	8

1987

782†	10c Yachts, Great Isaac	20	15
783†	40c Yachts, Bird Rock	70	70
784†	45c Fishing boats, Castle Island	75	75

786	10c Pirate ship (Anne Bonney)		
787	40c Pirate ship (Blackbeard)		
788	45c Pirate ship attacking merchantman (Edward England)		
789	50c British ship of the line (Woodes Rogers)		
	Set of 4	1.75	1.75

804†	40c Cruise liner and catamaran	50	55
805†	40c Cruise liner and speedboat	50	55
806†	40c Game fishing boat and cruising yachts	50	55
807†	40c Game fishing boat and cruising yachts	50	55
808†	40c Fishing boat and schooner	50	55

BAHRAIN

Arabian Peninsula
1955 16 annas = 1 rupee
1000 fils = 1 dinar

1955

No. 509 of Great Britain surcharged **BAHRAIN 2 RUPEES**

94	2r on 2s6d H.M.S. *Victory*	6.50	1.25

1966

145†	50f Freighters in dock	45	5
146†	75f Freighters in dock	70	10
150†	1d Dhow	10.00	3.50

151	10f Freighter		
152	20f Freighter		
153	40f Freighter		
154	200f Freighter		
	Set of 4	6.50	2.75

1972

184†	30f Dhow	1.40	30
185†	60f Dhow	2.25	60

1977

249a†	80f Dhow	1.40	1.00

1979

258	100f Dhow (Boom type)		
259	100f Dhow (Baghla type)		
260	100f Dhow (Shu'ai type)		
261	100f Dhow (Ghanja type)		
262	100f Dhow (Kotia type)		
263	100f Dhow (Sambuk type)		
264	100f Dhow (Jaliboot type)		
265	100f Dhow (Zarook type)		
	Set of 8	7.50	7.50

1984

324	15f Dhows, Manama		
325	50f Dhows, Manama		
326	100f Dhows, Manama		
	Set of 3	1.50	1.25

BANGLADESH

Indian sub-continent
100 paisa = 1 taka

1973

34†	5t Fishing boat	1.50	90

1974

As No. 34 but showing Bengali letter instead of "TA" in front of "5"

51†	5t Fishing boat	1.10	70

1976

As No. 51, but redrawn smaller (32 × 20 mm)

74†	5t Fishing boat	70	35

82†	5t Pilgrim Fathers' *Mayflower*	65	50

1978

129†	25p Local jute boat	5	5

1980

156	1t Early mail boat		
157	10t Modern mail boat		
	Set of 2	85	95

1983

218†	5t 15th-century sailing ship	45	45

220† 5p Local mail rowing boat 5 5

1987

288† 5t Paddle-steamer 20 25

OFFICIAL STAMPS

1973
No. 34 overprinted **SERVICE**
O10† 5t Fishing boat 2.25 1.50

1974
No. 51 overprinted **SERVICE**
O13† 5t Fishing boat 1.60 1.10

1976
No. 74 overprinted **SERVICE**
O23† 5t Fishing boat 60 45

1981
No. 129 overprinted **SERVICE**
O25† 25p Local jute boat 5 5

1983
No. 220 overprinted **SERVICE**
O31† 5p Local mail rowing boat 5 5

BARBADOS
West Indies
1906 12 pence = 1 shilling
20 shillings = 1 pound
1950 100 cents = 1 dollar

1906

152 1d *Olive Blossom*, 1605 .... 7.50 40

1949
As No. 115 of Antigua
268† 3d Paddle-steamer 40 35

1950

273† 3c *W.L. Eunica* (schooner)........... 15 50
276† 8c *Frances W. Smith* (schooner) 55 45
280† 60c *W. L. Edricia* (schooner) 5.00 3.25

1953
As Nos. 273, 276 and 280, and new design, all showing portrait of Queen Elizabeth II
291† 3c *W. L. Eunica* (schooner) 15 5
293† 5c Schooner and Harbour Police rowing boat 20 5
295† 8c *Frances W. Smith* (schooner) 60 5
299† 60c *W. L. Edricia* (schooner) 4.50 1.75

1967

365† 35c *BP I* (police launch) 20 10

1969

394† 25c Sea Scouts' rowing boat and H.Q ship 35 10

1971

429 1c "Sailfish" craft 5 5

1972

441† 10c *Stanley Angwin* (cable ship) 20 5

1974

480 15c Sail fishing boat
481 35c Rowing boat
482 50c Motor fishing boat
483 $1 *Calmar* (fishing boat)
Set of 4 2.00 2.00

504† $1 Sailing ship 70 1.10

1975

506† 8c Royal Yacht *Britannia* 20 15
507† 25c Royal Yacht *Britannia* 50 25

538† 4c 17th-century sailing ship 25 5

1976

560† 5c Coastguard launches 1.25 1.10

1979

613 12c Early mail steamer
614 25c *Queen Elizabeth 2* (liner)
615 50c *Ra II* (raft)
616 $1 Early mail steamer (*different*)
Set of 4 1.50 1.50

1981

681† $1 Harbour scene 60 75

1982

701 20c Lighter
702 35c Rowing boat
703 55c Speightstown schooner
704 $2.50 Inter-colonial schooner
Set of 4 2.75 2.75

1983

741† $2.50 18th-century warship, Carlisle Bay 1.90 2.10

1984

752† 75c *Philosopher*, 1857 .... 75 70
753† $1 *Sea Princess* (cruise liner) 95 95

1986

816† $2.50 *Lady Nelson* (liner) 2.00 2.25

MS821† $2 *Queen Elizabeth 2* (liner) 1.75 2.00

1988

866† $2 Olympic yachts 1.25 1.40

BARBUDA

West Indies
100 cents = 1 dollar

1968

30† 75c Yachts 65 90

1969

37 75c Sea Scouts' rowing boat 60 1.25

1971

95† 25c Yachts 20 60

1973

Nos. 269/85 of Antigua overprinted **BARBUDA**
116 ½c War canoe
104 1c *Nina* (Columbus)
105 2c Sir Thomas Warner's *Concepcion*
117 3c Viscount Hood and H.M.S. *Barfleur*
106 4c Sir George Rodney and H.M.S.
    Formidable
107 5c Nelson and H.M.S. *Boreas*
108 6c William IV and H.M.S. *Pegasus*
109 10c Blackbeard and pirate ketch
118 15c Collingwood and H.M.S. *Pelican*
110 20c Nelson and H.M.S. *Victory*
111 25c *Solent* (paddle-steamer)

112 35c George V and H.M.S. *Canada* (built
    1881)
113 50c H.M.S. *Renown* (battle cruiser)
114 75c *Federal Maple* (freighter)
119 $1 *Sol Quest* (yacht)
115 $2.50 H.M.S. *London* (cruiser)
121 $5 *Pathfinder* (tug)
                              Set of 17   9.00 10.50

1974

Nos. 387/8 of Antigua overprinted
(a) with **BARBUDA 13 JULY 1922**
150† 1c *Orinoco* (mail steamer) 8 8
152† 2c Hydrofoil 8 8
(b) with **BARBUDA 15 SEPT. 1874 G.P.U.**
151† 1c *Orinoco* (mail steamer) 8 8
153† 2c Hydrofoil 8 8

1975

Nos. 427/31 of Antigua overprinted **BARBUDA**
217 5c Carib war canoe
218 15c Ship of the line, 1770
219 35c H.M.S. *Boreas*, 1787, and Nelson
220 50c Yachts
221 $1 Yachts
                              Set of 5   1.75 1.75

223 35c Battle of the Saints, 1782
224 50c H.M.S. *Ramillies* (ship of the line),
    1782
225 75c Firing broadside
226 95c Burning ship
                              Set of 4   8.00 5.00

1977

345† 50c Royal Yacht *Britannia* 40 40

364† 75c German battleship (1914–18 War) .. 40 35

1978

Nos. 576/80 of Antigua overprinted **BARBUDA**
403 10c Yacht regatta
404 50c Fishing and work boat race
405 90c Yacht race
406 $2 Power boat race
                              Set of 4   1.75 1.75
MS407 $2.50 Guadeloupe—Antigua yacht race 1.25 1.60

1979

Nos. 623 and **MS**626 *of Antigua overprinted* **BARBUDA**
475† 50c H.M.S. *Endeavour* (Cook) 50 45
MS478† $2.50 H.M.S. *Resolution* (Cook) 1.25 1.50

1981

No. 715 of Antigua overprinted **BARBUDA**
600 90c Sailing dinghy................... 75 45

1984

Nos. 830/4 of Antigua overprinted **BARBUDA MAIL**
721 45c *Booker Vanguard* (freighter)
722 50c *Canberra* (liner)
723 60c Sailing boats
724 $4 *Fairwind* (liner)
                              Set of 4   4.25 3.75
MS725 $5 18th-century English man-o-war 3.75 4.00

1985

Nos. 911 and **MS**913 *of Antigua overprinted* **BARBUDA MAIL**
791† $1 Statue of Liberty and cadet ship 55 60
MS793† $5 Liner and New York skyline........ 2.75 3.00

1986

No. 944 of Antigua overprinted **BARBUDA MAIL**
840† $3 Windsurfing...................... 1.50 1.60

No. 967 of Antigua overprinted **BARBUDA MAIL**
844† $4 Royal Yacht *Britannia* 2.00 2.10

1987

Nos. 1009/13 of Antigua overprinted **BARBUDA MAIL**
918 30c Tug
919 60c Game-fishing boat
920 $1 Yacht
921 $4 Lugger
                              Set of 4   2.25 2.50
MS922 $5 Boat building 2.25 2.40

Nos. 1072/6 of Antigua overprinted **BARBUDA MAIL**
936 30c *Canada I* (yacht), 1981
937 60c *Gretel II* (yacht), 1970
938 $1 *Sceptre* (yacht), 1958
939 $3 *Vigilant* (yacht), 1893
                              Set of 4   2.00 2.25
MS940 $5 *Australia II* defeating *Liberty*
    (yachts), 1983 .... 2.25 2.40

Nos. 1100, 1102, 1104, 1106 and 1109 of Antigua overprinted
                              BARBUDA MAIL
950† 10c *Spirit of Australia* (powerboat), 1978 5 8
952† 30c U.S.S. *Triton* (submarine), 1960 .... 12 15
954† 60c U.S.S. *New Jersey* (battleship), 1942 25 30
956† 90c *United States* (liner), 1952 .... 40 45
959† $3 *Queen Elizabeth 2* (liner), 1969 ...... 1.40 1.50

1988

Nos. 1172/9 of Antigua overprinted **BARBUDA MAIL**
1043† 10c Fleet of Columbus, 1493 .... 5 8
1044† 30c Fleet of Columbus, 1493 .... 12 15
1045† 45c *Santa Mariagalante* (Columbus),
    1493 .... 20 25
1046† 60c *Painos* Indian canoe, 1493 .... 25 30
1048† $1 Fleet of Columbus and ship's boat,
    1493 .... 45 50
1049† $3 Fleet of Columbus at anchor, 1493 .. 1.40 1.50
1050† $4 Fleet of Columbus at sea, 1493 ...... 1.75 1.90

BASUTOLAND

Southern Africa
12 pence = 1 shilling
20 shillings = 1 pound

1949

As No. 115 of Antigua
39† 3d Paddle-steamer 65 50

BECHUANALAND

Southern Africa
12 pence = 1 shilling
20 shillings = 1 pound

1949

As No. 115 of Antigua
139† 3d Paddle-steamer 55 50

BELGIAN CONGO

Central Africa
100 centimes = 1 franc

1894

27† 40c Native canoe 3.00 2.00

29† 10f *Deliverance* (stern wheel paddle-
steamer) 7.00 11.00

1909
Nos. 27 and 29 overprinted **CONGO BELGE**
50† 40c Native canoe 1.50 1.50
55† 10f *Deliverance* (stern wheel paddle-
steamer) £150 90.00

1910
As Nos. 27 and 29 but inscribed "CONGO BELGE-BELGISCH CONGO"
64† 40c Native canoe (black and green) 1.50 1.50
69† 10f *Deliverance* (stern wheel paddle-
steamer) 15.00 12.00

1915
As No. 64 but colour changed
74† 40c Native canoe (black and red) 3.25 1.50

1918
As Nos. 69 and 74, with centres in blue, surcharged with red cross and premium
82† 40c + 40c Native canoe 35 45
86† 10f + 10f *Deliverance* (stern wheel
paddle-steamer) 60.00 60.00

1920

89† 2f Native canoes on beach 55 20

1921
No. 64 surcharged
91† 5c on 40c Native canoe 20 20

No. 69 overprinted **1921**
100† 10f *Deliverance* (stern wheel paddle-
steamer) 3.75 2.50

1922
No. 74 surch **.25c.** *without bars*
103 25c on 40c Native canoe 1.75 30

No. 74 surcharged **0.25** *with bars*
112 25c on 40c Native canoe 70 30

1925

141 25c + 25c Native canoe 20 20

1931

193† 4f Beached canoes 30 15

1949

293 4f 19th-century sailing ship 60 15

1953

319 3f Canoe, Lake Kivu
320 7f Canoe, Lake Kivu
Set of 2 2.25 45

BELGIAN OCCUPATION OF GERMANY
North-west Europe
100 centimes = 1 franc
100 pfennig = 1 mark

1919
No. 191 of Belgium overprinted **ALLEMAGNE DUITSCHLAND**
14 1f Shipping in the Scheldt 17.00 17.00

1920
No. 191 of Belgium surcharged **EUPEN & MALMEDY 1 MK 25**
24 1m25 on 1f Shipping in the Scheldt 16.00 40.00

No. 191 of Belgium overprinted **Eupen**
38 1f Shipping in the Scheldt 16.00 18.00

No. 191 of Belgium overprinted **Malmedy**
55 1f Shipping in the Scheldt 16.00 18.00

BELGIUM
North-west Europe
100 centimes = 1 franc

1915

191† 1f Shipping in the Scheldt 17.00 25

1918
No. 191 surcharged **1F** *and cross*
232† 1f + 1f Shipping in the Scheldt 38.00 38.00

1929

556† 1f75 + 25c *Aquitania* (liner) 2.50 2.50

1946

1174 1f35 *Prince Baudouin* (mail steamer)
1175 2f25 *Marie Henriette* (paddle-steamer)
1176 3f15 *Diamant* (paddle-steamer)
Set of 3 1.25 35

1197† 1f35 + 1f15 *Bobby* (fishing boat) 35 35

1947

1202† 2f25 *Belgica* (polar barque) 2.75 85

1948

1222† 2f25 Freighter in Antwerp Docks 1.75 30
1224† 3f Freighter in Antwerp Docks 12.00 10

1953

1442† 80c + 20c Fishing boats *Marcel, De
Meeuw* and *Jacqueline Denise* 90 35
1444† 2f + 50c Fishing boats and freighter 1.75 70

1957

1611 2f Steamer entering Zeebrugge harbour 70 10

1958

1665† 3f + 1f50 Rowing boat 3.25 1.25

1966

1991 1f + 50c *Erika Dan* (polar vessel)
1992 3f + 1f50 *Belgica* (polar barque)
1993 6f + 3f *Magga Dan* (polar vessel)
Set of 3 85 60
MS1994 10f + 5f *Magga Dan* (polar vessel) 1.25 1.25

1968

2082† 13f + 5f Yachts 45 45

2090†	6f *Mineral Seraing* (ore carrier)	25	15
2091†	10f Canal barges on "lift", Ronquieres ..	35	25

2101	6f Cargo ship in Ghent Canal	25	15

1969

2132†	3f Cargo ship on aqueduct	25	5

1970

2157†	2f50 Freighter, Zelzate	20	10

1971

2230	10f *Erika Dan* (polar vessel)	1.00	80

1973

2318†	10f + 5f 18th-century sailing ship from Ostend	2.25	2.50

1975

2384†	6f50 + 2f50 Gondola, Venice	40	50

COLLECT BIRDS ON STAMPS

Second revised edition of this Stanley Gibbons thematic catalogue – now available at £8.50 (p. + p. £2) from: Stanley Gibbons Publications Ltd, 5 Parkside, Christchurch Road, Ringwood, Hants BH24 3SH.

1981

2650†	6f50 Yacht	25	15

1982

2680†	50f + 14f *Treaty of Rome* (yacht)	2.25	2.25

1985

2844†	24f Freighter and landing craft	1.10	30

1988

2936	10f Trawler leaving harbour		
2937	10f Trawler		
2938	10f Cross-channel ferry and yacht		
2939	10f Container ship		
	Set of 4	1.25	55

OFFICIAL STAMP

1946

As No. 1224 but additionally inscribed "B"

O1242†	3f Freighter in Antwerp Docks	20.00	2.50

BELIZE

Central America
100 cents = 1 dollar

1979

481†	10c *Heron H*, 1949 (mail boat)	5	5
482†	35c Mail canoe, 1920)	20	20
485†	$2 *Eagle*, 1856 (mail boat)	1.00	1.25

1981

671	10c British 19th-century sail warship

672	25c *Madagascar* (sail merchantman), 1837		
673	35c *Whitby* (brig), 1838		
674	50c *China* (sail merchantman), 1850		
675	85c *Swiftsure* (sail merchantman), 1850		
676	$2 *Windsor Castle* (sail merchantman), 1857		
	Set of 6	2.75	80
MS677	$5 18th–19th-century naval battle	3.50	3.25

1983

755†	$2 *Heron H* (mail boat)	1.40	1.50

1985

847†	15c Packet ship and privateer	20	12
848†	25c *Duke of Marlborough* (P.O. packet)	30	25
849†	75c *Diana* (P.O. packet)	70	60
850†	$1 Falmouth packet ship)	80	80
851†	$3 *Conway* (mail boat)	2.25	2.50

864†	$4 Royal Yacht *Britannia*	2.75	3.00

1986

932†	75c U.S.S. *Constitution* (frigate)	50	50

No. 932 overprinted **STOCKHOLMIA 86** *and emblem*

953†	75c U.S.S. *Constitution* (frigate)	50	55

1987

985	75c *America II* (yacht), 1983		
986	75c *Stars and Strips* (yacht), 1987		
987	$1 *Australia II* (yacht), 1983		
988	$4 *White Crusader* (yacht)		
	Set of 4	3.25	3.50

BENIN

West Africa
100 centimes = 1 franc

1977

675†	60f Tourist boat, Ganvie stilt village	45	30

1978

727† 60f Pirogue 45 25

1979

750† 20f H.M.S. *Resolution* and H.M.S.
Discovery (Cook) 30 15

753† 50f Mail canoe 60 40

1980

806† 15f Fishing canoe 12 5

1983

886 125f Oil rig and support vessels 40 15

1984

968 90f 2nd-century Sidon merchant ship
969 120f Wavertree (sail merchantman), 1895
Set of 2 1.00 80

1985

987† 200f Oil rig 1.25 1.00

POSTAGE DUE STAMPS

1978

D721† 80f Postman in canoe 60 55

BERMUDA

North Atlantic Ocean
1902 12 pence = 1 shilling
20 shillings = 1 pound
1970 100 cents = 1 dollar

1902

34a	¼d Vessel in dry dock and schooner		
35	¼d Vessel in dry dock and schooner (black and green)		
41	¼d Vessel in dry dock and schooner (green)		
32	1d Vessel in dry dock and schooner (brown and red)		
42	1d Vessel in dry dock and schooner (red)		
37	2d Vessel in dry dock and schooner		
38	2½d Vessel in dry dock and schooner (brown and blue)		
43	2½d Vessel in dry dock and schooner (blue)		
33	3d Vessel in dry dock and schooner		
39	4d Vessel in dry dock and schooner		

Set of 10 55.00 48.00

1910

76a†	¼d Sailing ship, *c.* 1620	40	1.25
77†	½d Sailing ship, *c.* 1620	30	15
79†	1d Sailing ship, *c.* 1620	2.25	40
79b†	1½d Sailing ship, *c.* 1620	3.50	50
80†	2d Sailing ship, *c.* 1620	1.00	2.00
81a†	2½d Sailing ship, *c.* 1620 (green)	1.50	3.00
82†	2½d Sailing ship, *c.* 1620 (blue)	2.25	50
83†	3d Sailing ship, *c.* 1620 (blue)	16.00	25.00
84†	3d Sailing ship, *c.* 1620 (purple on yellow)	1.10	1.50
85†	4d Sailing ship, *c.* 1620	1.25	2.00
86†	6d Sailing ship, *c.* 1620	1.25	1.40
51†	1s Sailing ship, *c.* 1620	3.50	7.00

1918

No. 79 overprinted **WAR TAX**
56 1d Sailing ship, *c.* 1620 .... 25 65

1920

59	¼d Sailing ship, *c.* 1620	
60	½d Sailing ship, *c.* 1620	
65	1d Sailing ship, *c.* 1620	
61	2d Sailing ship, *c.* 1620	
66	2½d Sailing ship, *c.* 1620	
62	3d Sailing ship, *c.* 1620	
63	4d Sailing ship, *c.* 1620	
67	6d Sailing ship, *c.* 1620	
64	1s Sailing ship, *c.* 1620	

Set of 9 45.00 £110

1936

98†	½d *Song of the Wind* (yacht)	10	10
101†	2d *Lucie* (yacht)	4.50	3.50
106†	1s6d *Song of the Wind* (yacht)	30	20

1938

110a†	1d *J. W. Clise* (schooner) and *Monarch of Bermuda* (liner)	40	20
111b†	1½d *J. W. Clise* (schooner) and *Monarch of Bermuda* (liner)	70	55

1940

No. 110a surcharged **HALFPENNY**
122 ½d on 1d *J. W. Clise* (schooner) and
Monarch of Bermuda (liner) 20 45

1949

As No. 115 *of Antigua*
131† 3d Paddle-steamer 1.25 90

1953

138†	2d *Victory II* (racing dinghy)	40	15
139†	2½d Sir George Somers's *Sea Venture*, 1609	80	50
142†	4½d *Sea Venture* and inter-island boat	45	80
143b†	9d *Sea Venture* and inter-island boat ..	4.00	1.50

1964

183 3d *Tsotsi in the Bundu* (Finn class yacht) 10 10

1967

208†	3d *Mercury* (cable ship)	10	5
211†	2s6d *Mercury*	25	15

1968

220	3d Olympic yachts	
221	1s Olympic yachts	
222	1s6d Olympic yachts	
223	2s6d Olympic yachts	

Set of 4 60 30

1971

275	4c Building *Deliverance*, 1609			
276	15c *Deliverance* and *Patience* at Jamestown			
277	18c Wreck of *Sea Venture*, 1609			
278	24c *Deliverance* and *Patience* at sea			
		Set of 4	5.00	6.00

1975

336†	17c Rowing boats		50	30
337†	20c *Lady Catherine* (American sail merchantman), 1775		55	80

1976

357†	5c *Ready* (bathysphere)		35	10
359†	20c H.M.S. *Challenger* (survey ship), 1873		75	1.50

361†	5c *Christian Radich* (cadet ship)		35	15
362†	12c *Juan Sebastian de Elcano* (cadet ship)		70	85
363†	17c *Eagle* (U.S. coastguard cadet ship)		85	85
364†	20c *Winston S. Churchill* (cadet ship)		95	1.40
365†	40c *Kruzenshtern* (cadet ship)		1.25	1.90

1977

379	5c 17th-century merchant ship			
380	15c H.M.S. *Resolution* (ship of the line), 1795			
381	17c Pilots rowing out to *Marco Bozzaris* (paddle-steamer)			
382	20c Pilot gig and *Harvest Queen* (brig)			
383	40c Pilot cutter and *Queen Elizabeth 2* (liner)			
		Set of 5	2.75	3.25

1979

411†	25c Police launch		45	50

1980

418†	50c *Orduna* (mail ship), 1926		60	50
419†	$1 *Delta* (mail ship), 1856		1.00	1.25
420†	$2 *Lord Sidmouth* (mail ship), 1818		1.75	2.00

1981

434†	50c 19th-century onion boat		65	65
435†	$1 *Devonshire* (privateer) and *Felipe Quinto* (Spanish galleon)		1.50	2.00

1983

461	12c Early dinghy			
462	30c Modern dinghy			
463	40c Early dinghy (different)			
464	$1 Modern dinghy with spinnaker			
		Set of 4	2.50	2.75

468†	$1 U.S.S. *Patoka* (airship tender)		1.50	2.00

1984

472†	$1 *Lady Hammond* (packet boat)		2.00	2.25

475†	40c Wreck of the *Sea Venture*, 1609		90	75
476†	$1 Fleet leaving Plymouth, 1609		2.00	2.25

481†	$1 Olympic yachts		2.00	2.25

STAMP MONTHLY

— finest and most informative magazine for all collectors. Obtainable from your newsagent or by postal subscription — details on request.

1986

507	3c *Constellation* (schooner), 1943			
508	5c *Early Riser* (pilot boat), 1876			
509	7c *Madiana* (sail/steamer), 1903			
510	10c *Curlew* (sail/steamer), 1856			
511	12c *Warwick* (sailing ship), 1619			
512	15c H.M.S. *Vixen* (gunboat), 1890			
513	20c *San Pedro* (sailing ship), 1594			
514	25c *Alert* (sloop), 1877			
515	40c *North Carolina* (sail merchantman), 1880			
516	50c *Mark Antonie* (Spanish privateer), 1777			
517	60c *Mary Celestia* (paddle-steamer), 1864			
518	$1 *L'Herminie* (French frigate), 1839			
519	$1.50 *Caesar* (sailing ship), 1818			
520	$2 *Lord Amherst* (sailing ship), 1778			
521	$3 *Minerva* (sailing ship), 1849			
522	$5 *Caraquet* (steamer), 1923			
523	$8 H.M.S. *Pallas* (frigate), 1783			
		Set of 17	22.00	23.00

532†	$1 *Eagle* (cadet ship) (on stamp No. 363)		1.75	2.00
MS533†	$1.50 *Queen of Bermuda* (liner)		2.40	2.75

1987

538†	$1.50 *Prince David* (liner)		4.00	4.25

BHUTAN

Central Asia
100 chetrum = 1 ngultrum

1972

Appendix stamp surcharged

264†	90ch on 2n50 Liner		4.50	6.00

1974

285†	3ch Early and modern ships		15	5

1986

678	50ch *Mircea* (Rumanian full-rigged cadet ship)			

679	1n *Shalom* (Israeli liner)
680	2n *Leonardo da Vinci* (Italian liner)
681	3n *Libertad* (Argentine cadet barque)
682	4n *France* (French liner)
683	5n *United States* (American liner)
684	15n *Queen Elizabeth 2* (British liner)
685	20n *Europa* (West German liner)

Set of 8   5.00   5.00

1987

| 687† | 20ch *Santa Maria* (Columbus) .... | 5 | 5 |
| 689† | 50ch *Santa Maria* (Columbus) .... | 5 | 5 |

1988

731†	5n *Natchez* and *Robert E Lee*		
	(Mississippi paddle-steamers), 1870	50	50
733†	7n U.S.S. *Constitution* (frigate), 1797	65	65

Appendix

The following stamps have either been issued in excess of postal needs, or have not been made available to the public in reasonable quantities at face value. Miniature sheets, imperforate stamps etc. are excluded from this section.

1970

Famous Paintings. 3n Sailing dinghy
New U.P.U. Headquarters Building, Berne 3, 10, 20ch, 2n50 (all show liner)

BOLIVIA

South America
1916 100 centavos = 1 boliviano
1963 100 centavos = 1 peso boliviano

1916

| 144† | 2c Balsa boat, Lake Titicaca .... | 30 | 12 |

1930

No. 144 surch **R.S. 21-4 1930** *and value*

| 225† | 0.03c on 2c Balsa boat, Lake Titicaca .. | 85 | 70 |
| 227† | 25c on 2c Balsa boat, Lake Titicaca .... | 70 | 50 |

245†	15c Plane over river boat	50	35
246†	20c Plane over river boat	50	35
248†	50c Plane over river boat	50	15
250†	2b Plane over river boat	50	25

1941

| 380† | 10b Balsa boat on Lake Titicaca .... | 4.00 | 50 |
| 381† | 20b Balsa boat on Lake Titicaca .... | 4.50 | 85 |

1942

384	5c Balsa boat (on stamp No. 380)
385	10c Balsa boat (on stamp No. 380)
386	20c Balsa boat (on stamp No. 380)
387	40c Balsa boat (on stamp No. 380)
388	90c Balsa boat (on stamp No. 380)
389	1b Balsa boat (on stamp No. 380)
390	10b Balsa boat (on stamp No. 380)

Set of 7   20.00   11.50

1982

| 1079 | 14p Naval Base, Puerto Busch .... | 30 | 15 |

1987

| 1141 | 20c *Nina* (Columbus) |
| 1142 | 20c *Santa Maria* and *Pinta* (Columbus) |

Set of 2   20   10

BOTSWANA

Southern Africa
100 thebe = 1 pula

1978

| 432† | 25t "Mokoro" canoe .... | 40 | 40 |

1981

| 477 | 6t Paddle-steamer (on Bechuanaland | | |
| | stanp No. 139) .... | 10 | 10 |

COLLECT RAILWAYS ON STAMPS

A Stanley Gibbons thematic catalogue on this popular subject. Copies available at £7.50 (p. + p. £2) from: Stanley Gibbons Publications Ltd, 5 Parkside, Christchurch Road, Ringwood, Hants BH24 3SH.

BRAZIL

South America
1900 1000 reis = 1 milreis
1942 100 centavos = 1 cruzeiro

1900

| 226† | 100r Discovery of Brazil, 1500 .... | 2.00 | 1.50 |

1916

| 286 | 100r Ship of 1616 .... | 7.00 | 2.00 |

1920

| 361† | 600r Steamer .... | 50 | 10 |
| 342† | 1000r Steamer .... | 1.60 | 10 |

1935

| 583† | 300r Coutinho's *Gloria*, 1535 .... | 85 | 35 |

1948

| 774 | 5cr Ship of 1648 on arms of Paranagua | 1.75 | 10 |

1953

| 847 | 1cr50 *Admiral Saldanha* (cadet ship) .... | 55 | 20 |

1954

| 911† | 40c Battle of Riachuelo .... | 55 | 15 |

1957

969 2cr50 *Almirante Tamandare* (cruiser)
970 3cr30 *Minas Gerais* (aircraft carrier)
                                    Set of 2   90   20

1958

972 2cr50 19th-century sail merchantman   50   10

990 2cr50 Modern freighters   45   10

1960

1036 6cr50 Caravel of 1460   20   5

1967

1202 10c *Almirante Tamandare* (cruiser)   30   12

1204 5c *Minas Gerais* (aircraft carrier)   30   15

1968

1212† 10c Cabral and his fleet, 1500   25   15

1969

1281 5c *Pernambuco* (destroyer) and *Bahia*
          (submarine)   40   15

1970

1314 20c Modern destroyer 1.40   80

1971

1340 20c *Parati* (gunboat) 1.00   30

1972

1353† 40c Oil rig 2.00   50
1355† 1cr30 Ore carrier 2.25   1.25

1371† 45c Figurehead of local river craft   45   12

1423† 30c Naval sail-training ship 1.40   85

1973

1472 40c *Gailora* (river steamboat)
1473 70c *Regatao* (river trading boat)
1474 1cr *Jangada* (coastal raft)
1475 2cr *Saveiro* (passenger boat)
                                    Set of 4   6.50   3.50

1976

1587† 1cr40 Olympic yachts   25   10

1594† 20c Fishing pirogue   15   5

1977

1695† 1cr30 Naval patrol boat, Amazon   25   5

1979

1761 2cr50 "O'Day 23" class yacht
1762 10cr50 "Penguin" class dinghy
1763 12cr "Hobie Cat" class catamaran
1764 12cr50 "Snipe" class dinghy
                                    Set of 4   1.25   50

1980

MS1858 24cr Sao Francisco River sailing
          canoe 1.00   1.00

1982

1942 17cr *Ita* (freighter)   75   15

1995 24cr *Benjamin Constant* (cadet ship)
1996 24cr *Almirante Saldanha* (cadet ship)
1997 24cr *Brasil* (training frigate)
                                    Set of 3   30   25

1983

2003 150cr *Barao de Teffe* (Antarctic support
          ship)   65   30

2044† 57cr Fishing pirogue 20 15

1984

2062 620cr *Don Afonso* (sail/steam warship) and figurehead 55 35

2063† 585cr Fishing pirogue 55 40

2088† 620cr *Westfalen* (aircraft tender) 55 35

1985

2174 220cr Modern corvette 45 30

2194 500cr *Especuladora* (ferry), 1835
2195 500cr *Segunda* (ferry), 1862
2196 500cr *Terceira* (ferry), 1911
2197 500cr *Urca* (ferry), 1981
Set of 4 50 30

1986

2264† 50c *Minas Gerais* (cruiser), 1930s 5 5

1987

2281† 3cz Sailing canoes 8 5

2290 5cz Caravels, Recife, 1537 .... 10 5

2300 7cz Galleon, 1587 .... 15 10

BRITISH ANTARCTIC TERRITORY

Antarctica
1963 12 pence = 1 shilling
20 shillings = 1 pound
1971 100 pence = 1 pound

1963

1†	½d *Kista Dan* (polar supply ship)	35	45
6†	3d *John Biscoe II* (research ship)	85	35
8†	6d H.M.S. *Protector* (ice patrol ship)	1.25	40
14†	10s *Shackleton* (research ship)	48.00	26.00
15a†	£1 H.M.S. *Endurance* (ice patrol ship), 1956	£150	£120

1971

Nos. 1, 6, 8 and 14 surcharged in decimal currency

24†	½p on ½d *Kista Dan* (polar supply ship)	70	75
29†	3p on 3d *John Biscoe II* (research ship) ..	1.75	1.00
31†	5p on 6d H.M.S. *Protector* (ice patrol ship)	2.75	1.75
37†	50p on 10s *Shackleton* (research ship) ..	65.00	38.00

1973

64a†	½p H.M.S. *Resolution* (Cook)	30	45
65†	1p *Vostok* (Bellinghausen)..............	25	40
66†	1½p *Jane* (Weddell)	25	40
67†	2p *Tula* (Biscoe)	55	55
68†	2½p *L'Astrolabe* (D'Urville)	50	50
69†	3p H.M.S. *Erebus* (Ross)	75	75
70†	4p *Jason* (Larsen)	35	60
71†	5p *Belgica* (Gerlache)	1.50	1.25
72†	6p *Antarctic* (Nordenskjold)	60	1.25
73†	7½p *Scotia* (Bruce)	80	1.40
74†	10p *Pourquoi-pas?* (Charcot)	1.10	1.10
75†	15p *Endurance* (Shackleton)............	1.00	1.25
78a†	£1 *Penola* (Rymill)	2.00	2.50

1974

62† 15p *Trepassey* (supply ship) 2.25 2.00

1977

83† 6p Royal Yacht *Britannia* 95 35

1980

93†	3p *Tula* (brig) and Sir John Barrow	15	10
94†	7p *Discovery* (Scott) and Sir Clement Markham	20	25
95†	11p *James Caird* (Shackleton's launch) and Lord Curzon	25	30

1985

139† 7p *Penola* (Rymill), 1935 .... 20 20

1987

156† 24p *Discovery* (Scott), Ross Island, 1902–4 .... 50 55

BRITISH GUIANA

South America
100 cents = 1 dollar

1852

9	1c *Sandbach* (sail merchantman)	£8500	£4250
10	4c *Sandbach* (sail merchantman)	£10000	£4250

1853

12	1c *Sandbach* (sail merchantman)	£1800	£650
20	4c *Sandbach* (sail merchantman)	£650	£300

1856

Imperforate

23	1c *Sandbach* (sail merchantman)		
24	4c *Sandbach* (on magenta)	—	£5500
26	4c *Sandbach* (on blue)	—	£30000

1860

29	1c *Sandbach* (red)	£850	£150
40	1c *Sandbach* (brown)	£200	70.00
85	1c *Sandbach* (black)	7.50	2.50
87	2c *Sandbach*	6.50	1.75
90	4c *Sandbach*	48.00	5.00
69	6c *Sandbach*	65.00	32.00
95	8c *Sandbach*	70.00	11.00
100	12c *Sandbach* (lilac).................	75.00	14.00
99	12c *Sandbach* (grey)	75.00	14.00
64	24c *Sandbach* (oval frame)	£100	48.00
78	24c *Sandbach* (round frame)	70.00	8.00
82	48c *Sandbach*	£100	38.00

1876

170	1c *Sandbach*	
171	2c *Sandbach*	
172	4c *Sandbach*	
173	6c *Sandbach*	
174	8c *Sandbach*	
131	12c *Sandbach*	
132	24c *Sandbach*	
133	48c *Sandbach*	
134	96c *Sandbach*	

Set of 9 £500 £200

1878

Overprinted with thick horizontal or horizontal and vertical bars

(a) On Nos. 69 and 173

137	1c on 6c *Sandbach*
141	1c on 6c *Sandbach*

(b) On Nos. O1, O3 and O6/10

138	1c *Sandbach* (No. O1)
139	1c *Sandbach* (No. O6)
140	2c *Sandbach*
144	4c *Sandbach*
145	6c *Sandbach*
146	8c *Sandbach* (No. O3)
148	8c *Sandbach* (No. O10)

Set of 9 £600 £350

1881

Surcharged with figure. Old value barred out in ink

(a) On Nos. 82 and 134

152	"1" on 48c *Sandbach*
149	"1" on 96c *Sandbach*
150	"2" on 96c *Sandbach*

(b) On No. O4 and unissued stamps overprinted **OFFICIAL**

154	"1" on 12c *Sandbach* (No. O4)
153	"1" on 48c *Sandbach*
155	"2" on 12c *Sandbach*
158	"2" on 24c *Sandbach*

Set of 7 £300 £250

1882

164	1c *Sandbach*		
163	2c *Sandbach*		

Set of 2 72.00 50.00

Each stamp is perforated with the word "SPECIMEN".

1888

As Nos. 170, etc, but without value in bottom tablet, surcharged **INLAND REVENUE** *and value*

175	1c *Sandbach*
176	2c *Sandbach*
177	3c *Sandbach*
178	4c *Sandbach*
179	6c *Sandbach*
180	8c *Sandbach*
181	10c *Sandbach*
182	20c *Sandbach*
183	40c *Sandbach*
184	72c *Sandbach*
185	$1 *Sandbach*
186	$2 *Sandbach*
187	$3 *Sandbach*
188	$4 *Sandbach*
189	$5 *Sandbach*

Set of 15 £850 £650

1889

No. 176 surcharged with additional **2**

192	"2" on 2c *Sandbach*	55	25

193	1c *Sandbach* (purple and grey)		
213	1c *Sandbach* (green)		
194	2c *Sandbach* (purple and orange)		
234	2c *Sandbach* (purple and red)		
235	2c *Sandbach* (purple and black on red)		
253	2c *Sandbach* (red)		
195	4c *Sandbach* (purple and blue)		
254	4c *Sandbach* (brown and purple)		
255	5c *Sandbach* (blue)		
243	5c *Sandbach* (purple and blue on blue)		
198	6c *Sandbach* (purple and brown)		
236	6c *Sandbach* (black and blue)		
256	6c *Sandbach* (grey and black)		
199	8c *Sandbach* (purple and red)		
215	8c *Sandbach* (purple and black)		
200a	12c *Sandbach* (purple and mauve)		
257	12c *Sandbach* (orange and purple)		
201	24c *Sandbach*		
202	48c *Sandbach* (purple and red)		
247	48c *Sandbach* (grey and brown)		
248	60c *Sandbach*		
203	72c *Sandbach*		
205	96c *Sandbach* (purple and red)		
250	96c *Sandbach* (black and red on yellow)		

Set of 24 £170 £190

1890

Nos. 185/8 surcharged **ONE CENT**

207	1c on $1 *Sandbach*
208	1c on $2 *Sandbach*
209	1c on $3 *Sandbach*
210	1c on $4 *Sandbach*

Set of 4 5.00 6.50

1905

Design as Nos. 193, etc, overprinted **POSTAGE AND REVENUE**

251	$2.40 *Sandbach*	£160	£200

1913

272	1c *Sandbach*
260a	2c *Sandbach* (red)
274	2c *Sandbach* (violet)
275	4c *Sandbach*

262	5c *Sandbach*
263	6c *Sandbach* (grey and black)
276	6c *Sandbach* (blue)
264	12c *Sandbach*
278	24c *Sandbach*
279	48c *Sandbach*
280	60c *Sandbach*
281	72c *Sandbach*
282	96c *Sandbach*

Set of 13 32.00 60.00

1918

No. 260a optd **WAR TAX**

271	2c *Sandbach*	15	20

1934

294†	24c Sugar cane in punts	2.50	3.25

1938

As No. 294, but with portrait of King George VI

312a†	24c Sugar cane in punts	1.25	5

1944

As No. 115 of Antigua

325†	6c Paddle-steamer	35	30

1954

344†	$2 Gold dredger	4.75	1.25

OFFICIAL STAMPS

1875

Nos. 78, 85, 87, 95 and 100 overprinted **OFFICIAL**

O1	1c *Sandbach*	24.00	10.00
O2	2c *Sandbach*	80.00	14.00
O3	8c *Sandbach*	£175	75.00
O4	12c *Sandbach*	£650	£325
O5	24c *Sandbach*	£375	£140

1877

Nos. 170/4 overprinted **OFFICIAL**

O6	1c *Sandbach*	£125	50.00
O7	2c *Sandbach*	55.00	11.00
O8	4c *Sandbach*	60.00	20.00
O9	6c *Sandbach*	£1500	£300
O10	8c *Sandbach*	£1500	£250

BRITISH HONDURAS

Central America
100 cents = 1 dollar

1938

157†	25c "Dorey" (local canoe)	1.00	35

1949

169†	5c H.M.S. *Merlin* (sloop), 1798	20	15
170†	10c H.M.S. *Merlin*	20	15
171†	15c H.M.S. *Merlin*	25	20

As No. 115 of Antigua

173†	5c Paddle-steamer	40	20

1973

343†	3c Racing yachts.....................	5	5

BRITISH INDIAN OCEAN TERRITORY

Indian Ocean
100 cents = 1 rupee

1968

No. 203 of Seychelles overprinted **B.I.O.T.**

7†	45c Outrigger canoe	20	30

1969

32	45c Outrigger canoe	
33	75c Pirogue	
34	1r *Nordvaer* (travelling post office)	
35	1r50 *Isle of Farquhar* (schooner)	
	Set of 4	3.00	4.00

1974

56	85c *Nordvaer* (travelling post office)	
57	2r50 *Nordvaer*	
	Set of 2	1.25	1.75

BRITISH POSTAL AGENCIES IN EASTERN ARABIA

Arabia
16 annas = 1 rupee

1951

No. 509 of Great Britain surcharged **2 RUPEES**

41†	2r on 2s6d H.M.S. *Victory*...............	20.00	7.50

BRITISH VIRGIN ISLANDS

West Indies
1949 12 pence = 1 shilling
20 shillings = 1 pound
1951 100 cents = 1 West Indian dollar
1962 100 cents = 1 U.S. dollar

1949

As No. 115 of Antigua

127†	3d Paddle-steamer	35	25

1956

150†	1c Virgin Islands sloop	30	10
156†	12c *New Idea* under construction........	95	35

1962

Nos. 150 and 156 surcharged in U.S. currency

163†	2c on 1c Virgin Islands sloop...........	15	8
168†	10c on 12c *New Idea* under construction	20	10

1964

186†	12c *Youth of Tortola* (inter-island ferry) ..	70	55
191†	$1.40 Yachts	5.50	5.50

1966

203†	5c *Atrato* (paddle-steamer), 1866	10	10
206†	60c Mail packet ship at Road Town, 1866	75	50

No. 191 surcharged

208†	$1.50 on $1.40 Yachts	3.00	3.00

1967

217†	4c *Mercury* (cable ship)	10	5
219†	50c *Mercury*	30	20

1968

223†	40c Game fishing boat	75	40

1969

237†	10c Yachts, Tortola	20	5

1970

240	½c Carib canoe	
241	1c *Santa Maria* (Columbus)	
242	2c *Elizabeth Bonaventure* (Drake)	
243	3c Dutch buccaneer, 1660	
244	4c *Thetis* (sail merchantman), 1827	
245	5c Henry Morgan's ship	
246	6c H.M.S. *Boreas* (Nelson) (frigate), 1784	
247	8c H.M.S. *Eclair* (schooner), 1804	
248	10c H.M.S. *Formidable* (ship of the line), 1782	
249	12c H.M.S. *Nymph* (sloop), 1778	
250	15c *Windsor Castle* (P.O. packet), 1807	
251	25c H.M.S. *Astraea* (frigate), 1808	
252	50c Wreck of *Rhone* (mail steamer), 1860	
253	$1 Tortola sloop	

254	$2 H.M.S. *Frobisher* (cruiser)	
255	$3 *Booker Viking* (tanker)	
256	$5 *Sun Arrow* (hydrofoil)	
	Set of 17	26.00	28.00

1972

Nos. 244 and 251 overprinted **VISIT OF H.R.H. THE PRINCESS MARGARET 1972**

269	4c *Thetis* (sail merchantman), 1827	
270	25c H.M.S. *Astraea* (frigate), 1808	
	Set of 2	30	40

271	½c Seaman (1800) and H.M.S. *Naiad* (frigate)	
272	10c Boatswain (1787–1807) and ship	
273	30c Captain (1795–1812) and ship	
274	60c Admiral (1787–95) and ship	
	Set of 4	2.25	1.75

275	15c *Sir Winston Churchill* (cadet ship)	
276	25c *Sir Winston Churchill* (cadet ship)	
	Set of 2	40	30

1972

277	½c Game fishing boat and Blue Marlin	
278	½c Game fishing boat and Wahoo	
279	15c Game fishing boat and Allison Tuna	
280	25c Game fishing boat and White Marlin	
281	50c Game fishing boat and Sailfish	
282	$1 Game fishing boat and Dolphin	
	Set of 6	2.50	3.00

1973

289†	1c Yacht	8	8

1974

307	5c Crest of *Canopus* (French minesweeper)	
308	18c Crest of U.S.S. *Saginaw*	
309	25c Crest of H.M.S. *Rothesay* (frigate)	
310	50c Crest of H.M.C.S. *Ottawa* (frigate)	
	Set of 4	1.00	1.10

1975

325 5c Figurehead of H.M.S. *Boreas* (frigate)
326 18c Figurehead of *Golden Hind* (Drake)
327 40c Figurehead of H.M.S. *Superb* (ship of the line)
328 85c Figurehead of H.M.S. *Formidable* (ship of the line)

                Set of 4 1.10 1.25

1976

355 8c *Hazard* (Massachusetts brig)
356 22c *Spy* (American privateer)
357 40c *Raleigh* (frigate)
358 75c *Alliance* (frigate) & H.M.S. *Trepassy* (sloop)

                Set of 4 4.25 4.00

1978

375† 5c Wreck of *Rhone* 15 5
376† 8c Wreck of *Rhone* 20 5

1980

449† 75c *Golden Hind* (Drake) 80 80

453† 13c Island schooner, Virgin Gorda 15 10

1983

508 15c Traditional boat building—Frame
509 25c Traditional boat building—Planking
510 50c Traditional boat building—Launch
511 $1 Traditional boat building—Maiden voyage

                Set of 4 2.50 2.50

1984

528† 50c Wreck of *Rhone*, 1860 .... 90 95
529† $1 *Booker Viking* (tanker) 1.50 1.60
MS530 $1 *Boyne* (mail steamer) 1.60 1.90

533† 20c Wind-surfing 30 35
534† 20c Sail board 30 35
535† 30c Olympic yachts 40 50
536† 30c Yacht 40 50

543† 30c Green and yellow sailing dinghies .. 40 45
544† 30c Blue and red dinghies 40 45
545† 30c White and blue dinghies 40 45
546† 30c Red and yellow dinghies 40 45
547† 30c Blue and white dinghies 40 45

548 10c Sloop
549 35c Fishing boat
550 60c Schooner
551 75c Cargo boat

                Set of 4 2.75 3.00

1985

556 25c Cruising yachts 45 45

1986

592 35c *Flying Cloud* (sail cruise ship)
593 50c *Newport Clipper* (cruise liner)
594 75c *Cunard Countess* (cruise liner)
595 $1 *Sea Goddess* (cruise liner)

                Set of 4 4.25 4.50

612† $1 Loading rum barrels into rowing boat 1.00 1.00

615 35c *Sentinel* (cable ship)
616 35c *Retriever* (cable ship), 1961
617 60c *Cable Enterprise* (cable ship), 1964
618 60c *Mercury* (cable ship), 1962
619 75c *Recorder* (cable ship), 1955
620 75c *Pacific Guardian* (cable ship), 1984
621 $1 *Great Eastern* (cable ship), 1860s
622 $1 *Cable Venture* (cable ship), 1971

                Set of 8 6.25 7.25

MS622 Four sheets. (a) 40c *Sentinel*, 40c *Retriever*; (b) 50c *Cable Enterprise*, 50c *Mercury*; (c) 80c *Recorder*, 80c *Pacific Guardian*; (d) $1.50 *Great Eastern*, $1.50 *Cable Venture*

           Set of 4 sheets 8.00 8.25

1987

625 12c Wreck of 18th-century Spanish galleon
626 35c Wreck of H.M.S. *Astraea* (frigate), 1808
627 75c Wreck of *Rhone* (mail steamer), 1867
628 $1.50 Wreck of *Rocus* (freighter), 1929

                Set of 4 4.00 4.00
MS629 $2.50 Wreck of *Volvart* (brig), 1819 .... 4.00 4.25

662† 10c 18th-century sailing packet 12 15
MS666† $2.50 Mail steamer, 1880s 3.00 3.25

BRUNEI

South-east Asia
100 cents = 1 dollar

1949

As No. 115 of Antigua
97† 15c Paddle-steamer 1.50 1.40

1969

169 12c Oil rig
170 40c Oil rig
171 50c Oil rig

                Set of 3 1.50 1.10

1971

180† 75c *Pahlawan* (patrol boat) 2.50 3.25

1983

337†	50c Fishing canoe	40	45
338†	75c Trawler	60	65

1986

390†	50c *Seteria* (missile boat)	50	55

BUENOS AIRES

South America
8 reales = 1 peso

1858

P13	4r Early steamship	50.00	40.00
P17	1(IN)p Early steamship (brown)	60.00	40.00
P20	1(IN)p Early steamship (blue)	40.00	22.00
P25	1(TO)p Early steamship (blue)	70.00	50.00
P1	2p Early steamship	50.00	28.00
P4	3p Early steamship	£300	£150
P7	4p Early steamship	£1250	£900
P10	5p Early steamship	£1200	£700

BULGARIA

South-east Europe
100 stotinki = 1 lev

1947

694	50lev *Rodina* (freighter)	80	35

1948

735†	9lev *Radetski* (river paddle-steamer)	10	5

1950

775†	3lev Shipbuilding	35	5

815†	50lev Freighter	1.75	75

1953

892†	8s Crossing Danube by pontoon, 1877	20	5

1957

1071†	16s *Aurora* (Russian cruiser)	60	5

1962

1298†	2s Sailing ship, Varna	15	5

1302	1s *Varna* (freighter)		
1303	5s *Komsomol* (tanker)		
1304	20s *G. Dimitrov* (liner)		
	Set of 3	1.75	30

1307†	6s Fishing boats, Nesebur	40	5
1308†	8s Danube shipping	45	15

1966

1605†	10s River steamer, 1886	45	8

1619	2s *Radetski* (river paddle-steamer)	20	5

1968

1772†	1s Crossing Danube by pontoon, 1877	15	5

1799†	10s *Die Fregatte* (cruise ship)	40	5

1828	20s Viking ships	1.00	85

1969

1949†	1s Deep sea trawler	10	5

1970

2018†	4s Yachts, Albena	15	5
2019†	8s Yachts, Rousalka	25	5

1972

2138	18s *Vihren* (ore carrier)	1.10	20

1973

2216†	18s *NIV 100* (diving bell)	75	35

COLLECT MAMMALS ON STAMPS

A Stanley Gibbons thematic catalogue on this popular subject. Copies available at £7.50 (p. + p. £2) from: Stanley Gibbons Publications Ltd, 5 Parkside, Christchurch Road, Ringwood, Hants BH24 3SH.

2282 1s "Finn" class yacht
2283 2s "Flying Dutchman" class yacht
2284 3s "Soling" class yacht
2285 13s "Tempest" class yacht
2286 20s "470" class yacht
2287 40s "Tornado" class yacht
             Set of 6   4.00   2.40

1975

2410 13s Ryukyu sailing boat 20   10

2435 1s Egyptian galley
2436 2s Phoenician galley
2437 3s Greek trireme
2438 5s Roman galley
2439 13s Viking longship
2440 18s Venetian galley
             Set of 6   1.25   55

1977

2597 1s Hansa kogge
2598 2s Santa Maria (Columbus)
2599 3s Golden Hind (Drake)
2600 12s Santa Catherina (carrack)
2601 13s La Corona (galleon)
2602 43s Mediterranean galley
             Set of 6   1.75   65

1978

2655 23s Kor Karoli (circumnavigating yacht)   55   25

2703 13s Ferry, Varna–Ilichovsk   40   10

1980

2864 5s Jesus of Lubeck (Hansa kogge)
2865 8s Roman galley
2866 13s Eagle
2867 23s Mayflower (Pilgrim Fathers)
2868 35s Maltese galleon
2869 53s Royal Louis
             Set of 6   2.40   90

2883† 8s Tank landing-craft 20   5

1981

2935 35s Georgi Dimitrov (liner)
2936 43s Petimata of RMS (freighter)
2937 53s Khan Asparuch (tanker)
             Set of 3   3.25   1.25

1982

3051 13s Aurora (Russian cruiser)   30   10

1984

3135 5s General Vi Zaimov (bulk carrier)
3136 13s Mesta (tanker)
3137 25s Veleka (tanker)
3138 32s Geroite na Odesa (ferry)
3139 42s Rozhen (bulk carrier)
             Set of 5   2.50   1.25

MS3151 3lev Hamburg kogge 4.50   5.50

3209 13s Sofia (Danube cruise ship)   40   15

1985

MS3218 80s Akademik (research ship) 1.60   1.75

3286 5s 17th-century Dutch fly
3287 12s Sovereign of the Seas (English
       warship), 1637
3288 20s Mediterranean polacca
3289 25s Prince Royal (17th-century English
       warship)
3290 42s Xebec
3291 60s 17th-century English warship
             Set of 6   2.75   1.40

1986

3372 5s King of Prussia (galleon)
3373 13s 18th-century East Indiaman
3374 25s 18th-century xebec
3375 30s Sv. Pavel (Russian ship of the line)
3376 32s 18th-century topsail schooner
3377 42s Pobeda (Russian ship of the line)
             Set of 6   2.00   1.00

BURKINA FASO

West Africa
100 centimes = 1 franc

1986

853 250f Columbus before King of Portugal
       and Nina
854 300f Columbus using astrolabe and Santa
       Maria
855 400f Columbus in prison and Santa Maria
856 450f Landing on San Salvador and Pinta
       (air)
             Set of 4   5.50   4.25
MS857 1000f Fleet leaving Palos 4.50   4.75

BURMA

South-east Asia
1938 12 pies = 1 anna
16 annas = 1 rupee
1953 100 pyas = 1 kyat

1938

25†	2a6p Royal barge (red)	65	25
29†	8a Sailing craft on River Irrawaddy (green)	1.40	65

1940

No. 25 surcharged **COMMEMORATION POSTAGE STAMP 6TH MAY 1840 ONE ANNA 1A**

34	1a on 2a6p Royal barge	1.50	70

1945

Nos. 25 and 29 overprinted **MILY ADMN**

42†	2a6p Royal barge	12	35
46†	8a Sailing craft on River Irrawaddy	12	25

1946

As Nos. 25 and 29, but colours changed

57†	2a6p Royal barge (blue)	10	25
59†	8a Sailing craft on River Irrawaddy (mauve)	60	30

1947

ကြားဖြတ်
အစိုးရ။

Nos. 57 and 59 overprinted

74†	2a6p Royal barge	30	30
78†	8a Sailing craft on River Irrawaddy	35	35

OFFICIAL STAMPS

1939

Nos. 25 and 29 overprinted **SERVICE**

O21†	2a6p Royal barge	1.40	1.40
O23†	8a Sailing craft on River Irrawaddy	3.75	1.50

1946

Nos. 57 and 59 overprinted **SERVICE**

O34†	2a6p Royal barge	10	65
O36†	8a Sailing craft on River Irrawaddy	15	55

1947

Nos. O34 and O36 overprinted as on Nos. 74 and 78

O47†	2a6p Royal barge	90	75
O49†	8a Sailing craft on River Irrawaddy	90	60

BURUNDI

Central Africa
100 centimes = 1 franc

1970

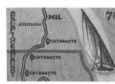

534†	7f Red Sea felucca	50	25
535†	14f Red Sea felucca	50	30

Nos. 534 and 535 each cover 18 different designs forming a map of the Nile.

1971

723†	31f + 1f Gondolas, Venice	80	35

1974

978†	14f Modern mail boat	50	25
979†	14f Modern mail boat	50	25
986†	31f Modern mail boat (air)	1.00	40
987†	31f Modern mail boat	1.00	40

Nos. 978/9 and 986/7 each form a composite design

1977

1278†	5f *Aurora* (Russian cruiser)	15	5

1294†	1f Tanker unloading	10	5

1979

1347†	27f *Hohenzollern* (on Tanganyika stamp No. 21)	40	20
1350†	60f Modern mail boat (on stamps Nos. 978/9)	80	45

1984

1436†	10f *Hohenzollern* (on Tanganyika stamp No. 21)	15	10
1439†	65f Modern mail boat (on stamps Nos. 978/9)	80	70

CAICOS ISLANDS

West Indies
100 cents = 1 dollar

1983

18†	35c Boat building, North Caicos	45	50
21†	$1.10 *Pinta* (Columbus)	1.40	1.50

1984

No. 21 overprinted **UNIVERSAL POSTAL UNION 1874-1984**

56†	$1.10 *Pinta* (Columbus)	1.25	1.50

59†	70c Fleet of Columbus	1.10	1.10
MS61†	$2 Fleet of Columbus	2.75	3.00

CAMBODIA

South-east Asia
100 cents = 1 riel

1960

98	2r Freighter	
99	5r Freighter	
100	20r Freighter	

	Set of 3 2.25	2.00

CAMEROUN

West Africa
1900 100 pfenning = 1 mark
1915 12 pence = 1 shilling
20 shillings = 1 pound
1915 100 centimes = 1 franc

GERMAN COLONY

1900

K 7	3pf *Hohenzollern* (German Imperial yacht)
K 8	5pf *Hohenzollern*
K 9	10pf *Hohenzollern*
K10	20pf *Hohenzollern*
K11	25pf *Hohenzollern*
K12	30pf *Hohenzollern*
K13	40pf *Hohenzollern*
K14	50pf *Hohenzollern*
K15	80pf *Hohenzollern*
K16	1m *Hohenzollern*
K17	2m *Hohenzollern*
K18	3m *Hohenzollern*
K19	5m *Hohenzollern*

	Set of 13 £190	£475

BRITISH OCCUPATION

1915

Nos. K7/19 surcharged **C.E.F.** *and value in English currency*

1	½d on 3pf *Hohenzollern* (German Imperial yacht)
2	½d on 5pf *Hohenzollern*
3	1d on 10pf *Hohenzollern*

4	2d on 20pf *Hohenzollern*		
5	2½d on 25pf *Hohenzollern*		
6	3d on 30pf *Hohenzollern*		
7	4d on 40pf *Hohenzollern*		
8	6d on 50pf *Hohenzollern*		
9	8d on 80pf *Hohenzollern*		
10	1s on 1m *Hohenzollern*		
11	2s on 2m *Hohenzollern*		
12	3s on 3m *Hohenzollern*		
13	5s on 5m *Hohenzollern*		
	Set of 13	£475	£650

FRENCH ADMINISTRATION

1915
Nos. 56/62 of Gabon overprinted **Corps Expeditionnaire Franco-Anglais CAMEROUN**

7†	25c Fishing boats, Libreville	27.00	10.00
8†	30c Fishing boats, Libreville	65.00	60.00
9†	35c Fishing boats, Libreville	20.00	10.00
10†	40c Fishing boats, Libreville	70.00	65.00
11†	45c Fishing boats, Libreville	70.00	60.00
12†	50c Fishing boats, Libreville	70.00	65.00
13†	75c Fishing boats, Libreville	£110	65.00

1931

109†	1f50 Liner	1.90	1.75

1937

110†	20c Liner	45	50
111†	30c Sailing ships	30	35

1941

190m†	50f Freighters in harbour	60	60

1953

262†	200f Freighters, Douala	4.50	80

1954

264	15f Landing craft, Normandy, 1944	1.75	1.40

1961
No. 262 surcharged **REPUBLIQUE FEDERALE 10/-**

296a†	10s on 200f Freighters, Douala	14.00	14.00

1965

383†	18f *De Grasse* (cruiser)	80	55
402†	50f Racing pirogues, Edea	1.60	50

1966

434†	60f *Vigilant* (gunboat)	80	40

1968

494†	60f Tug and freighters, Douala	1.10	60
505	30f Tanker, Port Gentil	55	35

1971

601†	20f Pirogue	30	25
606†	30f *Villalba* (deep sea trawler)	35	25
608†	70f Fishing boats, Douala	65	35
609†	150f Shrimp boats, Douala	1.60	75

COLLECT RAILWAYS ON STAMPS
A Stanley Gibbons thematic catalogue on this popular subject. Copies available at £7.50 (p. + p. £2) from: Stanley Gibbons Publications Ltd, 5 Parkside, Christchurch Road, Ringwood, Hants BH24 3SH.

614†	50f *Hohenzollern* (German Imperial yacht) (on stamp No. K19)	55	30
620	250f Pirogue	4.00	3.00

1972

639†	100f Gondolas, Venice	90	45
640†	200f Gondolas, Venice	2.25	90
644†	40f Pirogue, River Wouri	35	25

1973

679†	45f Pirogue (on stamp No. 620)	35	20
704†	50f Pirogue on beach	50	30

1975

745	40f Local fishing boats		
746	45f Local fishing boats		
	Set of 2	1.00	50

757† 100f Lafayette and French warship, 1776   80   55

1977

803 70f *Hohenzollern* (German Imperial yacht)
     (on stamp No. K16)   55   35

1978

835 100f Capt. Cook and Siege of Quebec
836 250f H.M.S. *Adventure* and H.M.S.
     Resolution (Cook)
                          Set of 2   1.75 1.25

1979

855 100f *Hohenzollern* (German Imperial
     yacht) (on stamp No. K9)   55   40

1981

913 60f *Cam Iroko* (freighter)   45   25

1983

966 500f Container ship 2.00 1.75

STANLEY GIBBONS
STAMP COLLECTING SERIES

Introductory booklets on *How to Start, How to Identify Stamps* and *Collecting by Theme.* A series of well illustrated guides at a low price.
Write for details.

CANADA

North America
100 cents = 1 dollar

1908

195† 20c *Grande Hermine* and *Petite Hermine*
     (Cartier), 1534 . . . . £100 55.00

1928

284† 50c *Bluenose* (fishing schooner) 80.00 24.00

1933

331 5c *Royal William* (paddle-steamer) 4.00 1.25

1935

340† 13c *Britannia* (Royal racing yacht), 1935   5.00 2.50

1937

371† 6c *Distributor* (stern paddle-steamer) 1.50 20

1942

386† 20c Launching H.M.C.S. *La Malbaie*
     (corvette) 1.50 15
388† $1 H.M.S. *Cossack* (destroyer) 48.00 4.00

1946

406† $1 *Abegweit* (train ferry) 27.00 1.00

1949

412 4c Cabot's *Matthew*, 1497   10   8

1951

437† 5c *City of Toronto* and *Prince George*
     (paddle-steamers)   65   1.50

1953

477† 10c Eskimo in kayak   15   5

1957

491† 5c Canadian canoe   25   10

1963

537 5c Frobisher's barque *Gabriel*, 1575   20   5

1967

606† 6c Bulk carrier (red)   45   5
607† 6c Bulk carrier (black)   25   5
609† 7c Bulk carrier   30   5

1968

624 5c *Nonsuch* (ketch), 1668   20   10

1972

724† 8c Alogonkian canoes   40   10

1975

818 8c *Wm. D. Lawrence* (sail merchantman)
819 8c *Neptune* (steamer)
820 8c *Beaver* (paddle-steamer)
821 8c *Quadra* (steamer)
                          Set of 4   2.00 55

1976

Canada 10

851	10c *Northcote* (paddle-steamer)		
852	10c *Passport* (paddle-steamer)		
853	10c *Chicora* (paddle-steamer)		
854	10c *Athabasca* (steamer)		
	Set of 4	1.10	45

1977

12 Canada

893†	12c *Arctic* (survey ship)	15	5

Canada 12

902	12c "Pinky" (fishing boat)		
903	12c Five-masted schooner		
904	12c "Tern" schooner		
905	12c Mackinaw boat		
	Set of 4	55	35

1978

Canada 14

925†	14c Sculpture of Inuitumiak	15	5

Canada 14

931	14c *Chief Justice Robinson* (paddle-steamer)		
932	14c *St.Roch* (steamer)		
933	14c *Northern Light* (steamer)		
934	14c *Labrador* (steamer)		
	Set of 4	80	45

1982

Canada 60

1041†	60c *Bluenose* (fishing schooner) (on stamp No. 284)	60	45

1984

1118	32c Cartier's *Grande Hermine*, 1534	45	25

Canada 32

1119	32c *Eagle* (U.S. Coastguard cadet ship)	45	25

1122	32c Freighter in St. Lawrence seaway	45	25

CANADA 32

1128†	32c 18th-century scow, Louisbourg	50	50
1130†	32c 19th-century three-masted ship, Ile Verte	50	50
1131†	32c Early paddle-steamer, Gibraltar Point	50	50

1209†	34c Viking ships	50	50
1210†	34c *Matthew* (Cabot), 1497	50	50
1211†	34c Henry Hudson cast adrift in rowing boat, 1611	50	50

1222	34c *Accommodation* (paddle-steamer)	35	40

1987

1232†	34c Indian canoe, Lake Superior	30	35

1245	36c *Segwun* (lake steamer)		
1246	36c *Princess Marguerite* (coastal steamer)		
	Set of 2	60	70

36 Canada

1247†	36c Figurehead from wreck of *Hamilton*, 1813	30	35
1248†	36c Wrecked hull of *San Juan*, 1565	30	35

1988

1286†	37c H.M.S. *Discovery* (Vancouver), 1795	35	40
1287†	37c Expedition portaging canoes, 1808	35	40

OFFICIAL STAMPS

1949
No. 406 overprinted **O.H.M.S.**

O9†	$1 *Abegweit* (train ferry)	45.00	40.00

1951
No. 406 overprinted **G**

O28†	$1 *Abegweit* (train ferry)	48.00	40.00

1953
No. 477 overprinted **G**

O45†	10c Eskimo in kayak	35	5

SPECIAL DELIVERY

1927

S5	20c *Ile de France* (liner)	8.00	6.50

CANAL ZONE

Central America
1917 100 centesimos = 1 balboa
1924 100 cents = 1 dollar

1915
Nos. 178/82 of Panama overprinted **CANAL ZONE**

59†	12c *Panama* (cargo liner) at Culebra Cut	13.50	4.75
60†	15c *Panama* (cargo liner) at Culebra Cut	35.00	20.00
61†	24c *Cristobal* (cargo liner) in Gatun Lock	35.00	10.00
62†	50c Freighters in Balboa docks	£250	£150
63†	1b *Nereus* (U.S. Navy collier) in Pedro Miguel Lock	£130	50.00

1924
No. 698 of U.S.A. overprinted **CANAL ZONE**

94†	20c Sailing ship, Golden Gate, San Francisco	6.00	3.25

1931

126	4c Steamer in Panama Canal		
127	5c Steamer in Panama Canal		
128	6c Steamer in Panama Canal		
129	10c Steamer in Panama Canal		
130	15c Steamer in Panama Canal		
131	20c Steamer in Panama Canal		
132	30c Steamer in Panama Canal		
133	40c Steamer in Panama Canal		
134	$1 Steamer in Panama Canal		
	Set of 9	17.00	5.50

1939

152†	5c *Andrea F. Luckenbach* (freighter)	1.40	95
154†	7c U.S.S. *Houston* (cruiser)	2.75	1.40
158†	12c *Santa Clara* (liner)	7.00	4.75
160†	15c *Panama* (liner)	11.00	4.00
162†	20c *Duchessa D'Aosta* and *President Polk* (liners)	13.00	3.25
145†	15c Freighter and fishing boat, Fort Amador (air)	3.25	1.10
146†	25c Fishing boat, Cristobal Harbour	12.00	7.50
147†	30c U.S.S. *Chester* (cruiser)	9.50	5.50

1949

198†	18c *Panama* (paddle-steamer) *c* 1848	2.75	1.60

1958

214 4c *Ancon* (freighter), 1939 .... 40 20

1976

249 13c *Cascadas* (dredger) 55 20

OFFICIAL STAMPS

1941

Nos. 127/34 overprinted **Official Panama Canal**

O167	5c Steamer in Panama Canal		
O168	6c Steamer in Panama Canal		
O169	10c Steamer in Panama Canal		
O170	15c Steamer in Panama Canal		
O171	20c Steamer in Panama Canal		
O172	30c Steamer in Panama Canal		
O173	40c Steamer in Panama Canal		
O174	$1 Steamer in Panama Canal		
	Set of 8	70.00	22.00

CAPE JUBY

North-west Africa
100 centimos = 1 peseta

1929

Nos. 506 and 508 of Spain overprinted **CABO JUBY**

38†	15c Caravel	20	15
40†	25c Caravel	20	15

1948

No. 317 of Spanish Morocco overprinted **CABO JUBY**

164† 10p *Arango* (freighter) at quay 1.50 1.10

CAPE VERDE ISLANDS

Atlantic Ocean
100 centavos = 1 escudo

1913

Surcharged **REPUBLICA CABO VERDE** *and new value*

(a) On Nos. 1/2, 5 and 7 of Portuguese Colonies

147†	½c on 2½r Departure of Vasco Da Gama's fleet	50	30
148†	½c on 5r Vasco Da Gama's fleet at Calicut	50	30
151†	5c on 50r *Sao Gabriel* (flagship)	70	60
153†	10c on 100r *Sao Gabriel*	70	70

(b) On Nos. 104/5, 108 and 110 of Macao

155†	½c on ½a Departure of Vasco da Gama's fleet	50	40
156†	½c on 1a Vasco da Gama's fleet at Calicut	50	40
159†	5c on 8a *Sao Gabriel* (flagship)	2.50	1.90
161†	10c on 16a *Sao Gabriel*	80	70

(c) On Nos. 58/9, 62 and 64 of Timor

163†	½c on ½a Departure of Vasco da Gama's fleet	50	40
164†	½c on 1a Vasco da Gama's fleet at Calicut	50	40
167†	5c on 8a *Sao Gabriel* (flagship)	2.50	1.90
169†	10c on 16a *Sao Gabriel*	80	70

1921

No. 153 surcharged

253† 4c on 10c on 100r *Sao Gabriel* (flagship) 60 60

1952

350† 1e Caravel 12 8

1967

403	1e *Mandovy* (Portuguese gunboat)		
404	1e50 *Augusto Castilho* (Portuguese minesweeper)		
	Set of 2	75	35

1968

409† 50c *Mauretania* (liner), 1939 .... 10 5

1972

425 5e Galleons at Cape Verde 40 15

1978

463 1e *Cabo Verde* (freighter) 15 5

1980

470 4e Sailing ships, Mindelo, 1880 .... 15 10

492	3e *Arca Verdel* (freighter)		
493	5e50 *Ilha do Maio* (freighter)		
494	7e50 *Ilha do Komo* (freighter)		
495	9e *Boa Vista* (freighter)		
496	12e *Santo Antao* (freighter)		
497	30e *Santiago* (freighter)		
	Set of 6	2.25	1.25

1982

532 12e *Morrissey Ernestina* (schooner) 50 20

1982

533 10e50 Freighters under construction, San Vicente shipyard 40 20

1987

586† 12e Fishing boats, Santiago 15 8

588	12e *Carvalho* (schooner)		
589	16e *Nauta* (cutter)		
590	50e *Maria Sony* (schooner)		
	Set of 3	1.00	45
MS591	60e × 2 *Madalan* (brigantine)	85	85

CAROLINE ISLANDS

Pacific Ocean
100 pfennig = 1 mark

1901

As Nos. K7/19 of Cameroun, but inscribed "KAROLINEN"

13	3pf *Hohenzollern* (German Imperial yacht)	
14	5pf *Hohenzollern*	
15	10pf *Hohenzollern*	
16	20pf *Hohenzollern*	
17	25pf *Hohenzollern*	
18	30pf *Hohenzollern*	
19	40pf *Hohenzollern*	
20	50pf *Hohenzollern*	
21	80pf *Hohenzollern*	
22	1m *Hohenzollern*	
23	2m *Hohenzollern*	
24	3m *Hohenzollern*	
25	5m *Hohenzollern*	
	Set of 13 £120	£550

CASTELROSSO

Mediterranean
100 centesimi = 1 lira

ITALIAN OCCUPATION

1932

No. 333 of Italy overprinted **CASTELROSSO**

30† 10c Fishing boats, Nice 42.00 38.00

CAYES OF BELIZE

Central America
100 cents = 1 dollar

Appendix

The following stamps have either been issued in excess of postal needs, or have not been made available to the public in reasonable quantities at face value. Miniature sheets, imperforate stamps etc, are excluded from this section.

1984

Marine Life. Map and Views. 75c Spanish Galleon, $5 Game fishing boat
Lloyd's List. 25c Queen Elizabeth 2, $1 Loss of the *Fishburn*
90th Anniv of "Caye Service" Local Stamps. 75c Steam yacht

1985

Shipwrecks. $1 *Santa Yaga*, $1 *Comet*, $1 *Yeldham*, $1 *Oxford*

CAYMAN ISLANDS

West Indies
1935 12 pence = 1 shilling
20 shillings = 1 pound
1969 100 cents = 1 Jamaican dollar

1935

101†	½d Cat boat	40	15
104†	2d Cat boat	1.00	1.00
108†	1s Cat boat	5.00	6.50

1938

120†	2½d *Rembro* (schooner) (blue)	20	35
120a†	2½d *Rembro* (orange)	1.25	30
125†	5s *Rembro*	9.00	9.00

1949

As No. 115 *of Antigua*

132†	3d Paddle-steamer	60	25

1950

135†	¼d Cat boat	15	60
145†	2s *Ziroma* (schooner)	6.50	7.50
146†	5s Boat building	8.50	11.00

1953

As Nos. 135 *and* 145/6, *but with portrait of Queen Elizabeth II*

148†	¼d Cat boat	20	12
159	2s *Ziroma* (schooner)	6.00	4.00
160	5s Boat building	7.00	4.75

1962

166†	1d Cat boat	20	12
172†	6d *Lydia E. Wilson* (schooner)	1.00	25
176†	1s9d Sailing dinghy	2.75	1.50

1966

203	1s Cayman schooner		
204	1s9d Cayman schooner		
	Set of 2	25	15

1967

205†	4d Speed boat	10	5
207†	1s Game fishing boat	12	5
208†	1s9d Sailing yachts	15	10

1969

229†	8d Motor vessels at berth	30	10

No. 229 *surcharged*

244†	7c on 8d Motor vessels at berth	12	10

1970

As No. 229, *but face value in decimal currency*

279†	7c Motor vessels at berth	30	10

1972

320	6c Cayman schooner (on currency note)	10	5

1974

360†	8c Cayman schooner	12	10

1976

410	20c Olympic yachts		
411	50c Olympic yachts		
	Set of 2	75	90

1977

427†	8c Prince Charles and sailing ship	12	20

1978

441†	3c *Southward* (cruise liner)		
442†	5c *Renaissance* (cruise liner)		
443†	30c Freighter in new harbour		
444†	50c *Daphne* (cruise liner)		
	Set of 4	1.50	1.40

1980

501†	10c Cat boat	15	10

1982

556†	50c Catamaran	85	85

1984

586	5c *Song of Norway* (cruise liner)		
587	10c Cat boats in George Town harbour		
588	25c Wreck of *Ridgefield*		
589	50c *Goldfield* (schooner)		
	Set of 4	1.75	1.75
MS590	$1 *Goldfield* (schooner) (different)	2.10	2.25

No. 589 *overprinted* **U.P.U. CONGRESS HAMBURG 1984**

591	50c *Goldfield* (schooner)	1.00	1.25

597†	5c Schooner	10	12
600†	25c Yachts	50	55
601†	25c Power boat	50	55

1985

609	5c Wreck of freighter		
610	25c Wreck of sailing ship		
611	35c Wreck of trawler		
612	40c Submerged wreck		
	Set of 4	2.40	2.25

1987

648†	15c Catamaran and sailboard	30	30
649†	25c Diving launch	45	45

STANLEY GIBBONS
STAMP COLLECTING SERIES

Introductory booklets on *How to Start*, *How to Identify Stamps* and *Collecting by Theme*. A series of well illustrated guides at a low price.

Write for details.

CENTRAL AFRICAN EMPIRE

Central Africa
100 centimes = 1 franc

1977

Nos. 395 and 432 of Central African Republic overprinted
EMPIRE CENTRAFRICAIN

491†	100f Dugout canoe	90	90
464†	200f Dr. Schweitzer in dugout canoe	1.75	1.75

1978

558†	60f Paddle-steamer	40	20

578†	60f H.M.S. *Endeavour* (Cook)	50	20
581†	350f Masked paddlers in canoe	2.00	1.00

609†	150f *Aurora* (Russian cruiser)	75	50
MS612†	500f *Aurora* (Russian cruiser)	2.75	2.75

CENTRAL AFRICAN REPUBLIC

Central Africa
100 centimes = 1 franc

1968

163	30f Tanker, Port Gentil, Gabon	50	25

177	10f *Ville de Bangui* (river vessel), 1958		
178	30f *J. B. Gouandjia* (river vessel), 1968		
179	50f *Lamblin* (river vessel), 1944		
180	100f *Pie X* (river vessel), 1894 (air)		
181	130f *Ballay* (river vessel), 1891		
	Set of 5	4.00	2.00

1975

395	200f Dr Schweitzer in dugout canoe	1.60	1.00

400†	150f River tug	1.00	65

1976

404	30f *Jean Bedel Bokassa* (river vessel)		
405	40f *Jean Bedel Bokassa*		
	Set of 2	70	45

432	100f Dugout canoe	80	50

1981

779	40f C. V. Rietschoten and ship		
780	50f M. Pajot and ship		
781	60f L. Jaworski and ship		
782	80f M. Birch and ship		
783	100f O. Kersauson and ship (air)		
784	200f Sir Francis Chichester and *Gipsy Moth*		
	Set of 6	2.75	1.75
MS785	500f A. Colas and ship	2.75	1.75

1982

835†	300f *Savannah* (nuclear-powered freighter)	1.75	1.25

1983

949	300f Olympic yacht	1.00	1.00

COLLECT MAMMALS ON STAMPS

A Stanley Gibbons thematic catalogue on this popular subject. Copies available at £7.50 (p. + p. £2) from: Stanley Gibbons Publications Ltd, 5 Parkside, Christchurch Road, Ringwood, Hants BH24 3SH.

1984

1012	65f *Le Pericles* (mail-ship)		
1013	120f *Pereire* (steamer)		
1014	250f *Admella* (passenger steamer)		
1015	400f *Royal William* (paddle-steamer)		
1016	500f *Great Britain* (steamer)		
	Set of 5	5.50	4.50

1060	90f Piccard's *Trieste* (bathysphere)	40	25

1985

Nos. 1014/15 overprinted

1083†	250f *Admella* (overprinted **ARGENTINA '85 BUENOS AIRES**)	90	80
1085†	400f *Royal William* (overprinted **ITALIA '85 ROME**)	1.40	1.25

1092	5f Yachts, Stockholm	10	5

1111†	400f Mississippi stern-wheeler	1.75	1.60

1986

1179†	240f Landing of Columbus	1.40	1.00
1181†	400f Fleet of Columbus (air)	2.00	1.50
1182†	500f Fleet of Columbus	2.40	1.75

Appendix

The following stamps have either been issued in excess of postal needs, or have not been made available to the public in reasonable quantities at face value. Miniature sheets, imperforate stamps, etc, are excluded from this section.

1981

Navigators. 1500f Riguidel and ship

CEYLON

Indian Ocean
100 cents = 1 rupee

1951

426†	50c Outrigger canoe	30	5

1956

438†   3c Ancient sailing craft 15   10

1958

As No. 426 but inscriptions changed
459†   50c Outrigger canoe 30   5

CHAD
Central Africa
100 centimes = 1 franc

1931
As No. 109 of Cameroun
61†   1f50 Liner 1.25   1.60

1959

62†   15f Fishing canoe 25   12

1964

109†   30f Canoe building 45   25

1969

222†   100f H. Barth in canoe, 1851 .... 1.10   55

251†   1f Olympic yacht 20   20

1972

369   40f Sailing ship, Venice
370   45f Gondolas, Venice
371   140f Gondolas, Grand Canal, Venice
                              Set of 3   2.50   1.40

1974

410†   30f Mail canoe 35   25

1976

MS447†   400f De Grasse and Battle of Virginia
Capes, 1781 .... 3.00   1.60

480†   120f 19th-century French sail warship .. 1.40   65

1977

485†   200f Harbour ferry, New York 1.60   55
MS486   500f Harbour ferry, New York 3.00   1.40

495†   100f Lafayette and French ships, 1777 .. 80   40

1979

MS577†   500f Olympic yachts 2.50   1.10

1972

578   65f Reed canoe
579   100f Sailing canoe
580   200f *Curacao* (paddle-steamer)
581   300f *Calypso* (liner)
                              Set of 4   3.50   1.50
MS582   500f *Normandie* (liner) 2.50   1.10

1981
Nos. 578/9 surcharged **POSTES 1981 60F**
594†   60f on 65f Reed canoe 30   20
595†   60f on 100f Sailing canoe 30   20

1983

654†   300f Paddle-tugs, London, 1837 .... 1.40   1.25

1984

730   50f Freighter
731   60f Freighter
732   70f Freighter
733   125f Freighter (air)
734   250f Freighter
                              Set of 5   2.50   1.75

741†   200f Sailing boat on Lake Chad 1.00   80

749   90f British East Indiaman
750   125f *Vera Cruz* (steamer)
751   200f *Carlisle Castle* (sail merchantman)
752   300f *Britannia* (steamer), 1887
                              Set of 4   3.00   2.40

1985

784†   350f Piccard's *Trieste* (bathysphere) 1.60   1.25

809† 250f Modern liner 1.40 1.00

POSTAGE DUE STAMPS

1930

D77† 1f Pirogue on Lake Chad 1.10 1.25
D78† 2f Pirogue on Lake Chad 2.25 2.50
D79† 3f Pirogue on Lake Chad 16.00 18.00

CHAMBA

Indian sub-continent
12 pies = 1 anna
16 annas = 1 rupee

1938

No. 256 of India overprinted **CHAMBA STATE**
91† 6a *Strathnaver* (liner) 6.00 13.00

CHILE

South America
1910 100 centavos = 1 peso
1960 100 centesimos = 1 escudo
1975 100 centavos = 1 peso

1910

123† 10c *Lautaro* and *Esmeralda* (sail
frigates) in battle 90 25
124† 12c Capture of *Maria Isabella* (sail
frigate) 2.40 90

1936

257† 10c Fishing boats 15 10
263† 1p *Orduna* (liner), Valparaiso 1.25 35

1938

274† 1p *Calbuco* (fishing boat) 15 5
275† 1p80 Lake steamer 60 20
338h† 2p Freighter, Valparaiso 60 5

1940

279 80c + 2p20 *Abtao* (armed steamer)
280 3p60 + 6p40 *Abtao*
Set of 2 3.25 2.75

1942

404c† 60c Fishing boat 15 5

1948

378 40c *Esmeralda* (sail frigate) at Battle of
Iquique, 1879 .... 25 5

1959

476† 40p Yacht 15 5

1965

561† 40c Fishing boats, Angelmo 15 5

1966

572 10c *Chile* and *Peru* (paddle-steamers)
573 70c *Chile* and *Peru* (air)
Set of 2 25 15

1967

578† 20c *Yelcho* (coastguard vessel), 1917 .. 15 5

1968

600† 30c Galleon and modern ferry 15 5

1970

640 40c Schooner, 1820
641 2e Schooner, 1820 (air)
Set of 2 30 10

1971

660 52c *Lago Maihue* (freighter)
661 5e *Lago Maihue* (air)
Set of 2 25 10

662 5e O'Higgins and fleet, 1821
663 1e O'Higgins and fleet, 1821 (air)
Set of 2 30 10

676 35c Magellan and caravel 10 5

1972

697 1e15 *Esmeralda* (cadet ship) 15 5

1973

707 20e Destroyer 20 5

1974

736† 200e Galleon, 1574 .... 40 12

1975

745† 150e Shipwreck 15 8
746† 150e Lifeboat 15 8

749 500e *Baquedano* (sail/steam corvette)
750 500e *Lautaro* (sail frigate)
751 500e *Chacabuco* (cruiser)
752 500e *Esmeralda* (cadet ship)
753 800e *Baquedano*
754 800e *Lautaro*
755 800e *Chacabuco*
756 800e *Esmeralda*
757 1000e *Baquedano*
758 1000e *Lautaro*
759 1000e *Chacabuco*
760 1000e *Esmeralda*
　　　　　　　　　　Set of 12　5.00　1.90

769 1p Lord Cochrane and fleet, 1820
770 1p Battle of Valdiva, 1820
771 1p Capture of *Esmeralda*, 1820
772 1p *Cochrane* (cruiser), 1874
773 1p *Cochrane* (destroyer), 1962
　　　　　　　　　　Set of 5　1.25　55

1977

790 2p Schooner 15 5

1978

799 10p Freighter loading timber 45 8

As No. 799, but inscribed "CORREOS" and Chilean flag added
800 20p Freighter 1.00 10

807 20p Chilean fleet, 1778 .... 1.00 80

1979

817 3p50 Battle of Iquique, 1879
818 3p50 Battle of Punta Gruesa, 1879
819 3p50 Battle of Angamos, 1879
　　　　　　　　　　Set of 3　1.25　55

838 3p50 Freighter, Puerto Williams 35 15

1981

875 3p50 Rowing boats, Arturo Prat Base 35 15

1982

917 20p Trawler 1.00 60

933 7p *Copiapo* (steamer), 1872 .... 40 12

1984

978† 9p Freighter, Valparaiso 25 12

1986

1053 40p *Santiaguillo* (caravel), 1536 .... 55 30

1060 35p *Ancud* (schooner) 40 30
1061 35p *Aguila* (brigantine) 40 30
1062 35p *Esmeralda* (sail corvette) 40 30
1063 35p *O'Higgins* (sail frigate) 40 30

1987

1096 100p Rowing boat, Arturo Prat Base
1097 100p Rowing boats, Arturo Prat Base
　　　　　　　　　　Set of 2　1.10　90

1110 60p *Almirante Latorre* (battleship), 1920
1111 60p *O'Higgins* (cruiser)
　　　　　　　　　　Set of 2　70　50

1134 50p Battle of Iquique, 1879 .... 30 25

1142 45p Antarctic supply ship 25 20

OFFICIAL STAMPS

1939

No. 274 overprinted **Servicio del ESTADO**
O280† 1p *Calbuco* (fishing boat) 3.25 2.00

1941

Nos. 274/5 and 338h overprinted **OFICIAL**
O339† 1p *Calbuco* (fishing boat) 1.60 85
O288† 1p80 Lake steamer 5.75 3.75
O442† 2p Freighter, Valparaiso 1.60 25

CHINA

Eastern Asia
100 cents = 1 dollar (yuan)

Chinese Republic

1913

309† ½c Junk 10 5
310† 1c Junk 10 5
311† 1½c Junk 60 45
312† 2c Junk 20 5
313† 3c Junk 20 5
292† 4c Junk (red) 30 8
314† 4c Junk (grey) 3.25 20
315† 4c Junk (olive) 25 5

316†	5c Junk	30	5
294†	6c Junk (grey)	45	20
317†	6c Junk (red)	40	10
318†	6c Junk (brown)	8.00	1.50
319†	7c Junk	70	75
320†	8c Junk	60	20
321†	10c Junk	45	5

1920

Nos. 292, 294 and 312/13 surcharged in Chinese with English figures at the bottom

349	1c on 2c Junk		
361	2c on 3c Junk		
350	3c on 4c Junk		
351	5c on 6c Junk		
	Set of 4	10.50	4.75

1925

Nos. 312/15 surcharged in Chinese with English figures at the top

366	1c on 2c Junk		
367	1c on 3c Junk		
369	1c on 4c Junk (olive)		
370	1c on 4c Junk (grey)		
	Set of 4	1.50	25

1936

449†	5c Freighters and junks	40	10

1947

985†	$100 *Momus* (liner)	5	50
988†	$400 Junk	5	50
989†	$500 Junk	5	30

1948

1001	$5000 Junk (on stamp No. 989) (red)		
1002	$5000 Junk (on stamp No. 984) (green)		
	Set of 2	55	1.85

1044	$20000 *Hai Tien* (freighter) and *Eton* (steamer), 1872		
1045	$30000 *Hai Tien* and *Eton*		
1046	$40000 *Kiang Ya* (freighter)		
1047	$60000 *Kiang Ya*		
	Set of 4	35	1.75

1949

Revenue stamps surcharged

1122	50c on $20 Liner	
1137	$1 on $15 Liner	
1127	$2 on $50 Liner	
1144	$3 on $50 Liner	
1138	$5 on $500 Liner	
1129	$10 on $30 Liner	
1140	$15 on $20 Liner	

1141	$25 on $20 Liner	
1145	$50 on $50 Liner	
1147	$50 on $300 Liner	
1130	$80 on $50 Liner	
1146	$100 on $50 Liner	
1124	$200 on $50 Liner	
1142	$200 on $500 Liner	
1125	$300 on $50 Liner	
1143	$500 on $15 Liner	
1134	$500 on $30 Liner	
1135	$1,000 on $50 Liner	
1150	$1,000 on $100 Liner	
1126	$1,500 on $50 Liner	
1151	$2,000 on $300 Liner	
	Set of 21	13.00 18.00

Surcharged as Nos. 1122/51 but key pattern inverted at top and bottom

1183	$50 on $10 Liner	
1184	$100 on $10 Liner	
1185	$500 on $10 Liner	
1186	$1,000 on $10 Liner	
1187	$5,000 on $20 Liner	
1188	$10,000 on $20 Liner	
1189	$50,000 on $20 Liner	
1190	$100,000 on $20 Liner	
1191	$500,000 on $20 Liner	
1192	$2,000,000 on $20 Liner	
1193	$5,000,000 on $20 Liner	
	Set of 11	£850 £250

Revenue stamps overprinted for type of service

1232	$10 Liner (B)	
1233	$30 Liner (A)	
1234	$50 Liner (C)	
1235	$100 Liner (D)	
1236	$200 Liner (A)	
1237	$500 Liner (A)	
	Set of 6	85.00 60.00

Overprint translation: (A) Domestic Letter fee: (B) Express Letter Fee: (C) Registered Letter Fee: (D) Air Mail Fee

Revenue stamps surcharged

1312	1c on $20 Liner	
1284	1c on $5,000 Liner	
1285	4c on $100 Liner	
1286	4c on $3,000 Liner	
1313	10c on $20 Liner	
1287	10c on $50 Liner	
1288	10c on $1,000 Liner	
1289	20c on $1,000 Liner	
1290	50c on $30 Liner	
1291	50c on $50 Liner	
1292	$1 on $50 Liner	
	Set of 11	30.00 35.00

On Nos. 1312/13 the Key pattern is inverted at top and bottom

Manchuria

KIRIN AND HEILUNGKIANG

1927

用貼黑吉限

Nos. 309/21 of Chinese Republic overprinted

1†	½c Junk	10	8
2†	1c Junk	10	5
3†	1½c Junk	60	50
4†	3c Junk	25	20
5†	3c Junk	40	40
6†	4c Junk (olive)	20	5
7†	5c Junk	40	15
8†	6c Junk (red)	50	30
9†	7c Junk	1.25	1.25
10†	8c Junk	1.10	1.10
11†	10c Junk	1.00	5

PORT ARTHUR AND DARIEN

1949

54†	S10 Liner	8.00	8.00

No. 54 surcharged

59†	$100 on $10 Liner	£250	£250
61†	$500 on $10 Liner	£400	£400

Sinkiang

1915

限新省貼用

Nos. 309/21 of Chinese Republic overprinted

47†	½c Junk	20	15
48†	1c Junk	20	10
49†	1½c Junk	90	90
50†	2c Junk	30	30
4†	3c Junk	20	8
5†	4c Junk (red)	30	30
52†	4c Junk (grey)	2.00	1.50
53†	4c Junk (olive)	90	40
6†	5c Junk	30	20
7†	6c Junk (grey)	40	50
55†	6c Junk (red)	1.00	70
56†	6c Junk (brown)	10.00	12.00
8†	7c Junk	85	1.00
9†	8c Junk	90	70
10†	10c Junk	70	25

1932

空航

Nos. 6 and 10 overprinted

83†	5c Junk	75.00	45.00
84†	10c Junk	75.00	38.00

Szechwan

1933

限川四貼用

Nos. 310 and 316 of Chinese Republic overprinted

1†	1c Junk	40	25
2†	5c Junk	1.00	5

Yunnan

1926

限滇省貼用

Nos 309/21 of Chinese Republic overprinted

1†	½c Junk	15	15
2†	1c Junk	25	5
3†	1½c Junk	60	60
4†	2c Junk	40	25
5†	3c Junk	35	20
6†	4c Junk (olive)	35	5
7†	5c Junk	40	25
8†	6c Junk (red)	1.00	60
9†	7c Junk	1.50	1.50
10†	8c Junk	1.10	90
11†	10c Junk	70	8

Chinese People's Republic
1949 100 cents = 1 yuan
1955 100 fen = 1 yuan

CENTRAL CHINA

1949

Revenue stamps as 1949 issue of Chinese Republic surcharged
CC71 $3 on $30 Liner
CC72 $15 on $15 Liner
CC73 $30 on $50 Liner
CC74 $60 on $50 Liner
CC75 $130 on $15 Liner
Set of 5 6.00 9.00

Nos. 1151, 1124, 1142, 1147, 1146 and 1141 of Chinese Republic surcharged
CC79 $5 on $2,000 on $300 Liner
CC80 $10 on $200 on $50 Liner
CC81 $10 on $200 on $500 Liner
CC82 $30 on $50 on $300 Liner
CC83 $50 on $100 on $50 Liner
CC84 $100 on $25 on $20 Liner
Set of 6 10.00 11.00

EAST CHINA

1949

No. 1122 of Chinese Republic surcharged
EC351 $5 on 50c on $20 Liner
EC352 $10 on 50c on $20 Liner
EC353 $20 on 50c on $20 Liner
EC354 $20 on 50c on $20 Liner
Set of 4 17.00 18.00

GENERAL ISSUES

1952

1563† $800 Destroyers 20 10

1955

1677† 8f Freighter 30 10

1957

1730† 52f Collier 12.00 50

1733† 8f Yellow River ferry 2.50 30

1960

1894† 10f Sampan 5.50 60

1965 8f Yue Jin (freighter) 4.25 1.00

1972

2485 8f Fenglei (freighter)
2486 8f Taching No 30 (tanker)
2487 8f Chang Seng (cargo-liner)
2488 8f Hsien-feng (dredger)
Set of 4 1.40 1.40

1976

2638† 8f Canal vessels 20 20
2644† 8f Freighters in shipyard 20 20

1978

2751† 8f Tanker 15 10
2752† 20f Exploration (drilling ship) and oil rig 30 20

1979

2871† 8f Sampan 15 12

2891† 8f Submarine 15 10

1980

2975† 2f Freighter 15 15

2983† 60f Ancient junk 50 35

3009† 60f Guilin ferry 40 30

1984

3317† 20f Freighter in lock 25 12

Taiwan
100 cents = 1 yuan

1957

265 40c Hai Min (freighter) and Kiang Foo
     (river vessel)
266 80c Hai Min and Kiang Foo
267 $2.80 Hai Min and Kiang Foo
Set of 3 1.75 50

1960

348 $1.60 Yu-Khi (postal launch) 70 20

1962

461 80c Liner
462 $3.60 Haimin (freighter)
Set of 2 2.10 5

1964

512 $2 Ancient ship and modern freighter
513 $3.60 Ancient ship and modern freighter
Set of 2 95 25

518 80c *Tai Ho, Tai Choa* and *Tai Tsang*
     (destroyers)
519 $6 *Tai Ho, Tai Choa* and *Tai Tsang*
     (destroyers)
Set of 2 1.10 35

1966

581† $2.50 Dragon boat race 1.25 5

1967

601 $5 Freighter 1.10 15

1970

782† $2.50 Dragon boat race 40 20

1971

850 $4 *Hai King* (freighter)
851 $7 Liner
Set of 2 1.00 45

1972

878† $1 Three Ming ceremonial barges 5 5
880† $1 Two Ming ceremonial barges 5 5
885† $8 Ming ceremonial barges 80 25

907† $2.50 Container ship 25 15

1973

923† $1 Bamboo model of sampan 25 5

1974

994† $5 Taiwan canoes, Lanya 30 8

1976

1099† $8 Mail ship 45 15

1979

1243† $10 Rowing boat 30 25

1980

1324† $2 Shipyard, Kaohsiung 8 5

1984

1553 $2 *Ming Comfort* (container ship)
1554 $18 *Prosperity* (tanker)
Set of 2 1.00 70

1985

1602† $2 Ching ivory model of dragon boat .. 10 8

1987

1764† $3 Sampan 12 8

CHRISTMAS ISLAND

Indian Ocean
100 cents = 1 dollar

1963

17† 12c *Islander* (freighter) 50 20
18† 20c *Triadic* (freighter) 1.25 50

1972

37 1c *Eagle*, 1714
38 2c H.M.S. *Redpole* (gunboat), 1890
39 3c *Hoi Houw* (freighter), 1959
40 4c *Pigot*, 1771
41 5c *Valetta* (cargo-liner), 1968
42 6c H.M.S. *Flying Fish* (survey ship), 1887
43 7c *Asia* (sail merchantman), 1805
44 8c *Islander* (freighter), 1929–60
45 9c H.M.S. *Imperieuse* (armoured cruiser),
    1888
46 10c H.M.S. *Egeria* (survey ship), 1887
47 20c *Thomas*, 1615
48 25c H.M.S. *Gordon* (sloop), 1864
49 30c *Cygnet*, 1688
50 35c *Triadic* (freighter), 1958
51 50c H.M.S. *Amethyst* (frigate), 1857
52 $1 *Royal Mary* (warship), 1643
Set of 16 10.00 8.50

1977

69† 3c H.M.S. *Flying Fish* (survey ship), 1887 15 5
77† 20c Ocean yacht 40 25

1981

143† 60c Freighter loading phosphate 65 65

1983

171 27c Mirror dinghy
172 35c Ocean yachts
173 50c Cargo ship and fishing launch
174 75c Sailing dinghies
Set of 4 1.75 1.75

1986

214†	60c Freighter loading phosphate	60	60
215†	90c Yachts	85	85

1987

227	36c H.M.S. *Flying Fish* (survey ship), 1887		
228	90c H.M.S. *Egeria* (survey ship), 1887		
	Set of 2	1.60	1.60

1988

As Nos. 1105/8 *of Australia, but inscribed* "CHRISTMAS ISLAND"

246†	37c Arrival of First Fleet, 1788	30	35
247†	37c Aborigine canoe	30	35
248†	37c First Fleet in cove	30	35
249†	37c Ship's boat	30	35

253†	95c H.M.S. *Imperieuse* (cruiser), 1888	90	95

CISKEI

Southern Africa
100 cents = 1 rand

1985

81	12c *Antelope* (sail troopship)		
82	25c *Pilot* (sail troopship)		
83	30c *Salisbury* (sail troopship)		
84	50c *Olive Branch* (sail troopship)		
	Set of 4	50	50

COCOS (KEELING) ISLANDS

Indian Ocean
1963 12 pence = 1 shilling
20 shillings = 1 pound
1969 100 cents = 1 dollar

1963

5†	2s Jukong (Cocos sailing boat)	9.00	4.75

1976

20	1c *Dragon*, 1609	
21	2c H.M.S. *Juno* (frigate), 1857	
22	5c H.M.S. *Beagle* (survey ship), 1836	
23	10c H.M.A.S. *Sydney* (cruiser), 1914	
24	15c *Emden* (German cruiser), 1914	
25	20c *Ayesha* (schooner), 1907	
26	25c *Islander* (freighter), 1927	
27	30c *Cheshire* (cargo liner), 1951	
28	35c Jukong (Cocos sailing boat)	
29	40c *Scotia* (cable ship), 1900	
30	50c *Orontes* (liner), 1929	
31	$1 *Gothic* (liner acting as Royal Yacht), 1954	
	Set of 12	8.50	6.50

1979

33†	50c Jukong (Cocos sailing boat)	40	55

48†	55c Jukongs (Cocos sailing boats)	25	35

1980

58†	22c *Eye of the Wind* (cadet ship)	20	20
60†	35c *Golden Hind* (Drake)	25	25
61†	60c *Eye of the Wind*	45	45

1981

77†	60c H.M.S. *Beagle* (Darwin), 1832	80	55

1984

112†	55c Jukongs (Cocos sailing boat)	60	60
113†	70c *Morea* (liner)	70	70
MS114	$1 Jukong (Cocos sailing canoe)	90	1.25

116†	65c *Hector* (Keeling), 1609	90	90

MS121†	$2 Jukongs	2.10	2.40

1985

126†	30c Jukong building	30	25

129	33c *Scotia* (cable ship)		
130	65c *Anglia* (cable ship)		
131	80c *Patrol* (cable ship)		
	Set of 3	2.00	1.75

1986

154†	$1 H.M.S. *Beagle* (Darwin), 1836	1.10	95

1987

158	36c Jukong (Cocos sailing boat)		
159	36c Ocean racing yachts		
160	36c *Sarimanok* (replica outrigger)		
161	36c *Ayesha* (schooner)		
	Set of 4	1.60	1.60

170†	65c Jukong building	60	65

1988

As Nos. 1105/8 *of Australia, but inscribed* "COCOS (KEELING) ISLANDS"

175†	37c Arrival of First Fleet, 1788	30	35
176†	37c Aborigine canoe	30	35
177†	37c First Fleet in cove	30	35
178†	37c Ship's boat	30	35

189† 90c Jukong (Cocos sailing boat) (on stamp No. 5) 85 90

COLOMBIA

South America
100 centavos = 1 peso

1903

225† 5c *Cartagena* (gunboat) (blue) 1.25 90
226† 5c *Cartagena* (brown) 1.75 1.50

1932

Overprinted **CORREO AEREO**
422† 1p Galleon 5.50 4.25
423† 2p Galleon 16.00 10.00
424† 3p Galleon 35.00 27.00
425† 5p Galleon 55.00 48.00

1954

801† 2p Schooner, Cartagena 2.50 25

1955

844† 20c *City of Manizales* (freighter) 30 12
847† 50c *City of Manizales* (air) 50 12

857† 23c *Santa Maria*, *Pinta* and *Nina* (Columbus) 35 20

1956

873† 4c Fishing boats, Cartagena 15 5

1959

No. 873 surcharged
955 2c on 4c Fishing boats, Cartagena 10 5

No. 801 overprinted **UNIFICADO** *within outline of aeroplane*
985† 2p Schooner, Cartagena 85 20

990† 10c River steamer 25 15

1961

1085† 35c Paddle steamer, Barranquilla 35 5

1965

1153† 10p *Manuel Mejia* (freighter) 2.00 25

1966

1171 5c 16th-century galleon
1172 15c Riohacha brigantine, 1850
1173 20c Uraba schooner
1174 40c Steamer and barge, Magdalena, 1900
1175 50c Modern freighter
                        Set of 5 1.50 60

1971

1290† 1p30 Yachts 65 30

1972

1311 1p20 *Almirante Padilla* (frigate), 1952 .... 40 5

1973

1341 10p Battle of Maracaibo, 1823 .... 2.25 25

1975

1380 3p *Elettra* (Marconi's steam yacht) 35 5

1979

1484† 5p Motorboats, Rio Prado Barrage 35 10

1983

1697† 35p Caravel, Cartagena 1.25 20

1984

1705† 10p 19th-century sail warship 30 10
1708† 20p Pirogue 35 15

1985

1723 20p *Gloria* (cadet ship) and *Caldas* (frigate) 30 10

COMORO ISLANDS

Indian Ocean
100 centimes = 1 franc

1950

1† 10c Local sailing craft 8 10
2† 50c Local sailing craft 15 15
3† 1f Local sailing craft 15 15

1954

As No. 264 of Cameroun
17 15f Landing craft, Normandy, 1944 .... 16.00 12.00

1964

42	15f Pirogue		
43	30f Felucca		
44	50f Pirogue		
45	85f Schooner		
	Set of 4	8.50	6.00

1970

91	5f Feluccas		
92	10f Feluccas		
93	40f Feluccas		
	Set of 3	1.40	1.40

1974

159†	90f Fishing boat, Mamutzu	1.40	90

1976

194†	35f Viking longship	25	10

1978

309†	35f Shipwreck	20	10

1980

419†	60f Pirogue	30	12

STAMP MONTHLY
— finest and most informative magazine for all collectors. Obtainable from your newsagent or by postal subscription — details on request.

1981

476†	75f Scout pirogue	45	20
477†	250f Scout felucca	1.25	5

1983

510	150f Type "470" Olympic yacht		
511	200f "Flying Dutchman" Olympic yacht		
512	300f Type "470" Olympic yacht		
513	400f "Finn" class Olympic yacht		
	Set of 4	3.75	3.50
MS514	500f "Soling" class yachts	2.25	2.50

1984

542	100f William Fawcett (paddle-steamer)		
543	150f Lightning (clipper)		
544	200f Rapido (barque)		
545	350f Sindia (barque)		
	Set of 4	3.50	3.00

1985
No. MS514 overprinted OLYMPHILEX '85 LAUSANNE

MS554	500f "Soling" class yachts	2.00	2.50

555†	200f Fishing boats at quay	1.00	60

559†	300f Mississippi paddle-steamer	1.25	90

578	25f Galleon		
579	75f Galleon		
580	125f Galleon		
581	500f Galleon		
	Set of 4	3.50	3.00

Appendix
The following stamps have either been issued in excess of postal needs, or have not been made available to the public in reasonable quantities at face value. Miniature sheets, imperforate staps etc., are excluded from this section.

1975
No. 159 surcharged ETAT COMORIEN. 100f on 90f Fishing boat, Mamutzu.

CONGO (BRAZZAVILLE)
Central Africa
100 centimes = 1 franc

1962

21	50f Freighter loading timber	80	50

1968
As No. 163 of Central African Republic

158	30f Tanker, Port Gentil, Gabon	50	25

1969

169	50f Freighter, Pointe Noire	1.40	1.00

1973

355†	260f Oil rig	3.00	1.50

359†	50f Fishing boat	55	35

375†	30f Oil rig	35	20
377†	100f Oil rig	90	60

1974

437†	30f Yachts, Argenteuil (Monet)	35	25

1975

463† 40f Pirogue 45 25

467† 40f Pirogue 45 25
469† 90f Pirogue 80 60

1976

504 5f *Alphonse Fondere* (river steamer)
505 10f *Hamburg* (paddle-steamer), 1839
506 15f *Gomer* (paddle-steamer), 1831
507 20f *Great Eastern* (paddle-steamer), 1858
508 30f *Alphonse Fondere*
509 40f *Hamburg*
510 50f *Gomer*
511 60f *Great Eastern*
512 95f *S.M. White II* (river steamer), 1878
Set of 9 2.75 2.00

1977

552 35f Pirogue racing
553 60f Pirogue racing
Set of 2 85 60

MS588† 500f *Mauretania* (liner), 1939 .... 3.00 1.40

1978

633† 200f Roman sailing ship, Alexandria 1.25 55

1979

662† 250f Hawaiian canoes 1.60 50
663† 350f Capt. Cook's ships at anchor 2.00 90

1983

908 100f Sailboard
909 200f Sailboard
910 300f Sailboard
911 400f Sailboard
Set of 4 3.50 3.50

1984

958† 100f Pusher tug 65 50
959† 150f Pusher tug 1.00 55
960† 300f Buoying boat 1.90 1.40
961† 500f Freighter 3.00 2.50

966† 20f Fishing pirogue 12 5

974 100f Sailboard
975 150f "Soling" class yachts
976 200f "470" class yachts
977 500f "Flying Dutchman" class yachts
Set of 4 6.00 5.00

978 60f Log raft and boats
979 100f Log raft and boats
Set of 2 75 60

1988

1117 240f Pirogues 1.00 85

POSTAGE DUE STAMPS

1961

D23† 2f Pirogue 5 5
D24† 2f River steamer, 1932 .... 5 5

CONGO (KINSHASA)

Central Africa
1963 100 centimes = 1 franc
1967 100 sengi = 1 (li)kuta
100 (ma)kuta = 1 zaire

1963

460 2f Pirogue
461 4f Pirogue
462 7f Pirogue
463 20f Pirogue
Set of 4 1.50 1.10

Nos. 460/3 *overprinted* **10 DECEMBRE 1948 10 DECEMBRE 1963 15e anniversaire DROITS DE L'HOMME**

507 2f Pirogue
508 4f Pirogue
509 7f Pirogue
510 20f Pirogue
Set of 4 45 45

1969

697† 8k Unloading freighter 40 25

COOK ISLANDS

South Pacific
1920 12 pence = 1 shilling
20 shillings = 1 pound
1967 100 cents = 1 dollar

1920

82† 1d Schooner 3.00 1.50
84† 4d Local sailing canoe 3.75 11.00

1932

106† ½d Captain Cook and ship 40 70
108† 2d Double Maori canoe 45 25
109† 2½d Schooner 30 80
111† 6d *Monowai* (liner) 75 2.25

1935

As Nos. 109 and 111 but colours changed, overprinted **SILVER JUBILEE OF KING GEORGE V. 1910 – 1935.**

114†	2½d Schooner	1.00	1.40
115†	6d *Monowai* (liner)	3.00	5.00

1938

145†	3s Canoe	12.00	15.00

1949

152†	2d *Messenger of Peace* (missionary schooner)	60	80
155†	6d Canoe	1.00	1.00
159†	3s *Matua* (inter-island ship)	6.50	10.00

1963

173†	5s *Tiare Taporo* (schooner)	8.50	5.50

1966

No. 173 overprinted **In Memoriam SIR WINSTON CHURCHILL 1874 – 1965**

184†	5s *Tiare Taporo* (schooner)	3.50	2.25

No. 173 overprinted **Airmail** *and aircraft*

191†	5s *Tiare Taporo* (schooner)	2.00	2.00

1967

No. 173 surcharged **50c**

217†	50c on 5s *Tiare Taporo* (schooner)	4.00	1.50

225†	18c (1s9d) *Moana Roa* (inter-island ship)	50	25

1968

269†	½c H.M.S. *Resolution* (Cook), Matavai Bay, Tahiti	5	5
270†	1c H.M.S. *Resolution* and H.M.S. *Discovery* at Huaheine	15	10
271†	2c H.M.S. *Resolution* and H.M.S. *Discovery*, Kamchatka	40	35
272†	4c H.M.S. *Resolution* in Antarctica	40	35
273†	6c H.M.S. *Resolution* and H.M.S. *Discovery* (Cook) (air)	90	65
275†	15c H.M.S. *Resolution* and H.M.S. *Discovery*, Hawaii	1.50	90

277†	1c Olympic yacht	5	5

1970

329†	30c H.M.S. *Endeavour* (Cook)	2.75	1.75

No. 329 overprinted **FIFTH ANNIVERSARY SELF-GOVERNMENT AUGUST 1970**

333†	30c H.M.S. *Endeavour*	1.50	75

1971

349†	25c Royal Yacht *Britannia*	1.50	2.00

1973

437	½c Tipairua (canoe type)		
438	1c Wa'a Kaulua (canoe type)		
439	1½c Tainui (canoe type)		
440	5c War canoe		
441	10c Pahi (canoe type)		
442	15c Amatasi (canoe type)		
443	25c Vaka (canoe type)		
	Set of 7	3.00	1.50

1975

515†	10c *Vitoria* (Juan Sebastian de Elcano), 1520	60	50
516†	25c Friar Andres de Urdaneta and ship, 1564	1.50	1.25
517†	30c Miguel Lopez de Legazpi and ship, 1564	1.60	1.50

528†	25c Motor launch	80	50

1976

541	$1 H.M.S. *Resolution* and Benjamin Franklin		
542	$2 H.M.S. *Resolution* and Capt. Cook		
	Set of 2	14.00	6.00
MS543	$3 H.M.S. *Resolution* with Cook and Franklin	12.00	10.00

Nos. 541/MS543 overprinted **Royal Visit July 1976**

544	$1 H.M.S *Resolution* and Benjamin Franklin		
545	$2 H.M.S. *Resolution* and Capt. Cook		
	Set of 2	9.00	6.00
MS546	$3 H.M.S. *Resolution* with Cook and Franklin	10.00	10.00

1978

584†	50c H.M.S. *Resolution*	1.50	75
585†	$1 H.M.S. *Resolution* at Hawaii	2.00	1.25

Nos. 584/5 overprinted **1728 · 250th ANNIVERSARY OF COOK'S BIRTH · 1978**

613†	50c H.M.S. *Resolution*	1.50	75
614†	$1 H.M.S. *Resolution* at Hawaii	2.00	1.25

1979

629†	30c H.M.S. *Resolution*	45	35
630†	35c H.M.S. *Endeavour*	55	45

637†	35c *Cap Horniers* (sailing ship)	40	40
638†	35c River steamer	40	40
639†	35c *Deutschland* (liner)	40	40
640†	35c *United States* (liner)	40	40

1980

Nos. 637/40 overprinted **ZEAPEX STAMP EXHIBITION– AUCKLAND 1980** *and New Zealand 1865 2d stamp*

691†	35c *Cap Horniers*	30	35
692†	35c River steamer	30	35
693†	35c *Deutschland*	30	35
694†	35c *United States*	30	35

1984

999†	48c H.M.S. *Endeavour* careened (Cook)	50	50
MS1002†	90c H.M.S. *Endeavour* careened (Cook) (sheet also contains three other designs)	3.50	3.75

1986

MS1064†	$4 Royal barge on Thames, 1759	3.25	3.75

1069†	$1 H.M.S. *Resolution* (Cook)	1.00	1.00
1071†	$2 H.M.S. *Resolution* (Cook)	1.90	1.90

1987
No. 999 surcharged

1141†	$1.30 on 48c H.M.S. *Endeavour* careened (Cook)	1.40	1.50

Nos. 1069 and 1071 surcharged **HURRICANE RELIEF + 50c**

1172†	$1 + 50c H.M.S. *Resolution* (Cook)	35	40
1174†	$2 + 50c H.M.S. *Resolution*	35	40

OFFICIAL STAMPS

No. 542 overprinted **O.H.M.S.**

O29†	$2 H.M.S. *Resolution* and Capt. Cook	4.50	3.00

COSTA RICA
Central America
100 centimos = 1 colon

1911

Surcharged **Correos Un centimo** *or* **Correos 5 5 centimos**

94	1c on 10c *Antilles* (liner), 1906		
96	1c on 25c *Antilles*		
97	1c on 50c *Antilles*		
98	1c on 1col *Antilles*		
99	1c on 5col *Antilles*		
100	1c on 10col *Antilles*		
101	5c on 5c *Antilles*		
	Set of 7	4.00	2.75

1923

144†	12c *Santa Maria* (Columbus)	3.25	1.60

1926
No. 144 surcharged **10 10** *between bars*

163	10c on 12c *Santa Maria* (Columbus)	1.25	45

1928
No. 144 surcharged **LINDBERGH ENERO 1928 10 10** *and aircraft*

169	10c on 12c *Santa Maria* (Columbus)	8.00	6.50

1936

226	5c Fleet of Columbus		
227	10c Fleet of Columbus		
	Set of 2	45	15

1947
No. O228 overprinted **CORREOS 1947**

431	5c Fleet of Columbus	10	5

435	25c Fleet of Columbus		
436	30c Fleet of Columbus		
437	40c Fleet of Columbus		
438	45c Fleet of Columbus		

439	50c Fleet of Columbus		
440	65c Fleet of Columbus		
	Set of 6	3.50	2.00

1948
No. 437 surcharged **HABILITADO PARA C 0.35**

472	35c on 40c Fleet of Columbus	30	30

1952

502	15c 16th-century caravels		
503	20c 16th-century caravels		
504	25c 16th-century caravels		
505	55c 16th-century caravels		
506	2col 16th-century caravels		
	Set of 5	2.50	1.40

1953
Nos. 436/8 and 440 surcharged **HABILITADO PARA CINCO CENTIMOS 1953**

515a	5c on 30c Fleet of Columbus		
516	5c on 40c Fleet of Columbus		
517	5c on 45c Fleet of Columbus		
518	5c on 65c Fleet of Columbus		
	Set of 4	1.25	1.25

1963

666†	25c *William le Lacheur* (sail merchantman)	15	5

1970

843	1col *Santa Maria* (on stamp No. 144)		
844	2col *Santa Maria* (on stamp No. 144)		
	Set of 2	80	45

853†	80c Fishing boats	55	10

1976

1055†	2col 20 Sail merchantman, Boston Tea Party, 1773	50	20

OFFICIAL STAMPS

1936
Nos. 226/7 overprinted **OFICIAL**

O228	5c Fleet of Columbus		
O229	10c Fleet of Columbus		
	Set of 2	20	15

CROATIA
South-east Europe
100 banicas = 1 kuna

1943

85†	1k + 50b Motor torpedo boats	10	15

CUBA
West Indies
100 centavos = 1 peso

1899

304†	5c *Umbria* (liner)	3.00	45

1936

403†	4c *Rex* (liner)	85	20
404†	5c Freighter in harbour	1.25	20
408†	50c Sailing ship and steamer	7.00	3.25
412†	50c Liner, San Severino (air)	7.00	2.00

1937

422	1c Caravel		
423	2c Caravel		
424	5c Caravel		
	Set of 3	2.75	1.00

424o	25c Fleet of Columbus	24.00	18.00

1944

478†	13c Caravels at Pinar del Rio (Columbus)	3.50	1.50
479†	5c Fleet of Columbus (air)	75	35

STANLEY GIBBONS
STAMP COLLECTING SERIES

Introductory booklets on *How to Start*, *How to Identify Stamps* and *Collecting by Theme*. A series of well illustrated guides at a low price.
Write for details.

1952

585 2c Fleet of Columbus
586 25c Fleet of Columbus (air)
　　　　　　　　　　　　　　　Set of 2　5.50　2.00

1955

728† 10c 19th-century sailing ships, Havana　2.50　65
732† 24c *Umbria* (liner) (on stamp No. 304)
　　　(air)　　　　　　　　　　　　　　1.40　55

757† 8c *Three Friends* (tug) ....　1.25　45

1960

922† 2c *Granma* (launch) ....　60　15

954† 1c Olympic yachts ....　45　20

1962

1022 10c 18th-century mail ship ....　1.75　60

1028b† 3c Speed boat ....　55　15
1028e 3c Racing yacht ....　55　15

1964

1122 1c *Rio Jibacoa* (freighter)
1123 2c *Camilo Cienfuegos* (freighter)
1124 3c *Sierra Maestra* (freighter)
1125 9c *Bahia de Siguanea* (freighter)
1126 10c *Oriente* (freighter)
　　　　　　　　　　　　　　Set of 5　2.75　1.00

1965

1193† 13c Merchantman ....　2.00　65

1196 1c *Goleta* (fishing schooner)
1197 2c *Omicron* (fishing boat)
1198 3c *Victoria* (fishing boat)
1199 9c *Cardenas* (fishing boat)
1200 10c *Sigma* (fishing boat)
1201 13c *Lambda* (fishing boat)
　　　　　　　　　　　　　　Set of 6　4.50　1.50

1216† 3c 18th-century mail ship ....　1.00　15

1249† 13c *Granma* (launch) ....　1.40　40

1315† 10c *Remolcador* (tug) ....　75　25
1316† 13c *15 de Marzo* (freighter) ....　1.40　45

1966

1320† 3c Torpedo-boat ....　35　5

1340† 2c 18th-century English yacht ....　25　5

1351† 3c *Houston* (freighter) sinking ....　20　5

1413† 3c *Havana* (tanker) ....　25　5

1431† 10c *Granma* (launch) ....　1.10　35

1967

1460† 13c *Corynthia* (launch) ....　1.50　50

1971

1823† 30c Weather ship ....　2.50　80

1846 13c Burning ship, Giron, 1961 ....　1.50　40

1847 13c *Windsor Castle* (packet) attacked by
　　Jeune Richard, 1807
1848 30c *Orinoco* (mail steamer), 1851
　　　　　　　　　　　　　　Set of 2　3.25　1.40

1972

1906† 30c Fishing boats, Valencia ....　1.75　60

Drakkar S.VI al IX

1978 1c Viking longship
1979 2c Caravel
1980 3c Galley
1981 4c Galleon
1982 5c Clipper
1983 13c Steam packet
1984 30c *Lenin* (atomic ice-breaker)
Set of 7   3.50   1.60

1973

2027† 30c *Yuri Gagarin* (research ship)   1.75   65

2047 3c Destroyer   45   20

1974

2087 3c *Granma* (launch) (on stamp No. 922)   20   5

1975

2187 1c Fishing boat (Bonito)
2188 2c Fishing boat (Tunny)
2189 3c Fishing boat (Grouper)
2190 8c Fishing boat (Hake)
2191 13c Fishing boat (Prawn)
2192 30c Fishing boat (Lobster)
Set of 6   2.00   90

1976

2262† 3c Yacht, Guadalquivir River   15   5

2319 1c *Imias* (freighter)
2320 2c *Commandante Camilo Cienfuegos* (freighter)
2321 3c *Commandante Pinares* (cargo liner)
2322 5c *Vietnam Heroico* (cargo liner)
2323 13c *Presidente Allende* (ore carrier)
2324 30c *XIII Congresso* (bulk carrier)
Set of 6   2.00   90

2333† 1c *Granma* (launch)   5   5

1977

2347† 5c 18th-century sailing ships, Venice ..   10   5

2411† 3c *Aurora* (Russian cruiser)   15   5

2423† 13c *Corynthia* (launch)   45   10

1978

2434† 13c Fishing boats, Guadalquivir River   40   10

2436 13c Patrol boat   40   15

2487 1c Tunny fishing boat
2488 2c Fish-processing ship
2489 5c Shrimp fishing boat
2490 10c Stern trawler
2491 13c Stern trawler (air)
2492 30c Refrigeration and processing ship
Set of 6   1.50   70
MS2493 50c Venetian fishing boat 1.25   1.25

1980

2652 1c Building *Our Lady of Atocha*, 1620
2653 3c Building *El Rayo*, 1749
2654 7c Building *Santissima Trinidad*, 1769
2655 10c *Santissima Trinidad* at sea, 1805
2656 13c Building *El Colon* and *El Congreso* (steamships), 1851
2657 30c Cardenas and Chullima shipyards
Set of 6   1.50   70

1981

MS2753 1p Sailing packet 1.90   1.90

2762† 1p *Granma* (launch) 1.75   1.00

1982

2791† 4c Lobster fishing boat   15   5

2818† 9c Sailing ships in bay   25   5

MS2822 1p *Louisiane* (steamer) 1.90   1.90

2855 5c *Santa Maria* (Columbus)
2856 20c *Santa Maria* (Columbus)
2857 25c *Pinta* (Columbus)
2858 50c *Nina* (Columbus)
Set of 4   2.50   1.40

MS2864 1p *Almendares* (paddle-steamer) 1.75   1.75

1983

2910 30c Sailing ships in harbour, 1883 ...... 90 45

1984

MS3009 1p Early mail steamer 2.00 2.00

3051† 20c Departure of Columbus from Palos 55 35
3052† 30c *Santa Maria, Pinta, Nina*
(Columbus) 70 55

1985

3085† 5c Carib canoe 15 5
3088† 50c Caribs building canoe 1.00 80

MS3119 1p Roman cargo ship 2.00 2.00

1986

3187 5c Container ship 8 5

1987

MS3274 1p Galleon, Coruna, 1525 .... 1.60 1.60

3283† 5c Ship's boat, 1492 (on Spain stamp
No. 602) 8 5

SPECIAL DELIVERY STAMPS

1936

E413 15c Liner 6.50 2.00

1962

E1023 10c 18th-century sailing packet 3.50 1.10

CURACAO

West Indies
100 cents = 1 gulden

1928

112	6c Liner and freighter			
113	7½c Liner and freighter			
114	10c Liner and freighter			
115	12½c Liner and freighter			
116	15c Liner and freighter			
117	20c Liner and freighter			
118	21c Liner and freighter			
119	25c Liner and freighter			
120	27½c Liner and freighter			
121	30c Liner and freighter			
122	35c Liner and freighter			

Set of 11 32.00 24.00

1929

No. 113 *surcharged* **6 ct.**
126 6c on 7½c Liner and freighter 1.00 75

1934

146† 20c *Johannes van Walbeeck*, 1634 ...... 2.50 1.75
147† 21c *Johannes van Walbeeck*, 1634 ...... 8.50 12.00
148† 25c *Johannes van Walbeeck*, 1634 ...... 8.50 8.50

CYPRUS

Mediterranean
1949 40 paras = 1 piastre
180 piastres = 1 pound
1955 1000 mils = 1 pound
1983 100 cents = 1 pound

1949

As No. 115 *of Antigua*
169† 2pi Paddle-steamer 80 95

1955

180† 30m Yachts, Kyrenia 40 5
182† 40m *Maltese Prince* (freighter) 50 55

1960

Nos. 180 and 182 overprinted in Greek and Turkish
195† 30m Yachts, Kyrenia 1.25 10
197† 40c *Maltese Prince* (freighter) 2.00 75

1967

301† 100m Freighters, Famagusta 20 35

1976

449† 50m *Marcel Bayard* (cable ship) 20 5

1977

484† 120m Barges 45 70

1982

586† 40m Byzantine dromons, 965 .... 20 10

1983

619† 3c Motor launch 10 10
621† 13c *Sol Olympia* (liner) and *Polys*
(tanker) 40 35

1985

652†	5c Speed boat	12	5
655†	13c Sailboards	30	15

1986

No. 655 surcharged **18c**

685†	18c on 13c Sailboards	55	45

1987

706	2c Remains of ancient ship		
707	3c *Kyrenia II* (replica of ancient ship) under construction		
708	5c *Kyrenia II* at Paphos, 1986		
709	17c *Kyrenia II* at New York, 1986		
	Set of 4	60	70

Turkish Cypriot Posts

1977 1000 mils = 1 pound
1978 100 kurus = 1 lira

1977

50†	100m Motor yachts, Kyrenia	40	60

1978

66†	100k Hydrofoil	10	10

1982

126†	30k Remains of ship from 300 B.C.	30	30

1988

228†	200li *Piyale Pasha* (tug)	20	20

CYRENAICA

North Africa
100 centesimi = 1 lira

1924

No. 157 of Italy overprinted **CIRENAICA**

13†	30c Ferry boat	20	1.75

1933

103†	5li Roman galley	2.25	17.00
105†	12li Roman galley	2.25	50.00

CZECHOSLOVAKIA

Central Europe
100 haleru = 1 koruna

1936

362†	10k River tug and barge, Bratislava	65	40

1939

No. 362 surcharged **Otvorenie slovenskeho snemu 18.1.1939 300 h** *and arms*

393b	300k on 10k River tug and barge, Bratislava	75	90

1949

547†	13k Sailing ship	1.50	55

1952

732	1k50 River steamers, Bratislava	20	10

1953

796†	1k20 *Stalingrad* (tug)	2.75	1.40

1959

1130†	60h *Elettra* (Marconi's steam yacht)	20	5

1960

1136	30h Dredger		
1137	60h *Komarno* (tug)		
1138	1k *Komarno* (river boat)		
1139	1k20 *Lidice* (freighter)		
	Set of 4	3.00	1.25

1166	60h River tug and barge, Bratislava (on stamp No. 362)		
1167	1k River tug and barge, Bratislava (on stamp No. 362)		
	Set of 2	1.25	15

1962

1318†	60h Sailing dinghy	25	5

1319	30h *Aurora* (Russian cruiser)		
1320	60h *Aurora* (Russian cruiser)		
	Set of 2	45	10

1964

1409†	1k80 Sailing dinghies, Cesky Krumlow	75	25

1419†	1k U.S.S. *Intrepid* (aircraft carrier)	75	25

1966

1584†	20h Red Indian canoe	5	5

1967

1694†	2k Freighter in dock, Amsterdam	65	25

1971

1931†   50h Local trading punt   20   5

1972

2053	50h *Jiskra* (freighter)		
2054	60h *Mir* (freighter)		
2055	80h *Republika* (freighter)		
2056	1k *Kosice* (tanker)		
2057	1k60 *Dukla* (freighter)		
2058	2k *Kladno* (freighter)		
		Set of 6 3.75	80

1976

2292	40h 16th-century warship		
2293	60h 17th-century Dutch merchantman		
2294	1k 17th-century ship at anchor		
2295	2k 18th-century galleon		
		Set of 4 1.90	80

1977

2372†   30h *Aurora* (Russian cruiser)   15   5

1979

2500	3k Danube ferry, Bratislava, *c.* 1787		
2501	3k60 Danube ferry, Bratislava, *c.* 1815		
		Set of 2 2.50	2.50

COLLECT BIRDS ON STAMPS

Second revised edition of this Stanley Gibbons thematic catalogue – now available at £8.50 (p. + p. £2) from: Stanley Gibbons Publications Ltd, 5 Parkside, Christchurch Road, Ringwood, Hants BH24 3SH.

1980

2545	3k Danube ferry, Bratislava, *c.* 1810		
2546	4k Danube ferry, Bratislava, *c.* 1820		
		Set of 2 3.25	3.25

1982

2639	3k *Kamzik* (ferry)		
2640	3k60 *TR 100* (tug)		
		Set of 2 2.40	1.10

2642	3k Paddle-steamer, Bratislava, 1818		
2643	4k 19th-century river craft, Bratislava		
		Set of 2 3.00	2.00

1984

2754†   2k River barge   90   30

DAHOMEY
West Africa
100 centimes = 1 franc

1931
As No. 109 of Cameroun
99†   1f50 Liner 1.40   1.90

1937
As Nos. 110/11 of Cameroun
100†   20c Liner   25   30
101†   30c Sailing ship   30   40

1941

133†	80c Sailing pirogue on Lake Nokoue	15	15
134†	1f Sailing pirogue on Lake Nokoue	20	20
135†	1f30 Sailing pirogue on Lake Nokoue	35	35
136†	1f40 Sailing pirogue on Lake Nokoue	40	40
137†	1f50 Sailing pirogue on Lake Nokoue	40	40
138†	2f Sailing pirogue on Lake Nokoue	55	55

1960

144†   25f Pirogues, Ganvie   35   15

1961
No. 144 overprinted **JEUX SPORTIFS D'ABIDJAN 24 AU 31 DECEMBRE 1961**
162†   25f Pirogues, Ganvie   45   30

1963

172†   2f Ganvie girl in pirogue   5   5
183†   85f Ganvie girl in pirogue 1.50   75

1965

228†   25f Freighter, Cotonou Port 1.60   85

1966
No. 229 surcharged **ACCORD DE COOPERATION FRANCE – DAHOMEY 5e Anniversaire – 24 Avril 1966 15F**
247†   15f on 100f Freighter, Cotonou Port   35   25

1967
No. 183 surcharged **30F**
280†   30f on 85f Ganvie girl in pirogue   40   30

284	30f *Suzanne* (barque)		
285	45f *Esmerelda* (schooner)		
286	80f *Marie Alice* (schooner)		
287	100f *Antonin* (barque)		
		Set of 4 3.50	2.10

1968

341†   55f Mail pirogue   60   35

1970

396   100f Pirogue 1.25   50

405† 40f *La Justice* and *La Concorde* (French
warships), 1670 .... 65 35

1971

440† 100f *General Mangin* (liner) 1.40 70

1972

479 40f Freighter 50 20

1973

499† 15f Scout pirogue 25 15

1974
No. 499 *surcharged* **100F XIe JAMBOREE PANARABE DE
BATROUN - LIBAN**
547† 100f on 15f Scout pirogue 65 45

POSTAGE DUE STAMPS

1967

D308†1f Pirogue 5 5

DANISH WEST INDIES
West Indies
100 bit = 1 franc

1905

57† 1f *Ingolf* (training ship) 15.00 24.00
58† 2f *Ingolf* (training ship) 20.00 38.00
59† 5f *Ingolf* (training ship) 50.00 £140

DANZIG
Baltic
1921 100 pfennige = 1 mark
1923 100 pfennige = 1 Danzig gulden

1921

44 5pf Hanse kogge (medieval sailing vessel)
45 10pf Hanse kogge (medieval sailing vessel)
46 25pf Hanse kogge (medieval sailing vessel)
55 40pf Hanse kogge (medieval sailing vessel)
48 80pf Hanse kogge (medieval sailing vessel)
49 1m Hanse kogge (medieval sailing vessel)
50 2m Hanse kogge (medieval sailing vessel)
51 3m Hanse kogge (medieval sailing vessel)
52 5m Hanse kogge (medieval sailing vessel)
53 10m Hanse kogge (medieval sailing vessel)
Set of 10 10.00 12.50

1924

201† 2g Freighter and tugs, River Mottlau
(black and purple) 42.00 65.00
206† 2g Freighter and tugs, River Mottlau
(black and red) 1.60 2.50

1932
No. 201 *surcharged* **15 15 Luftpost-Ausstellung 1932**
222† 15pf + 15pf on 2g Freighter and tugs,
River Mottlau (black and purple) 7.50 10.00

1936

242† 25pf Fishing boats, Brosen Beach 80 1.50

245† 15pf + 5pf Tug 1.00 2.00

1938

276 5pf + 5pf *Peter von Danzig* (yacht), 1936
277 10pf + 5pf *Fu Shing* (dredger)
278 15pf + 10pf *Columbus* (liner)
279 25pf + 10pf *Hansestadt Danzig* (liner)
280 40pf + 15pf *Peter von Danzig*, 1472
Set of 5 6.50 11.50

STANLEY GIBBONS
STAMP COLLECTING SERIES
Introductory booklets on *How to Start, How to Identify
Stamps* and *Collecting by Theme*. A series of well
illustrated guides at a low price.
Write for details.

DENMARK
Northern Europe
100 ore = 1 krone

1927

Solid background
246 15ore Caravel
247 20ore Caravel
248 25ore Caravel
249 30ore Caravel
250 35ore Caravel
251 40ore Caravel
Set of 6 22.00 60

1933
As Nos. 246/51, but with lined background
277b 15ore Caravel (red)
277d 15ore Caravel (green)
278a 20ore Caravel (grey)
278b 20ore Caravel (red)
279 25ore Caravel (blue)
279ab 25ore Caravel (brown)
280a 30ore Caravel (orange)
280b 30ore Caravel (blue)
281 35ore Caravel
282 40ore Caravel (green)
282b 40ore Caravel (blue)
Set of 11 60.00 4.25

1934
Nos. 279 and 280a surcharged
285 "4" on 25ore Caravel (blue)
286 "10" on 30ore Caravel (orange)
Set of 2 3.50 1.60

1937

306† 5ore *Rita* (King Christian X's yacht), 1930 1.50 15

1940
Nos. 277b, 280b and 282 surcharged
319a† 15ore on 40ore Caravel (green) 90 75
320† 20ore on 15ore Caravel (red) 1.10 5
321† 40ore on 30ore Caravel (blue) 1.00 20

1941

324 10ore *St. Peter* (Vitus Bering)
325 20ore *St. Peter* (Vitus Bering)
326 40ore *St. Peter* (Vitus Bering)
Set of 3 1.75 45

1947

355† 40ore *Fyn* (train ferry) 1.25 75

1951

378 25ore *Fredericus Quartus* (Danish
warship), c. 1700
379 50ore *Fredericus Quartus*
Set of 2 3.00 55

383	25ore + 5ore *Jutlandia* (hospital ship)	60	80

1960

426	30ore Sailing ship of 1560	30	5

1962

448	60ore *Selandia* (freighter)	1.75	1.25

1963

453	60ore *Copenhagen* (paddle-steamer)	25	15

1970

517	30ore Figurehead from *Elephanten*	10	5

520	30ore Bronze-age ship		
521	50ore Viking shipbuilding		
522	60ore *Emanuel* (schooner)		
523	90ore *A.P. Moller* (tanker)		
	Set of 4	1.10	65

1971

534	90ore Yachts	35	40

1974

594†	90ore English warships, 1808	40	10

1976

618	70ore + 20ore Viking longship		
619	90ore + 20ore *Thingvalla* (freighter)		
620	100ore + 20ore *Frederik VIII* (liner)		
621	130ore + 20ore *Danmark* (training ship)		
	Set of 4	2.50	3.00

1978

662†	1k80 Fishing boats	35	20

1980

690†	280ore Fishing boats, Vorupor	50	60

1982

740	1k60 *Argus* (revenue cutter)	45	10

1983

760†	3k50 Yacht	65	40

765†	3k50 Lifeboat	80	50

1984

774†	2k70 Pilot boat	50	15

783†	2k70 Fishing fleet	55	10
784†	3k30 Deep sea fishing boat	60	60
785†	3k70 Trawler	70	30

1985

812	2k80 Rowing boat	55	30

1986

MS817	25ore Ice boat, 1880 (sheet also contains three other designs)	2.25	2.75

825	2k80 Sailing dinghies, Aalberg	85	45

PARCEL POST STAMPS

1914
Nos. 246, 249 and 251 overprinted **POSTFAERGE**

P252†	15ore Caravel	12.00	8.00
P253†	30ore Caravel	12.00	8.50
P254†	40ore Caravel	11.00	5.50

1936
Nos. 277b, 280a/b, 282 and 282b overprinted **POSTFAERGE**

P303†	15ore Caravel (red)	65	75
P304†	30ore Caravel (blue)	3.50	3.00
P305†	30ore Caravel (orange)	50	50
P306†	40ore Caravel (green)	3.50	3.00
P307†	40ore Caravel (blue)	60	70

DJIBOUTI
East Africa
100 centimes = 1 franc

1894

103†	5f *Pingouin* (French gunboat)	90.00	65.00

1899
No. 103 surcharged **0,75**

111†	0,75 on 5f *Pingouin* (French gunboat)	£300	£250

DJIBOUTI REPUBLIC
East Africa
100 centimes = 1 franc

1979

749†	40f Freighter	60	20

1980

799	55f H.M.S. *Endeavour* (Cook)		
800	90f Capt. Cook's ships		
	Set of 2	1.50	1.25

1981

804	100f Tanker	1.50	90

818	100f H.M.S. *Victory* (Nelson)		
819	175f H.M.S. *Victory*		
	Set of 2	2.50	2.00

1982

854†	25f Ferry and dhow	30	15

1983

884†	90f Yacht	1.40	90

1984

MS905	250f *Leon Thevenin* (cable ship)	3.50	3.75

1985

957†	80f Oil rig	95	85

COLLECT MAMMALS ON STAMPS

969†	100f Sailboards	1.25	90

1986

977	60f *Santa Maria* (Columbus)		
978	90f *Nina* and *Pinta* (Columbus)		
	Set of 2	1.75	1.75

1987

1011†	100f Dhow-building, 1887	75	70

DOMINICA

West Indies
100 cents = 1 dollar

1949

As No. 115 of Antigua

115†	6c Paddle-steamer	35	35

1954

147†	5c Canoe building	1.25	20

1963

164†	3c Sailing canoe	5	5
168†	8c Dugout canoe	10	10
170†	12c Canoes on beach	12	10

1967

206†	10c *Santa Maria* (Columbus)	8	5

1968

Nos. 164, 168 *and* 170 *overprinted* **ASSOCIATED STATEHOOD**

216†	3c Sailing canoe	5	5
220†	8c Dugout canoe	5	5
222†	12c Canoes on beach	10	5

No. 164 *overprinted* **NATIONAL DAY 3 NOVEMBER 1968**

234†	3c Sailing canoe	5	5

1969

261†	24c Freighter and tug	15	10

279†	8c Cargo liner	20	5

1971

328†	10c Boat building	10	5
329†	30c Yacht	20	20
330†	50c Motor yacht and speed boat	35	45

1974

441†	10c *Orinoco* (mail boat), 1851, and *Geesthaven* (freighter), 1974	15	5

1975

467	½c *Yare* (cargo-liner)		
468	1c *Thames* (liner)		
469	2c *Lady Nelson* (liner)		
470	20c *Lady Rodney* (liner)		
471	45c *Statesman* (freighter)		
472	50c *Geestecape* (freighter)		
473	$2 *Geestestar* (freighter)		
	Set of 7	6.00	4.50

1976

509†	1c British three-deck warship, 1782	5	5

1977

581†	$3 Sailing dinghies	2.00	2.00

1978

608† 40c Tug and barge (launch of Zeppelin *LZ1*), 1900 .... 20 20

1979

655† 30c Canoe 25 15

667† 10c H.M.S. *Endeavour* (Cook) 20 10
668† 50c H.M.S. *Resolution* (Cook) 45 45
669† 60c H.M.S. *Discovery* (Cook) 55 55

1982

828† $3 Canoe 2.50 3.00

1984

890 45c *Atlantic Star* (freighter)
891 60c *Atlantic* (liner)
892 90c Carib fishing boat
893 $4 *Norway* (liner)

       Set of 4 4.50 4.50
MS894 $5 *Santa Maria* (Columbus) 4.00 4.50

1985

956† $3 Rowing boat 2.25 2.50

965† $4 Royal Yacht *Britannia* 2.50 2.75

1986

988† 15c Police rowing boat, New York, 1890 15 10
989† 25c New York Police Dept launch, 1986 20 15

1987

1052 45c *Reliance* (yacht), 1903
1053 60c *Freedom* (yacht), 1980
1054 $1 *Mischief* (yacht), 1881
1055 $3 *Australia* (yacht), 1977

       Set of 4 2.40 2.50
MS1056 $5 *Courageous* (yacht), 1977 .... 2.40 2.75

1076† 10c Fleet of Columbus, 1493 .... 5 8
1077† 15c Fleet of Columbus, 1493 .... 8 10
1079† 60c Wreck of *Santa Maria*, 1492 ...... 25 30
1080† 90c Fleet of Columbus, 1492 ...... 40 45
1083† $5 Fleet of Columbus, 1493 .... 2.25 2.40
MS1084† Two sheets. (a) $5 Fleet off Dominica, 1493 (other sheet shows map)
      Price for 2 sheets 4.50 4.75

1085† 10c H.M.S. *Warrior* (ironclad) 5 8
1087† 25c *Flying Cloud* (sailing clipper) 12 15
1090† 60c *Spray* (yacht), 1895 .... 25 30
1091† 90c *Sea-Land Commerce* (container ship), 1973 .... 40 45
1094† $4 *Clermont* (first commercial steamboat), 1807 .... 1.75 1.90

DOMINICAN REPUBLIC

West Indies
100 centavos = 1 peso

1899

89† 1c 15th-century sailing boat (purple) 4.00 3.50
90† 1c 15th-century sailing boat (green) 75 40

1902

125† 1c Galleon and early steamship 25 25
126† 2c Galleon and early steamship 25 25
127† 5c Galleon and early steamship 25 25
128† 10c Galleon and early steamship 25 25
129† 12c Galleon and early steamship 25 25
130† 20c Galleon and early steamship 25 25

1937

385† 10c Fleet of Columbus 2.50 1.25
392† 1p Fleet of Columbus 8.50 2.25

1940

443† 10c Caravels 75 50
447† 50c Caravel 2.50 1.60

1958

747 7c *Rhadames* (freighter) 35 10

756† 17c Olympic yachts 45 35

1959

No. 756 surcharged **ANO GEOFISICO INTERNACIONAL 1957-1958 + 2c** *and globe*
772† 17c + 2c Olympic yachts 1.00 1.00

1974

1199† 7c *Eider* (mail steamer) 25 10

1976

1255 20c *Separacion Dominicana* (schooner) 50 25

1273† 6c Caravel and map 25 10

1977

1297 20c Battle of Tortuguero, 1844 .... 50 25

1978

1316   7c *Duarte* (schooner) 25   10

1982

1509† 7c Rowing boats, San Pedro de
       Macoris 30   15

1510† 7c *Santa Maria* (Columbus) 30   15
1511† 10c *Santa Maria* (Columbus) 50   20

1983

1527   15c *Mella* (frigate) 40   15

1543   10c Caravels
1544   21c *Santa Maria* (Columbus) (trophy)
1545   33c *Sotavento* (yacht)
       Set of 3   1.50   90
MS1546 50c *Santa Maria, Nina* and *Pinta*
       (Columbus) 1.40   1.40

1984

1569   10c Coastguard patrol boat 15   5

STANLEY GIBBONS
STAMP COLLECTING SERIES

Introductory booklets on *How to Start, How to Identify
Stamps* and *Collecting by Theme*. A series of well
illustrated guides at a low price.
Write for details.

1985

1617† 35c Racing yachts 40   15

1626† 10c Harbour scene, Haina 15   5

1986

1637   10c *Leonor* (schooner) 20   5

1649† 25c Racing yachts 30   10

DUBAI

Persian Gulf
1963 100 naye paise = 1 rupee
1966 100 dirhams = 1 riyal

1963

26†   1np Dhow 8   8
30†   20np Dhow (air) 45   25

1964

74†   75np *Rigorous* (tug) 60   40
75†   2r *Rigorous* 1.25   70
76†   3r *Rigorous* 1.75   1.10

82†   20np Dhows 15   5
84†   40np Dhows 30   5
85†   1r Tug and launches (air) 65   25
86†   2r Dhow and barge 1.40   65
87†   3r Tug and launches 2.00   1.25
88†   5r Dhow and barge 3.75   2.25

No. 30 overprinted **ANTI TUBERCULOSE**, in English and Arabic,
with Cross of Lorraine
101†   20np Dhow 3.00   2.50

1966

173†   10np Oil rig 20   5
175†   30np Oil rig 40   8
177†   50np Oil rig 70   15
179†   75np Oil rig 1.25   35

1967

263†   1r25 Dhow 80   35
264†   3r Dhow 1.75   1.00
265†   5r Dhow 2.50   1.50
266†   10r Dhow 4.50   4.00

1969

318†   25d *Bamora* (freighter), 1914 20   8
320†   60d *Sirdhana* (liner), 1947 55   12
322†   1r25 *Chandpara* (freighter), 1949 90   40
MS324† 1r25 *Bombala* (freighter), 1961 ...... 1.00   95

342†   20d *Thames* (tug) 20   10
343†   35d Tankers 45   15
344†   60d Oil rig 85   30
345†   1r Pipe-laying ship 1.40   60

1970

349†   60d *Weather Reporter* (weather ship) 35   12

363†   10d Dhow building 15   5
364†   20d Speedboat 30   5
366†   60d Dhows 50   12

STAMP MONTHLY
— finest and most informative magazine for all
collectors. Obtainable from your newsagent or by
postal subscription — details on request.

ECUADOR

South America
100 centavos = 1 sucre

1930

477†	10c Freighter	40	8

1936

522†	20c H.M.S. *Beagle* (Darwin)	90	15

1948

829†	10c *Santa Maria* (Columbus)	15	5
830†	20c *Santa Maria*	20	5
831†	30c *Santa Maria*	35	5
832†	50c *Santa Maria*	45	5
833†	1s *Santa Maria*	65	8
834†	5s *Santa Maria*	2.00	25

1956

1044†	10c Manta fishing canoe (blue)	15	5
1044a†	10c Manta fishing canoe (brown)	25	5
1045†	20c Canoe, River Babahoya (brown)	15	5
1045a†	20c Canoe, River Babahoya (pink)	15	5
1045b†	20c Canoe, River Babahoya (green)	25	5
1047†	50c Canoe, River Pital (green)	20	5
1047a†	50c Canoe, River Pital (violet)	25	5
1050b†	1s Raft, San Pablo (black)	35	5
1053†	1s Raft, San Pablo (blue) (air)	35	5
1053a†	1s Raft, San Pablo (orange)	25	5

1975

1582	2s Naval landing ship	25	8

1976

1658	5s Battle of Flamborough Head, 1779	1.00	25

1979

1741	5s Deep sea trawler	75	25

1982

1864	3s50 *Isla Solango* (freighter)	50	20

1985

1949†	10s *Calderon* (gunboat)	20	5

OFFICIAL STAMPS

1936

No. 522 overprinted **OFICIAL**

O527†	20c H.M.S. *Beagle* (Darwin)	35	10

EGYPT

North Africa
1000 milliemes = 100 piastres = 1 pound

1914

73†	1m Nile felucca	15	5

1922

No. 73 overprinted

98†	1m Nile felucca	40	8

1926

138	5m Ancient Egyptian ship, Temple of Deir-el-Bahari		
139	10m Ancient Egyptian ship, Temple of Deir-el-Bahari		
140	15m Ancient Egyptian ship, Temple of Deir-el-Bahari		
	Set of 3	3.75	2.10

Nos. 138/40 overprinted **PORT FOUAD**

141†	5m Ancient Egyptian ship, Temple of Deir-el-Bahari	£120	80.00
142†	10m Ancient Egyptian ship, Temple of Deir-el-Bahari	£120	80.00
143†	15m Ancient Egyptian ship, Temple of Deir-el-Bahari	£120	80.00

1948

351	10m Battle of Navarino, 1827	25	25

1956

517	10m Freighter and Suez Canal	40	35

1957

As No. 517, but with inscription in English instead of French and also inscribed "PORT SAID" and "REOPENING 1957"

524	100m Freighter and Suez Canal	70	50

530	10m *Sudan* (paddle-steamer) and felucca	25	15

1959

597†	10m *Al Mokattam* (freighter)	30	15
598†	10m Motorised Nile barge	30	15

1961

668	10m *Al Nasser* (destroyer)	15	8

1964

771†	3m Ancient funerary barge (alabaster model)	5	5
780†	40m Nile felucca	35	5

1965

850† 10m Oil rig 15 12

1966

886† 10m Ship building 20 8

891† 10m *Southern Cross* (liner) and freighter 30 8

1967

937 80m + 20m Gondola, Venice
938 115m + 30m Gondola, Venice
Set of 2 2.50 2.50

1969

1035† 20m Merchant ships of 1869 and 1969 30 12

1974

1226 110m Solar boat of Cheops 1.25 80

1977

1309 20m Pharaonic ship 30 5

COLLECT MAMMALS ON STAMPS
A Stanley Gibbons thematic catalogue on this popular subject. Copies available at £7.50 (p. + p. £2) from: Stanley Gibbons Publications Ltd, 5 Parkside, Christchurch Road, Ringwood, Hants BH24 3SH.

1332 20m Marine gas rig 30 5

1978

1337† 140m Nile feluccas 55 30

1983

1518† 3p Pharaonic ship and modern freighter 20 10

1988

1689 5p Container ship 5 5

OFFICIAL STAMPS

1915
No. 73 overprinted **O.H.H.S.** *in English and Arabic*
O83† 1m Nile felucca 1.00 1.00

1922
No. 73 overprinted **O.H.E.M.S.** *in English and Arabic*
O111† 1m Nile felucca 50 40

EGYPTIAN OCCUPATION OF PALESTINE
Western Asia
1000 milliemes = 100 piastres = 1 pound

1964
As Nos. 771 and 780 of Egypt, but additionally inscribed "PALESTINE" *in English and Arabic*
142† 3m Ancient funerary barge (alabaster model) 5 5
150† 40m Nile felucca 25 8

EL SALVADOR
Central America
1896 100 centavos = 1 peso
1912 100 centavos = 1 colon

1896

162† 10c Steamship 15 25
163† 12c Steamship 15 30

1933

810 15c Fleet of Columbus
811 20c Fleet of Columbus
812 25c Fleet of Columbus
813 40c Fleet of Columbus
814 1col Fleet of Columbus
Set of 5 16.00 13.00

1954

1051† 1c Fishing boats 10 5
1061† 7c Fishing boats 20 8
1067† 22c *Fle-Ja-Lis* (coastguard cutter) 50 35
1070† 1col *Fle-Ja-Lis* 1.75 70
1072† 5c Fishing boats (air) 30 5
1075† 10c *Fle-Ja-Lis* 40 8
1080† 25c *Fle-Ja-Lis* 70 15

1957
No. 1061 surcharged
1123† 6c on 7c Fishing boats 25 15

1962
No. 1070 surcharged
1171† 10c on 1 col *Fle-Ja-Lis* (coastguard cutter) 25 8

1969

1308† 40c Dugout canoe, Jaltepeque estuary 45 25

1970

1327† 50c *Nohuba* (coastguard patrol boat) .. 45 20

1971
No. 1327 overprinted **1951-12 Octubre-1971 XX Aniversario MARINA NACIONAL**
1374 50c *Nohaba* (coastguard patrol boat) 50 20

1979

1632† 1col Freighter 75 45

COLLECT RAILWAYS ON STAMPS
A Stanley Gibbons thematic catalogue on this popular subject. Copies available at £7.50 (p. + p. £2) from: Stanley Gibbons Publications Ltd, 5 Parkside, Christchurch Road, Ringwood, Hants BH24 3SH.

1983

1799† 1col Canoes on beach 85 60

1811† 25c Trawler and rowing boat 35 20

1985

1879 55c Inflatable inshore lifeboat 50 25

1986

1948† 20c Fishing boat 10 5

EQUATORIAL GUINEA

West Africa
1968 100 centimos = 1 peseta
1973 100 centimos = 1 ekuele (plural = bikuele)

1979

29† 1e Freighter, Bata 5 5

1984

72 125b Whaling pirogues
73 150b Pirogue on beach

Set of 2 1.75 1.10

Appendix

The following have either been issued in excess of postal needs, or have not been made available to the public in reasonable quantities at face value. Miniature sheets, imperforate stamps etc. are excluded from this section.

1972

Olympic Games, Munich. Sailing events at Kiel. 1, 2, 3, 5, 8p

---

1973

Transatlantic Yacht Race. Postage 1, 2, 3, 5, 8p; Air 15, 50p

1974

Centenary of U.P.U. 2e25 Mail canoe

1975

Historical Ships. Postage 30, 35, 40, 45, 50, 55, 60, 65, 70, 75c; Air 8, 10, 50, 60e

1976

Olympic Games, Montreal. 7e Yacht
Olympic Games, Montreal. Sailing. Postage 70, 80, 90c; Air 30, 60e
Steamships. Postage 80, 85, 90, 95c, 1p; Air 15, 40p
Ship Paintings. Postage 5, 10, 15, 20, 25, 30e; Air 50, 60, 65, 70e

---

ERITREA

North-east Africa

ITALIAN ADMINISTRATION
100 centesimi = 1 lira

1924

No. 157 of Italy overprinted **ERITREA**
76† 30c Ferry boat 20 1.75

BRITISH ADMINISTRATION
100 cents = 1 shilling

1951

Nos. 509/10 of Great Britain surcharged **B.A.ERITREA** *and value*
E30† 2s50 on 2s6d H.M.S. *Victory* (Nelson) 4.50 6.50
E31† 5s on 5s Yacht and Thames sailing
barge, Dover 11.00 18.00

ESTONIA

1919 100 penni = 1 Estonian mark
1928 100 senti = 1 kroon

1919

11† 1m Viking longship 20 45
12† 5m Viking longship 50 45
13† 15m Viking longship 2.25 1.60
14† 25m Viking longship 4.50 2.25

1936

127† 2k *Aegna* (cargo liner) 1.00 1.50

ETHIOPIA

East Africa
1947 100 cents = 1 dollar
1976 100 cents = 1 birr

1947

373a† 60c Canoe, Lake Tana 1.50 60
374† 70c Canoe, Lake Tana 1.75 65

1949

No. 374 surcharged **EXPOSITION 1949** *+***70c** *and two lines of Amharic*
394† 70c + 70c Canoe, Lake Tana 10.00 7.00

1951

No. 394 further overprinted **1951** *and date in Amharic*
420† 70c + 70c Canoe, Lake Tana 7.00 5.00

1952

435† 15c Dhows, Assab 1.00 30
437† 30c Dhows, Assab 1.75 70

1953

444 10c Freighter, Massawa
445 15c Freighter and pilot boat
446 25c Freighter, Massawa
447 30c Freighter and pilot boat
448 50c Freighter, Massawa

Set of 5 16.00 6.50

1960

No. 373a overprinted **World Refugee Year 1959-1960** *in English and Amharic*
499† 60c Canoe, Lake Tana 65 75

1962

554† 20c Kaleb's Fleet, 520 .... 45 20

1972

808 10c Reed Raft Lake Haik
809 20c Canoes, Lake Abaya
810 30c Punts, Lake Tana
811 60c Dugout canoes, River Baro

Set of 4 2.00 80

1981

1186† 15c Canoes, River Baro 15 5

1983

1263† 1b Liner 85 55

FALKLAND ISLANDS

South Atlantic
1933 12 pence = 1 shilling
20 shillings = 1 pound
1971 100 pence = 1 pound

1933

129† 1½d *Bransfield* (whale catcher) 4.25 9.00

1938

155† 6d *Discovery II* (research vessel) (black and brown) 4.50 5.00
156† 6d *Discovery II* (research vessel) (black) 2.50 7.00
157† 9d *William Scoresby* (research vessel) .. 2.50 80

1949

As No. 115 of Antigua
169† 3d Paddle-steamer 4.50 1.50

1952

173† 1d *Fitzroy* (supply ship) 80 40
178† 6d *John Biscoe* (research ship) 9.00 1.25
185† £1 Hulk of *Great Britain* (liner) 25.00 30.00

1953

As Nos. 173 and 178 but with portrait of Queen Elizabeth II
188† 1d *Fitzroy* (supply ship) 1.25 65
190† 6d *John Biscoe* (research ship) 2.50 90

1964

215† 2½d H.M.S. *Glasgow* (cruiser), 1914 .... 6.00 2.25
216† 6d H.M.S. *Kent* (cruiser), 1914 .... 1.00 25
217† 1s H.M.S. *Invincible* (battle cruiser), 1914 .... 1.75 60

1970

258 2d *Great Britain* (steam/sail in 1843)
259 4d *Great Britain* (steam/sail in 1845)
260 9d *Great Britain* (steam/sail in 1876)
261 1s *Great Britain* (sailing ship in 1886)
262 2s *Great Britain* (as a hulk in 1970)
Set of 5 9.50 6.25

1974

301† 5p Packet ship, 1841 .... 35 45
303† 16p *Ile de France* (liner), 1920 .... 60 75

305† 20p H.M.S. *Inflexible* and H.M.S. *Invincible* (battle cruisers), 1914 ...... 1.90 1.60

307 2p H.M.S. *Exeter* (cruiser), 1939
308 6p H.M.N.Z.S. *Achilles* (cruiser), 1939
309 8p *Admiral Graf Spee* (German pocket battleship)
310 16p H.M.S. *Ajax* (cruiser), 1939
Set of 4 15.00 14.50

1976

324† 20p *Monsunen* (wool freighter) 1.50 1.50

1978

331 1p *A.E.S.* (mail ship 1957–74)
332 2p *Darwin* (mail ship 1957–73)
333 3p *Merak-N* (mail ship 1951–52)
334 4p *Fitzroy* (mail ship 1936–57)
335 5p *Lafonia* (mail ship 1936–41)
336 6p *Fleurus* (mail ship 1924–33)
337 7p *Falkland* (mail ship 1914–34)
338 8p *Oravia* (mail ship 1900–12)
339 9p *Memphis* (mail ship 1890–97)
340 10p *Black Hawk* (mail ship 1873–80)
341 20p *Foam* (mail ship 1863–72)
342 25p *Fairy* (mail ship 1857–61)
343 50p *Amelia* (mail ship 1852–54)
344 £1 *Nautilus* (mail ship 1846–48)
345 £3 *Hebe* (mail ship 1842–46)
Set of 15 15.00 23.00

1979

370† 25p *Gwendolin* (schooner) 75 1.00

1982

417 5p *Lady Elizabeth* (shipwreck), 1913
418 13p *Capricorn* (shipwreck), 1882
419 15p *Jhelum* (shipwreck), 1870
420 25p *Snowsquall* (shipwreck), 1864
421 26p *St. Mary* (shipwreck), 1890
Set of 5 2.40 3.00

425† 34p H.M.S. *Beagle* (Darwin), 1831 ...... 85 95

Nos. 335 and 342 overprinted **1st PARTICIPATION COMMONWEALTH GAMES 1982**
431 5p *Lafonia*
432 25p *Fairy*
Set of 2 75 95

1983

442† 10p *Lenita* (ship repairing) 40 40
444† 20p H.M.S. *Invincible* (battle cruiser), 1914 .... 60 60

455† 13p *Canberra* (liner) and *Norland* (ferry) at San Carlos, 1982 .... 30 35
457† 50p H.M.S. *Hermes* (aircraft carrier), 1982 .... 1.00 1.10

1984

484 6p *Wavertree* (sail merchantman)
485 17p Freighter at Port Stanley quay, c. 1910
486 22p *Oravia* (liner)
487 52p *Cunard Countess* (cruise liner)
Set of 4 2.00 2.25

488 22p 19th-century sailing ship 45 50

1985

501† 7p *Merchant Providence* (freighter) 20 20

510 7p H.M.S. *Jason* (frigate), 1765
511 22p H.M.S. *Dolphin* (frigate) and H.M.S. *Tamar* (sloop), 1765
512 27p H.M.S. *Beagle* (Darwin), 1831
513 54p H.M.S. *Philomel* (brig), 1842
Set of 4 2.25 2.50

STANLEY GIBBONS STAMP COLLECTING SERIES

Introductory booklets on *How to Start, How to Identify Stamps* and *Collecting by Theme*. A series of well illustrated guides at a low price.
Write for details.

1986

527 10p *Great Britain* crossing Atlantic, 1845
528 24p *Great Britain* beached at Sparrow Cove, 1937
529 29p *Great Britain* on pontoon, 1970
530 58p *Great Britain* undergoing restoration, Bristol, 1986

Set of 4   2.25   2.50

1987

541† 29p Coasters and accommodation ship, Stanley   60   65

FALKLAND ISLANDS DEPENDENCIES

South Atlantic
1944 12 pence = 1 shilling
20 shillings = 1 pound
1971 100 pence = 1 pound

1944

Nos. 155 and 157 of Falkland Islands overprinted **GRAHAM LAND DEPENDENCY OF**
A6† 6d *Discovery II* 6.50   2.75
A7† 9d *William Scoresby* 1.75   1.50

Nos. 155 and 157 of Falkland Islands overprinted **SOUTH GEORGIA DEPENDENCY OF**
B6† 6d *Discovery II* 6.50   2.75
B7† 9d *William Scoresby* 1.75   1.50

Nos. 155 and 157 of Falkland Islands overprinted **SOUTH ORKNEYS DEPENDENCY OF**
C6† 6d *Discovery II* 6.50   2.75
C7† 9d *William Scoresby* 1.75   1.50

Nos. 155 and 157 of Falkland Islands overprinted **SOUTH SHETLANDS DEPENDENCY OF**
D6† 6d *Discovery II* 6.50   2.75
D7† 9d *William Scoresby* 1.75   2.50

1949

As No. 115 of Antigua
G22 2d Paddle-steamer 6.50   3.00

1954

G26 ½d *John Biscoe I* (research ship), 1947–52
G27 1d *Trepassey* (supply ship), 1945–47
G28 1½d *Wyatt Earp* (Ellsworth), 1934–36
G29 2d *Eagle* (sealer), 1944–45
G30 2½d *Penola* (Rymill), 1934–37
G31 3d *Discovery II* (research ship), 1929–37
G32 4d *William Scoresby* (research ship), 1926–46
G33 6d *Discovery* (research ship) (Scott), 1925–27
G34 9d *Endurance* (Shackleton), 1914–16
G35 1s *Deutschland* (German expedition), 1901–12
G36 2s *Pourquoi-pas?* (Charcot), 1908–10
G37 2s6d *Francais* (Charcot), 1903–05
G38 5s *Scotia* (Bruce), 1902–04
G39 10s *Antarctic* (Nordenskjold), 1901–03
G40 £1 *Belgica* (Gerlache), 1897–99

Set of 15   £200   95.00

1956

Nos. G27, G30/1 and G33 overprinted **TRANS-ANTARCTIC EXPEDITION 1955-1958**
G41 1d *Trepassey*
G42 2½d *Penola*
G43 3d *Discovery II*
G44 6d *Discovery*

Set of 4   1.25   1.40

1980

82† 9p *Louise* (coaling hulk)   30   30
150† 50p *John Biscoe II* (research ship), 1956   1.25   1.40
151† £1 *Bransfield* (research ship), 1970 ....   2.00   2.40
152† £3 *H.M.S. Endurance* (ice patrol ship) ..   5.50   6.00

FAROE ISLANDS

North Atlantic
100 ore = 1 krone

1940

No. 277b of Denmark surcharged **20**
1† 20ore on 15ore Caravel (red) 45.00   10.00

1975

7† 10ore 16th-century sailing ship   10   8
9† 60ore 16th-century sailing ship 1.50   1.50
11† 80ore 16th-century sailing ship   35   35
13† 120ore 16th-century sailing ship   50   25

1976

20† 125ore Faroese rowing boat 2.00   1.25

1977

23 100ore Motor fishing boat
24 125ore Inshore fishing cutter
25 160ore Modern seine fishing boat
26 600ore Deep-sea trawler

Set of 4   9.00   6.00

1981

60† 150ore Fishing boats, Torshavn   25   25
61† 200ore Fishing boats, Torshavn   30   30

COLLECT RAILWAYS ON STAMPS

A Stanley Gibbons thematic catalogue on this popular subject. Copies available at £7.50 (p. + p. £2) from: Stanley Gibbons Publications Ltd, 5 Parkside, Christchurch Road, Ringwood, Hants BH24 3SH.

1983

78 220ore *Arcturus* (cargo liner)
79 250ore *Laura* (cargo liner)
80 700ore *Thyra* (cargo liner)

Set of 3   2.00   2.00

1984

100† 280ore *Westward Ho* (fishing ketch)   40   40

1987

146 300ore *Joannes Patursson* (trawler)
147 550ore *Magnus Heinason* (trawler)
148 800ore *Sjurdarberg* (stern trawler)

Set of 3   3.25   3.25

150† 300ore Fishing boats, Hestur Island   55   55

FERNANDO POO

Off West Africa
100 centimos = 1 peseta

1929

Nos. 506 and 508 of Spain overprinted **FERNANDO POO**
211† 15c Spanish caravel, Seville   10   10
213† 25c Spanish caravel, Seville   10   10

1960

234† 20c + 5c Whaling canoe   10   5
236† 50c + 20c Whaling canoe   30   8

1962

248 25c *Okume* (Spanish freighter)
249 50c *San Francisco* (Spanish freighter)
250 1p *Okume*

Set of 3   20   15

252† 35c Liner 35 10

1964

261† 25c 19th-century sail warship 10 5
263† 1p 19th-century sail warship 10 5

264† 25c Canoe 10 5
266† 1p Canoe 10 5

FEZZAN

North Africa
100 centimes = 1 franc

1943

Nos. 54/5 and 59 of Libya surcharged **FEZZAN Occupation Francaise** *and value*

4† 2f on 30c Roman galley £140 £130
7† 5f on 50c Roman galley 7.50 7.50
8† 10f on 1li Roman galley £550 £550

FIJI

South Pacific
1891 12 pence = 1 shilling
20 shillings = 1 pound
1969 100 cents = 1 dollar

1891

87† 1d Fijian canoe (black) 2.50 2.50
101† 1d Fijian canoe (mauve) 3.25 60
89† 2d Fijian canoe 4.25 1.50
85† 5d Fijian canoe 7.00 7.50

1938

249† ½d Outrigger canoe 10 20
252† 1½d Outrigger canoe 55 75
257† 3d Outrigger canoe 35 15

1949

As No. 115 of Antigua

273† 3d Paddle-steamer 1.00 80

1954

285† 3d *Komowai* (copra freighter) 70 5

296† 1½d + ½d Bamboo trading raft 10 12

1963

Overprinted **COMPAC CABLE IN SERVICE DECEMBER 1963**
and illustration of Retriever (cable ship)
335 1s *Retriever* (on map design) 25 10

1966

351† 3d H.M.S. *Pandora* (frigate), 1791 ...... 15 5
353† 1s6d H.M.S. *Pandora* 30 15

1967

363† 2s *Oriana* (cruise liner) 40 25

364† 4d H.M.S. *Providence* (sloop), 1792 .... 15 5
365† 1s *Bounty*'s longboat and canoes, 1789 15 10

1968

377† 9d Bamboo raft 15 15
382† 2s6d Outrigger canoes 1.25 90

389† 9d *Vuniwai* (hospital ship) 20 15

1969

As Nos. 377 and 382, but with face values in cents
397† 8c Bamboo raft 20 5
402† 25c Outrigger canoes 75 30

412† 8c Racing yacht 15 5

1970

No. 402 overprinted **ROYAL VISIT 1970**
419† 25c Outrigger canoes 20 20

425† 3c H.M.S. *Endeavour* (Cook) 1.25 35
426† 8c *Bounty*'s longboat, 1789 .... 1.25 35
427† 25c Fijian ocean going-canoe 1.50 40

1974

496† 8c *Fijian Princess* (mail ship) 15 5

1977

545 4c Drua canoe
546 15c Tabilai canoe
547 25c Takai canoe
548 40c Camakua canoe
Set of 4 1.25 1.10

1979

571† 40c *Leonidas* (emigrant ship), 1879 .... 50 40

1980

596 6c *Southern Cross* (freighter), 1873
597 20c *Levuka* (freighter), 1910
598 45c *Matua* (cargo liner), 1936
599 50c *Oronsay* (liner), 1951
Set of 4 1.10 1.40

1981

618† 60c *Retriever* (cable ship) 90 90

1982

20c FIJI

629† 20c Scout catamaran 50 40

Fiji 70c

635† 70c *Kiro* (minesweeper) 1.00 95

FIJI $1

MS646† $1 Royal Yacht *Britannia* (sheet also contains two other designs) 2.10 2.50

1984

LLOYD'S LIST
FIJI 8c

675 8c *Tui Lau* (shipwrecked freighter)
676 40c *Tofua* (freighter)
677 55c *Canberra* (liner)
678 60c Freighter at wharf, Suva
Set of 4 2.10 2.25

FIJI $1

687† $1 *Fua Kavenga* (container ship) 1.60 1.60

1985

697† 20c Outrigger canoe, Toberua Island 25 30

1988

30c FIJI

770 30c Sailboard 25 30

FINLAND

Northern Europe
100 pennia = 1 markka

1929

1M SUOMI FINLAND

260† 1m *Bore* (freighter) 1.25 2.00

1930

M2+20P SUOMI·FINLAND

280† 2m + 20p Viking longship 2.00 19.00

1935

2M SUOMI

307† 2m Viking longship 1.75 60

1937

SUOMI·FINLAND

312 1¼m + 15p *Thorborg* (warship), 1772
313 2m + 20p *Lodbrok* (warship), 1771
314 3½m + 35p *Styrbjorn* (warship), 1789
Set of 3 10.50 6.00

1938

SUOMI·FINLAND

327† 1¼m Postal sledge-boat, 1700 . . . . 90 2.00

1942

SUOMI 100 FINLAND

370† 100m *Ilmatar* and *Rigulus* (freighters) 1.50 5

1946

SUOMI FINLAND 8mk

420 8m Sailing ship 30 30

SUOMI·FINLAND 8

424 8m Rowing boats, Tammisaari 20 30

1949

SUOMI·FINLAND

482 15m 18th-century sailing ship, Kristiinankaupunki 1.00 1.10

1955

25 SUOMI

542 25m *Ilma* (barque), 1863 . . . . 85 70

1956

5 SUOMI·FINLAND

553a† 5m Rowing boat 25 5
557b† 100m *Ilmatar* and *Rigulus* (as No. 370 but "FINLAND" without scroll, "100" upright and "mk" omitted) 22.00 5

1961

30 SUOMI·FINLAND

624 30m *Pommern* (barque) 90 50

1963

1,75 SUOMI·FINLAND

660† 5p Rowing boat 15 5
670† 1m *Ilmatar* and *Rigulus* 50 5
674† 1m75 River launch 1.00 5

1964

SUOMI·FINLAND 0,25+0,04

694† 25p + 4p *Polaris* (Red Cross hospital ship) 60 70

1968

SUOMI·FINLAND 1968 0.40

747 40p Container ship 30 15

1971

1971 0,30+0,06 SUOMI·FINLAND

780† 30p + 6p *Rauma II* (tug) 50 60

787   50p "Lightning" class yachts   80   25

1972

795   50p *Suomen Joutsen* (cadet ship)   90   25

832†   60p Rowing boat, Heinavesi 1.75   15

1975

880   70p Salvage tug and sinking ship   65   10

1977

917   90p Ice-breaker and freighter   60   10

1978

931   1m Freighter at wharf   55   10

1981

992   1m10 *Furst Menschikoff* (paddle-steamer),
       1842 ....   1.40   2.00

993†   1m10 Rowing to church in local
        longboats   35   8

1983

1040†   1m30 Tourist canoe, River Kitajoki   30   10

1986

MS1107   1m60 *Aura* (paddle-steamer), 1858;
       1m60 *Alexander* (steamer), 1858; 2m20
       Nicolai (steamer), 1858; 2m20 *Express II*
       (ice-breaker), 1877 ....   2.40   2.75

1987

1116   1m70 Cruise liner
1117   2m30 Yachts
                              Set of 2   1.40   30

1988

1147   3m *Calmare Nyckei* and *Fagel Grip*
       (emigrant ships), 1638 ....   1.00   20

FIUME

1919 100 centesimi = 1 corona
1920 100 centesimi = 1 lira

1919

75†   45c + 5li 13th-century Venetian war
       galley   50   40
76†   60c + 5li 13th-century Venetian war
       galley   50   40
77†   80c + 5li 13th-century Venetian war
       galley   50   40
78†   1cor + 5li 13th-century Venetian war
       galley   50   40

Nos. 75/8 surcharged **Valore globale** *and value*
123†   45c on 45 + 5li 13th-century Venetian
        war galley   5   5
110†   60c on 60c + 5li 13th-century Venetian
        war galley   10   10
111†   80c on 80c + 5li 13th-century Venetian
        war galley   10   10
112†   1cor on 1cor + 5li 13th-century Venetian
        war galley   10   10

1921

Nos. 75/8 overprinted **24 – IV – 1921 Costituente Fiumana** *and* **L**
over the "C" on No. 185
182†   45c + 5li 13th-century Venetian war
        galley   15   15
183†   60c + 5li 13th-century Venetian war
        galley   25   25
184†   80c + 5li 13th-century Venetian war
        galley   25   30
185†   1li on 1cor + 5li 13th-century Venetian
        war galley   40   40

1922

Nos. 75/8 overprinted **24 – IV – 1921 Costituente Fiumana 1922**
and **L** *over the "C" on No. 197*
194†   45c + 5li 13th-century Venetian war
        galley   5   10
195†   60c + 5li 13th-century Venetian war
        galley   5   10
196†   80c + 5li 13th-century Venetian war
        galley   5   10
197†   1li on 1cor + 5li 13th-century Venetian
        war galley   5   10

1923

201†   5c Medieval ship   5   5
202†   10c Medieval ship   5   5
203†   15c Medieval ship   5   5

1924

Nos. 201/3 overprinted **REGNO D'ITALIA** *and arms*
213†   5c Medieval ship   5   20
214†   10c Medieval ship   5   20
215†   15c Medieval ship   5   20

Nos. 201/3 overprinted **ANNESSIONE ALL'ITALIA 22 Febb 1924**
and arms
225†   5c Medieval ship   5   20
226†   10c Medieval ship   5   20
227†   15c Medieval ship   5   20

NEWSPAPER STAMPS

1920

N145   1c Mail steamer   5   5

POSTAGE DUE STAMPS

Nos. 110/12 and 123 surcharged **Segnatasse** *and value*
D188†   20c on 45c 13th-century Venetian war
         galley   12   20
D183†   30c on 1cor 13th-century Venetian war
         galley   12   25
D184†   40c on 80c 13th-century Venetian war
         galley   10   15
D185†   50c on 60c 13th-century Venetian war
         galley   10   15
D189†   60c on 45c 13th-century Venetian war
         galley   12   20
D190†   80c on 45c 13th-century Venetian war
         galley   12   20

FRANCE

Western Europe
100 centimes = 1 franc

1918

378   15c + 5c *Charles Roux* (hospital ship) 90.00   40.00

1927

458   90c *Paris* (liner)
459   1f50 *Paris*
                              Set of 2   2.00   70

1929

474b† 10f Fishing boats, La Rochelle 65.00 3.00

1934

521 75c *Grande Hermine* and *Petite Hermine* (Cartier), 1534
522 1f50 *Grande Hermine* and *Petite Hermine*
                        Set of 2 45.00 1.75

1935

526 1f50 *Normandie* (liner) 12.00 45

1937

585 50c + 20c Fishing boats, Constantinople 1.75 1.50

1938

601† 20f Grand Banks fishing barquentine, St. Malo 32.00 9.50

1939

637 90c *Clemenceau* (battleship) 30 20

1940

No. 601 surcharged
688† 10f on 20f Grand Banks fishing barquentine, St. Malo 60 75

1941

707 1f + 1f on 70c *Pasteur* (liner) 10 15

1942

739 2f50 + 7f50 *L'Astrolabe* and *La Boussole* (La Perouse), 1788 .... 70 70

744 1f50 + 8f50 Liner and sampan 40 50

748 1f50 + 8f50 14th-century ship of Jean de Vienne 50 50

1946

965 2f + 3f *Emile Bertin* (cruiser) and *Lorraine* (battleship) 20 20

1947

1011† 6f Tug and barges, Paris 40 25

1954

1204 15f Landing craft, Normandy, 1944 ...... 60 25

1955

1261 30f *La Capricieuse* (sail warship), 1855 3.75 2.00

1263† 8f Fishing boats, Marseilles 20 5

1956

1281† 15f Early refrigerated freighter 60 40

1305 30f Rhine barges, Strasbourg 3.00 1.10

1957

1322 12f + 3f 18th-century felucca 1.25 95

1344† 12f Freighters, Brest 55 35

1958

1386† 15f Nautical jousting in rowing boats 65 45

1959

1428† 15f + 5f Medieval ships 90 1.25

1960

1475 20c + 5c *Ampere* (cable ship) 80 90

1961

1543† 30c Yachts, Arcachon 15 5

1962

1557 30c *France* (liner) 35 20

1566 95c Freighter, Dunkirk 80 10

1963

1595 30c *Archimede* (bathyscaphe) 15 15

1965

1675 25c + 10c *La Guienne* (steam packet), 1860 .... 30 40

1685† 60c Yacht, Aix-les-Bains 25 5
1687† 95c Punt, Vendee 45 15

1692 30c *Le Taureau* (warship), 1665 .... 10 5

1966

1722 60c Norman ships, 1066 .... 20 10

1967

1759† 95c *Cap Nord* (trawler), Boulogne 40 30

1968

1799 25c *Velox* (freighter) 10 8

1969

1837† 45c Landing craft, Provence, 1944 .... 20 20

1849 70c *Le Redoutable* (submarine) 30 20

1970

1855 70c *Firecrest* (yacht) 30 20

1856 45c Police patrol boat 25 20

1883† 50c Fishing boat, Martinique 25 5

1896† 45c Siege of La Rochelle, 1628 .... 20 20

1971

1912 80c Bathysphere 30 20

1920 80c *Antoinette* (barque) 30 30

1972

1947† 2f River barges 2.00 90

1948 90c Antarctic exploration ship, 1772 .... 80 40

1955† 50c + 10c 18th-century French warship 65 85

1967 90c *Cote d'Emeraude* (Grand Banks fishing barquentine) 50 25

1973

1993† 50c + 10c 18th-century French warships 55 65

1998† 90c Tanker, Le Havre 45 15

2011 90c *France II* (barque) 35 25

1974

2040 90c Shipwreck and modern lifeboat 35 25

1975

2095 1f40 Tanker, St. Nazaire 55 20

2100 90c *La Melpomene* (cadet ship) 35 20

1976

2122	1f *Duguay Trouin VIII* (cruiser), 1926 and *Duguay Trouin IX* (destroyer), 1976	45	25

2139	1f20 Olympic yacht	30	25

2149	1f45 *Duchesse Anne* (cadet ship)	40	30

1977

2152†	2f10 Canal barge	75	35

2161	50c Container ships and bunker, Dunkirk	20	8

2181	1f40 Breton fishing boats	45	15

1978

2247†	1f40 Gas tanker	45	20
2248†	1f70 Ancient Norman ship	55	20

1979

2303	1f50 19th-century French warship	40	20

COLLECT MAMMALS ON STAMPS

A Stanley Gibbons thematic catalogue on this popular subject. Copies available at £7.50 (p. + p. £2) from: Stanley Gibbons Publications Ltd, 5 Parkside, Christchurch Road, Ringwood, Hants BH24 3SH.

1980

2375	2f50 Rochambeau's fleet, Rhode Island, 1780	60	35

1981

2436	1f40 *Borda* (warship), 1831	35	12

1982

2503	1f60 Fishing boats, St. Pierre et Miquelon	45	10

2553	3f25 La Salle's ships, 1682	65	40

1984

2623	2f *Grande Hermine* (Cartier), 1534	65	10

1985

2686	2f50 19th-century lifeboat, Lake Geneva	65	20

FRENCH EQUATORIAL AFRICA

Central Africa
100 centimes = 1 franc

1936

Nos. 127/31 *of Gabon overprinted* **AFRIQUE EQUATORIALE FRANCAISE**

17†	1c Log raft	5	5
18†	2c Log raft	5	5
19†	4c Log raft	25	20
20†	5c Log raft	25	20
21†	10c Log raft	25	20

1937

As Nos. 110/11 *of Cameroun*

27†	20c Liner	50	80
28†	30c Sailing ships	80	80

1938

97	65c *La Malouine* (warship), 1838		
98	1f *La Malouine*		
99	1f75 *La Malouine*		
100	2f *La Malouine*		
	Set of 4	2.10	2.10

1947

248†	5f Fishing pirogue	20	5
249†	6f Fishing pirogue	20	10
250†	10f Fishing pirogue	25	10

1953

273†	50f Log raft	75	20
274†	100f Sailing canoe	2.50	30

1954

As No. 264 *of Cameroun*

277	15f Landing craft, Normandy, 1944	2.50	2.25

FRENCH GUIANA

South America
100 centimes = 1 franc

1929

126†	30c Native canoe shooting rapids, River Maroni (green)	20	20
127†	30c Native canoe shooting rapids, River Maroni (brown & green)	10	10
128†	35c Native canoe shooting rapids, River Maroni	25	15
129†	40c Native canoe shooting rapids, River Maroni	10	10
130†	45c Native canoe shooting rapids, River Maroni (brown & green)	30	30
131†	45c Native canoe shooting rapids, River Maroni (green & olive)	15	15
132†	50c Native canoe shooting rapids, River Maroni	10	10
133†	55c Native canoe shooting rapids, River Maroni	45	45
134†	60c Native canoe shooting rapids, River Maroni	15	15
135†	65c Native canoe shooting rapids, River Maroni	30	30
136†	70c Native canoe shooting rapids, River Maroni	35	35
137†	75c Native canoe shooting rapids, River Maroni	55	55
138†	80c Native canoe shooting rapids, River Maroni	25	20
139†	90c Native canoe shooting rapids, River Maroni (red)	30	30
140†	90c Native canoe shooting rapids, River Maroni (brown & mauve)	40	35
141†	1f Native canoe shooting rapids, River Maroni (brown & mauve)	30	30
142†	1f Native canoe shooting rapids, River Maroni (red)	90	75
143†	1f Native canoe shooting rapids, River Maroni (blue & black)	15	10

1931
As No. 109 of Cameroun
163† 1f50 Liner 1.10 1.40

1935

172† 40c D'Estrees' fleet, Cayenne, 1676 .... 1.75 1.75
173† 50c D'Estrees' fleet, Cayenne, 1676 .... 4.00 2.75
174† 1f50 D'Estrees' fleet, Cayenne, 1676 .... 1.75 1.75

1937
As Nos. 110/11 of Cameroun
178† 20c Liner 30 30
179† 30c Sailing ships 30 30
MS183a† 3f Sailing ships 1.25 1.25

1947

230† 2f Pirogue 20 10
231† 2f50 Pirogue 20 20
232† 3f Pirogue 25 20

FRENCH GUINEA

West Africa
100 centimes = 1 franc

1931
As No. 109 of Cameroun
122† 1f50 Liner 4.00 4.25

1937
As Nos. 110/11 of Cameroun
123† 20c Liner 40 40
124† 30c Sailing ships 40 40

FRENCH INDIAN SETTLEMENTS

East coast of Indian sub-continent
24 caches = 1 fanon
8 fanons = 1 rupee

1931
As No. 109 of Cameroun
111† 1f12 Liner 1.25 1.25

1937
As Nos. 110/11 of Cameroun
112† 8c Liner 60 60
113† 12c Sailing ships 60 60

1941
Nos. 112/13 overprinted **FRANCE LIBRE**
154† 8c Liner 2.25 2.25
157† 12c Sailing ships 1.60 1.60

1942
Nos. 112/13 overprinted **FRANCE LIBRE** *and Cross of Lorraine*
189† 8c Liner 2.75 2.50
190† 12c Sailing ships 2.40 2.40

1954
As No. 264 of Cameroun
287 1f Landing craft, Normandy, 1944 .... 2.25 2.25

FRENCH MOROCCO

North-west Africa
100 centimes = 1 franc

1933

179† 45c Local rowing boat, Rabat 15 20
180† 50c Local rowing boat, Rabat 15 5
181† 65c Local rowing boat, Rabat 5 5

1938
No. 181 surcharged **O.S.E. + 65 c**
207† 65c + 65c Local rowing boat, Rabat 1.60 2.00

1939
No. 180 surcharged **40c**
213 40c on 50c Local rowing boat, Rabat 20 10

224† 50c Xebec, Sale (red) 55 30
225† 50c Xebec, Sale (green) 15 5
226† 60c Xebec, Sale (blue) 55 30
227† 60c Xebec, Sale (brown) 15 5
232† 90c Xebec, Sale 10 5
237† 1f50 Xebec, Sale (pink) 5 5
297† 1f50 Xebec, Sale (red) 5 5

1940
No. 181 surcharged **35c**
258 35c on 65c Local rowing boat, Rabat 50 30

1942
No. 232 surcharged **Enfants de France au Maroc +4f**
260† 90c + 4f Xebec, Sale 1.40 2.00

1947

345† 9f + 16f Freighter at quay 50 60

1948

351 6f + 9f *Dunkerque* (battleship) 50 55

1954

436 15f Schooner and destroyer
437 30f Schooner and destroyer
Set of 2 1.40 1.40

FRENCH POLYNESIA

South Pacific
100 centimes = 1 franc

1958

16† 200f Fishing pirogues at night, Moorea 23.00 9.50

1964

38† 2f Outrigger canoe, Tuamotu 40 40
43† 23f Outrigger canoes, Moorea (air) 3.75 2.00

1966

56 10f Pirogue
57 11f Schooner
58 12f Fishing launch
59 14f Pirogues
60 19f Early schooner
61 22f *Oiseau des Iles II* (coaster)
Set of 6 12.00 5.75

1967

72† 21f Pirogue-racing 3.00 1.75

1968

81† 40f Ship's stern and Tahitian canoe, 1767 4.00 3.00

1971

130† 10f Outboard motor boat 3.75 1.75

137† 15f Yacht 2.00 1.25

1972

153 28f Shipping in Papeete harbour 6.00 2.75

STAMP MONTHLY
— finest and most informative magazine for all
collectors. Obtainable from your newsagent or by
postal subscription — details on request.

158	16f *Kon Tiki* (raft)	3.00	2.25

1974

182†	6f Fishing canoe	75	50
184†	15f *Regina Maris* (schooner)	1.50	75

1976

212	24f Battle of the Saints, 1782		
213	31f Battle of the Chesapeake, 1781		
	Set of 2	4.50	3.25

218	90f *Firecrest* (yacht)	5.50	3.75

227	25f Marquesas pirogue		
228	30f Raiatea pirogue		
229	75f Tahiti pirogue		
230	100f Tuamotu pirogue		
	Set of 4	12.00	8.50

1977

262	20f Cutter		
263	50f Schooner		
264	85f Barque		
265	120f Full-rigged ship		
	Set of 4	10.00	6.00

1978

266	33f H.M.S. *Discovery* (Cook)		
267	39f H.M.S. *Resolution* (Cook)		
	Set of 2	4.25	2.75

284	15f *Tahiti* (inter-island ship)		
285	30f *Monowai* (inter-island ship)		
286	75f *Tahitien* (inter-island ship)		
287	100f *Mariposa* (inter-island ship)		
	Set of 4	8.25	6.00

1979

Nos. 266/7 overprinted **"1779 – 1979" BICENTAIRE DE LA MORT DE**

290	33f H.M.S. *Discovery*		
291	39f H.M.S. *Resolution*		
	Set of 2	3.25	2.25

Inscribed "DELRIEU" at foot

297†	4f Outboard motor boat, Raiatea	35	10
298†	5f Outrigger canoe, Motu	45	20

1981

349	200f Racing pirogue	4.50	2.75

356†	40f 18th-century ships in Matavai Bay	85	60
359†	120f 18th-century ships off Pointe Venus	2.25	1.50

1982

373	90f "Hobie Cat 16" class catamaran	1.90	1.25

1983

392	600f Pirogue	8.00	6.00

409†	40f Beached schooner, Moorea	1.00	60

1985

458	130f 19th-century French warship, Papeete	2.50	1.75
MS459	240f 19th-century French warship, Papeete	4.25	4.50

1986

As Nos. 297/8, but inscribed "CARTOR" at foot

470a†	4f Outboard motor boat, Raiatea	5	5
471†	5f Outrigger canoe, Motu	8	5

476	300f Game fishing boat	3.50	2.25

484	400f Sailing ships in harbour, 1880	4.50	3.00

490	46f Building pirogue		
491	50f Building pirogue		
	Set of 2	1.50	1.00

1987

523† 115f Fishing boat, Tuamotu Archipelago 1.25 90

1988

528† 11f Raft and outrigger canoes, Raiatea 15 10

FRENCH SOMALI COAST

East Africa
100 centimes= 1 franc

1931

As No. 109 of Cameroun
236 1f50 Liner 1.60 2.00

1937

As Nos. 110/11 of Cameroun
237† 20c Liner 40 45
238† 30c Sailing ships 50 55

1954

As No. 264 of Cameroun
428 15f Landing craft, Normandy, 1944 ...... 3.25 3.75

1956

431 15f Freighter at wharf 1.00 40

1962

453 100f *Forbin* (steam warship), 1862 ...... 3.50 1.75

1964

476 15f Houri (dhow)
477 25f Sambuk (dhow)
478 50f Building sambuks (air)
479 85f Zaruk (dhow)
480 300f Ziema (dhow)
Set of 5 16.00 8.25

COLLECT RAILWAYS ON STAMPS

A Stanley Gibbons thematic catalogue on this popular subject. Copies available at £7.50 (p. + p. £2) from: Stanley Gibbons Publications Ltd, 5 Parkside, Christchurch Road, Ringwood, Hants BH24 3SH.

FRENCH SOUTHERN AND ANTARCTIC TERRITORIES

Antarctica and nearby Islands
100 centimes = 1 franc

1960

23 25f *Dauphine* (Kerguelen-Tremarec), 1772 18.00 17.00

1962

24 25f *Pourquois Pas?* (Charcot), 1936 ...... 18.00 17.00

1968

44 30f *Astrolabe* (Dumont d'Urville), 1840 .... 85.00 70.00

1972

78 100f *Mascarin* and *Marquis de Castries* (Dufresne), 1772
79 250f Kerguelen's ships, 1772
Set of 2 35.00 27.00

82 100f *Gallieni* (Antarctic supply ship) 12.00 11.00

85 120f *Mascarin* (Dufresne), 1772
86 145f *Astrolabe* (Dumont d'Urville), 1840
87 150f *Roland* (Kerguelen-Tremarec), 1774
88 185f *Victoria* (Del Cano), 1522
Set of 4 11.50 11.50

1974

93 100f *Francais* (Charcot), 1903–05
94 200f *Pourquois Pas?* (Charcot), 1908–10
Set of 2 6.00 6.00

1975

95 75f *Sapmer* (modern mail ship) 4.50 4.50

104 1f90 *La Curieuse* (topsail schooner)
105 2f70 *Commandant Charcot* (ice patrol ship)
106 4f *Marion Dufresne* (Antarctic supply ship)
Set of 3 5.75 5.75

1976

109 3f50 H.M.S. *Discovery* and H.M.S. *Resolution* (Cook), Kerguelen 7.00 6.50

1977

118† 1f20 *Magga Dan* (Antarctic supply ship) 1.25 1.25
119† 1f40 *Thala Dan* (Antarctic supply ship) 1.25 1.25

1979

133 40c *Forbin* (destroyer)
134 50f *Jeanne d'Arc* (helicopter carrier)
Set of 2 2.00 2.00

135 2f70 H.M.S. *Challenger* (survey ship), 1872–76 .... 1.25 1.25

STANLEY GIBBONS
STAMP COLLECTING SERIES

Introductory booklets on *How to Start, How to Identify Stamps* and *Collecting by Theme.* A series of well illustrated guides at a low price.
Write for details.

1980

136	1f10 *Doudart de Lagree* (frigate)			
137	1f50 *Commandant Bourdais* (frigate)			
		Set of 2	1.10	1.10

142†	4f *Victoria* (Del Cano), 1522		1.50	1.25

145	1f90 *Le Recherche* and *L'Esperance*, Amsterdam Island, 1792		75	70

146	2f70 H.M.S. *Terror* (bomb ketch) (Ross), Kerguelen, 1840		85	75

155	3f50 *Saint Marcouf* (Antarctic supply ship)			
156	7f30 *Norsel* (Antarctic supply ship)			
		Set of 2	3.00	3.00

1981

166	8f40 *Antares* (dispatch vessel), 1916–36		1.50	1.50

1982

168	5f *Commandant Charcot* (ice patrol ship)		1.25	1.25

COLLECT BIRDS ON STAMPS

Second revised edition of this Stanley Gibbons thematic catalogue – now available at £8.50 (p. + p. £2) from: Stanley Gibbons Publications Ltd, 5 Parkside, Christchurch Road, Ringwood, Hants BH24 3SH.

1983

169	55c *Le Gros Ventre* (lighter)		30	30

175	2f30 *Austral* (trawler)		50	50

181	5f *Lady Franklin* (Antarctic supply ship)		3.25	3.00

1984

189	2f60 H.M.S. *Erebus* (bomb ketch) (Ross), 1842		70	70

194	11f30 *Albatros* (patrol boat)		2.50	2.50

195	9f *Gauss* (survey topsail schooner), 1901–03		2.75	2.75

1985

200	1f80 Research vessel			
201	5f20 Research vessel			
		Set of 2	1.75	1.75

204	12f80 *La Novara*, (frigate), St. Paul, 1857		3.25	3.25

206	2f Kerguelen's ships, 1772			
207	12f80 Kerguelen's ships, 1772			
		Set of 2	3.25	3.25

1986

212	2f10 *Var A 608* (patrol boat)			
213	3f *Polarbjorn* (Antarctic supply ship)			
		Set of 2	1.25	1.25

214	2f10 *Pourquois Pas?* (Charcot)		50	50
215	14f *Pourquois Pas?* (Charcot)		3.50	3.50

1987

227	3f20 *Eure* (sail despatch vessel)		70	70

228	14f60 *J. B. Charcot* (schooner)		3.25	3.25

COLLECT MAMMALS ON STAMPS

A Stanley Gibbons thematic catalogue on this popular subject. Copies available at £7.50 (p. + p. £2) from: Stanley Gibbons Publications Ltd, 5 Parkside, Christchurch Road, Ringwood, Hants BH24 3SH.

229 16f80 Research vessel and drilling ship 3.75 3.75

230 16f80 Research vessel 3.00 3.00

1988

237 3f50 *Le Gros Ventre* (French sail frigate)
238 4f90 *Jules Verne* (Antarctic supply ship)
239 5f *La Fortune* (French sail warship)
　　　　　　　　　　　　　　　Set of 3 3.00 3.00

FRENCH SUDAN

West Africa
100 centimes = 1 franc

1931

162†	1f25 Pirogue (purple & mauve)	1.25	20
163†	1f25 Pirogue (red)	15	15
164†	1f40 Pirogue	15	15
165†	1f50 Pirogue	15	8
166†	1f60 Pirogue	15	15
167†	1f75 Pirogue (blue & brown)	20	20
168†	1f75 Pirogue (blue)	20	20
169†	2f Pirogue	20	5
170†	2f25 Pirogue	25	25
171†	2f50 Pirogue	35	35
172†	3f Pirogue	20	5
173†	5f Pirogue	60	35
174†	10f Pirogue	80	50
175†	20f Pirogue	1.25	60

As No. 109 *of Cameroun*
189 1f50 Liner 70 70

1937
As Nos. 110/11 *of Cameroun*
190† 20c Liner 40 40
191† 30c Sailing ships 40 40

1941
Nos. 165 *and* 169 *surcharged* **SECOURS NATIONAL** *and value*
215† +2f on 1f50 Pirogue 1.75 2.00
216† +3f on 2f Pirogue 2.00 2.50

COLLECT RAILWAYS ON STAMPS
A Stanley Gibbons thematic catalogue on this popular subject. Copies available at £7.50 (p. + p. £2) from: Stanley Gibbons Publications Ltd, 5 Parkside, Christchurch Road, Ringwood, Hants BH24 3SH.

FRENCH TERRITORY OF THE AFARS AND THE ISSAS

East Africa
100 centimes = 1 franc

1970

550† 48f Speedboats 2.00 1.50
552† 55f Yacht 2.25 1.75

556 48f *Goubet* (car ferry) 2.00 1.50

1973

584† 30f Freighters in port 5.50 3.25

FRENCH WEST AFRICA

West Africa
100 centimes = 1 franc

1947

36† 40c Canoe 10 5

1951

74† 25f Sailing canoe 60 10

1954
As No. 264 *of Cameroun*
81 15f Landing craft, Normandy, 1944 .... 2.00 1.75

1955

84 15f Freighter at wharf 85 35

1958

99† 20f Liner and freighters, Dakar 70 35
102† 50f *L'Arachide* (freighter) 1.00 55

FUJEIRA

Arabia
100 dirhams = 1 riyal

1968

32† 25np Yacht 20 8

Appendix

The following have either been issued in excess of postal needs or have not been made available to the public in reasonable quantities at face value. Miniature sheets, imperforate stamps etc. are excluded from this section.

1968
Historical Ships. Postage 15, 25, 50, 75d, 1r; Air 2, 3, 4, 5r

1971
Olympic Games, Munich. Sports. 12d Yacht
Olympic Games, Munich. Venues. 35d Yacht

GABON

West Africa
100 centimes = 1 franc

1932

127†	1c Log raft	5	5
128†	2c Log raft	5	5
129†	4c Log raft	5	5
130†	5c Log raft	10	5
131†	10c Log raft	15	10
132†	15c Log raft	35	25
133†	20c Log raft	35	35
134†	25c Log raft	15	10

1965

230 25f 16th-century galleon
231 50f 17th-century merchantman
232 85f 18th-century frigate
233 100f 19th-century brig
　　　　　　　　　　　　　　　Set of 4 3.50 2.00

1966

267† 85f Oil rig 1.00 50

1967

311   30f *Belgrano* and *Jean Guiton*
       (19th-century steam packets)
312   30f *Ango* and *Lucie Delmas* (modern mail
       carriers)
                              Set of 2   70   50

1968

323   30f Tanker, Port Gentil   35   25

335   30f *Junon* (19th-century sail/steam
       warship)   35   25

1969

346   50f Log raft (on stamp No. 134)   75   75

372†   50f Oil rig   40   30

377   30f Mail pirogue, Adoumas   35   25

1972

443   60f Gondolas
444   70f Gondolas
445   140f Gondolas
                              Set of 3   3.00   1.50

1974

517†   40f Yachts   30   20

521†   30f Pirogue, River Ogooue   25   20

1976

578†   100f Ships of the Boston Tea Party, 1773   75   50

       No. 578 *overprinted* **4 JUILLET 1976**
583†   100f Ships of the Boston Tea Party, 1773   65   50

1978

650†   50f Container ships, Owendo Port   35   15

1979

691†   100f Olympic yachts   50   35

698   500f H.M.S. *Resolution* and H.M.S.
       Discovery (Cook) 3.50   2.00

1982

805   75f Freighter
806   100f *Correze* (container ship)
807   200f Oil tanker
                              Set of 3   1.75   1.50

1983

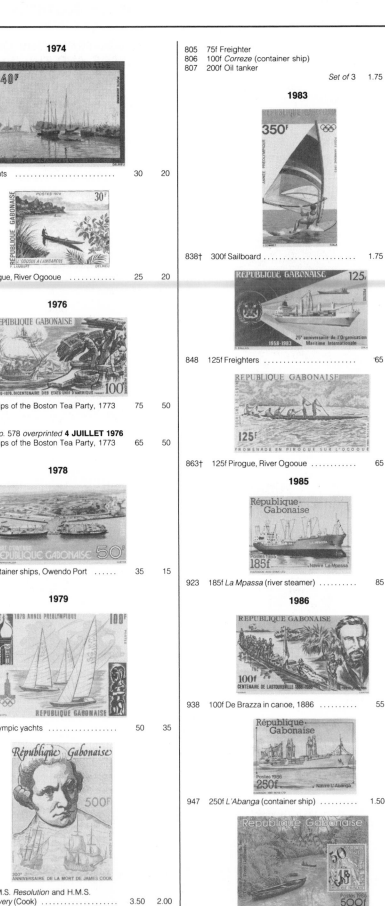

838†   300f Sailboard 1.75   1.40

848   125f Freighters . . . .   ·65   45

863†   125f Pirogue, River Ogooue   65   45

1985

923   185f *La Mpassa* (river steamer)   85   70

1986

938   100f De Brazza in canoe, 1886   55   45

947   250f *L'Abanga* (container ship) 1.50   1.25

948   500f River pirogues 2.25   2.00

GAMBIA

West Africa
1949 12 pence = 1 shilling
20 shillings = 1 pound
1971 100 bututs = 1 dalasy

1949

As No. 115 *of Antigua*

167†	3d Paddle-steamer	70	45

1953

172†	1d Sailing cutter	35	10
174†	2½d Barra canoe	35	30
175†	3d *Lady Wright* (river steamer)	35	10
179†	1s3d Sailing cutter	2.00	15
180†	2s Barra canoe	2.50	2.00
184†	10s *Lady Wright* (river steamer)	6.50	6.50

1969

259†	2d *Westfalen* (catapult ship)	15	5

1971

285†	25b Dugout canoe	25	10
286†	37b Dugout canoe	40	30

1978

396†	1d25 Local rowing longboat	60	70

404	8b *Lady Wright* (river steamer)	
405	25b *Lady Chilel Jawara* (river vessel)	
406	1d *Lady Chilel Jawara*	
	Set of 3	1.60 1.25

1980

436	10b *Vampire* (steam launch)	
437	25b *Lady Denham* (river steamer)	
438	50b *Mansa Kila Ba* (river steamer)	
439	1d *Prince of Wales* (river steamer)	
	Set of 4	1.25 1.25

441	8b Ancient Phoenician trading vessel	
442	67b Ancient Egyptian sea-going galley	
443	75b Portuguese caravel	
444	1d Spanish galleon	
	Set of 4	1.25 1.25

1983

494	1b Canoes	
495	2b River ferry	
496	3b Dredger	
497	4b *Sir Dawda* (harbour launch)	
498	5b Cargo liner	
499	10b *Lady Dale* (launch)	
500	20b Container ship	
501	30b Large sailing canoe	
502	40b *Lady Wright* (river steamer)	
503	50b Container ship	
504	75b Fishing boats	
505	1d Tug and groundnut barges	
506	1d25 Groundnut canoe	
507	2d50 *Banjul* (car ferry)	
508	5d *Bintang Bolong* (car ferry)	
509	10d *Lady Chilel Jawara* (river vessel)	
	Set of 16	3.00 3.50

514†	10b Local ferry boat	5	8

1984

MS533†	5d Olympic yachts	2.00	2.25

550†	85b Bulk carrier	50	40
551†	90b *Dagomba* (freighter) on fire	50	55
552†	1d25 19th-century British sail frigate	75	85

Nos. 507/8 *overprinted* **19th UPU CONGRESS HAMBURG**

553	2d50 *Banjul*		
554	5d *Bintang Bolong*		
	Set of 2	3.00	3.25

560†	85b *Westfalen* (catapult ship)	60	40

1985

No. **MS**533 *overprinted* **GOLD MEDAL STAR CLASS U.S.A.**

MS606†	5d Olympic yachts	1.75	1.90

1986

615†	60b Fishing boat, Fotoba, Guinea	20	25

1987

700	20b *America* (yacht), 1851		
701	1b *Courageous* (yacht), 1974		
702	2b *Volunteer* (yacht), 1887		
703	10b *Intrepid* (yacht), 1967		
	Set of 4	2.50	2.50
MS704	12b *Australia II* (yacht), 1983	2.25	2.40

706†	2b Launch	5	5
707†	3b Schooner	5	5
708†	5b *Queen Elizabeth 2* (liner) and aircraft carrier	5	5

GERMANY

Central Europe, divided after the Second
World War into West Germany, West Berlin and
East Germany
100 pfennige = 1 reichsmark

1937

639	3pf + 2pf *Bremen* (lifeboat), 1931		
640	4pf + 3pf *Elbe I* (lightship)		
641	5pf + 3pf Fishing smacks		
642	6pf + 4pf *Wilhelm Gustloff* (liner)		
643	8pf + 4pf *Padua* (barque)		
644	12pf + 6pf *Tannenberg* (liner)		
645	15pf + 10pf *Schwerin* (train ferry)		
646	25pf + 15pf *Hamburg* (liner)		
647	40pf + 35pf *Europa* (liner), 1928		
	Set of 9	21.00	11.50

1939

No. 206 *of Danzig surcharged* **2 Reichsmark Deutsches Reich**

717†	2rm on 2 g Freighters and tugs on River Mottlau	16.00	25.00

1943

819†	3pf + 2pf U-Boat Type V11A (submarine)	20	35
823†	8pf + 7pf Pontoon	20	35
830†	50pf + 50pf Motor torpedo-boat	85	1.25

1944

861†	3pf + 2pf Landing craft	15	25
869†	16pf + 10pf Motor torpedo-boat	15	25

Allied Occupation—French Zone

BADEN

1947

FB2†	3pf Yachts	5	10
FB5†	15pf Yachts (violet)	5	10
FB9†	45pf Yachts	5	20

1948

Design as Nos. FB2, etc, but new value and colour changed

FB15†	6pf Yachts	20	8
FB18†	15pf Yachts (blue)	40	25

Design as Nos. FB2, etc, but "PF" omitted

FB30†	5pf Yachts	60	55
FB31†	6pf Yachts	19.00	8.00

West Germany

100 pfennige = 1 deutschmark

1952

1078	20pf *Senator Schaffer* (trawler)	14.00	4.25

1957

1183	15pf *Bayernstein* (freighter)	1.00	1.10

1964

1331†	20pf *Lichtenfels* (liner), Hamburg	12	12
1332†	20pf *Kronprinz Harald* (ferry), Kiel	12	12

1965

1395†	70pf *Bremen* (liner) and *Hammonia* (19th-century steamship)	25	15
1399	20pf *Theodor Heuss* (rescue vessel)	10	5

1970

1528	20pf Liner in Kiel Canal	15	10

1972

1622†	25pf + 10pf Olympic yacht	60	75
1641†	30pf *Wappen von Hamburg* (liner), Heligoland	25	10

1973

1655	40pf Container ship, Hamburg		
1656	40pf *Loreley* (Rhine steamer), Rudesheim		
	Set of 2	60	20

1974

1680†	30pf Barge, Saarbrucken	25	10
1682†	40pf Freighters, Bremen	35	10

1975

1746†	70pf Tanker under construction	35	10

1977

1819	30pf + 15pf *Wappen von Hamburg* (11th- century warship)		
1820	40pf + 20pf *Preussen* (full-rigged sailing ship), 1902		
1821	50pf + 25pf *Bremen* (liner), 1929		
1822	70pf + 35pf *Sturmfels* (container ship), 1972		
	Set of 4	3.75	4.00

1982

1996	60pf Racing yachts	50	12

1983

2030	80pf *Concord* (emigrant ship), 1683	70	15

1984

2071	80pf Merchant ship, 1784	70	12

1987

2177†	80pf + 40pf Racing yachts	90	90

West Berlin

100 pfennige = 1 deutschmark

1955

B123	10pf *Berlin* (liner)		
B124	25pf *Berlin*		
	Set of 2	4.75	3.25

1962

B214†	10pf Barges on River Spree	5	5
B220†	60pf Barges on River Spree	20	30

1975

B467	30pf *Princess Charlotte* (pleasure boat)		
B468	40pf *Siegfried* (pleasure boat)		
B469	50pf *Sperber* (pleasure boat)		
B470	60pf *Vaterland* (pleasure boat)		
B471	70pf *Moby Dick* (pleasure boat)		
	Set of 5	2.00	2.25

As No. 1746 of West Germany, but additionally inscribed "BERLIN"

B484†	70pf Tanker under construction	40	15

1976

B512†	30pf Yacht	20	15

1977

B527 30pf + 15pf Bremen kogge, 1380
B528 40pf + 20pf Helena Sloman (steamship), 1850
B529 50pf + 25pf Cap Polonio (liner), 1914
B530 70pf + 35pf Widar (bulk carrier), 1971
Set of 4   2.50 2.75

East Germany
100 pfennige = 1 mark

1953

E118† 24pf Sailing barge, River Oder 60 65

E318† 50pf Launching a ship 5 30
E135† 60pf Launching a ship (design in dots) 3.75 1.00
E173† 60pf Launching a ship (design in lines) 6.00 50

1957

E295† 20pf Frieden (freighter) 5 5

1958

E371† 10pf Freundschaft (freighter) 10 5
E373† 25pf Frieden (freighter) 70 50

1959

E463† 70pf Shipbuilding 15 5

1960

E482† 25pf Olympic yacht 8 5

No. E371 overprinted Inbetriebnahme des Hochsee-hafens 1. Mai 1960
E494 10pf Freundschaft 10 5

E501 5pf Model and plan of Fritz Heckert (cruise liner)
E502 10pf + 5pf Fritz Heckert under construction
E503 20pf + 10pf Fritz Heckert at sea
E504 25pf Fritz Heckert and Aurora (Russian cruiser)
Set of 4   2.40 2.40

E537† 20pf Sassnitz (train ferry) 10 5

1961

E552† 10pf Trawler 5 5
E554† 25pf Robert Koch (trawler) 5 5

1962

E618† 25pf Ernst Thalmann (destroyer) 15 5

E639† 25pf Frieden (freighter) 1.25 1.00

1963

E678† 25pf Topsail schooner 1.25 80

1964

E777† 10pf + 5pf Freundschaft (freighter) (on stamp No. E371) 5 5

1967

E1027 10pf Friedrich der Grosse (battleship), 1914–18
E1028 15pf Prinzregent Leopold (battleship), 1914–18
E1029 20pf Seydlitz (battle cruiser), 1914–18
Set of 3   35 30

E1035† 40pf Aurora (Russian cruiser) 1.40 1.10

1968

E1070† 15pf Deep sea trawler 25 15

E1105† 20pf Kogge, Rostock 5 5

1969

E1252† 25pf Fishing boats 75 75

1970

E1311† 25pf River police patrol boat 70 55

1971

E1375† 15pf Takraf (dredger) 10 8

E1413 10pf Ivan Franko (liner)
E1414 15pf "Type 17" freighter
E1415 20pf Rostock (freighter), 1966
E1416 25pf Junge Welt (fish-factory ship)
E1417 40pf Hansel (container ship)
E1418 50pf Akademik Kurtschatow (research ship)
Set of 7   1.75 1.00

1972

E1495† 35pf Brigantine 15 5

E1508† 15pf Sea rescue launch 20 15

1974

E1700† 10pf 19th-century paddle-steamer and
        modern freighter 5 5

1976

E1835† 25pf *Prometey* (deep sea trawler) 25 12

1977

E1973† 35pf River Elbe passenger steamer,
        1837 .... 1.25 1.25

E1974† 10pf *Aurora* (Russian cruiser) 15 10

E1995† 50pf Fire-fighting tug 2.00 1.75

1978

E2044† 70pf *Boltenhagen* (container ship) 1.50 1.50

1979

E2119† 35pf H.M.S. *Resolution* (Cook) 25 10

E2121 20pf Container ship 15 5

E2139 20pf *Rostock* (train ferry), 1977
E2140 35pf *Rugen* (train ferry)
                            Set of 2 1.25 1.00

1980

MSE2250† 1m Olympic yachts 1.25 1.25

1981

E2361 10pf Tug
E2362 20pf Tug and barges
E2363 25pf Diesel-electric paddle-ferry, River
            Elbe
E2364 35pf Ice-breaker, River Oder
E2365 50pf *Schonewalde* (motor barge)
E2366 85pf Dredger
                            Set of 6 3.00 2.25

1982

E2417 5pf *Frieden* (freighter)
E2418 10pf *Fichtelberg* (roll-on roll-off
            freighter)
E2419 15pf *Brocken* (heavy cargo carrier)
E2420 20pf *Weimar* (container ship)
E2421 25pf *Vorwarts* (freighter)
E2422 30pf *Berlin* (container ship)
                            Set of 6 2.25 1.75

E2434† 5pf 17th-century ships in storm 5 5

1983

E2488† 10pf Tanker 15 5
E2489† 20pf Container ship 20 5

1986

E2714† 50pf *Atlantik 488* (factory trawler) 45 25

E2739† 50pf Barges, Magdeburg 45 25

E2762† 50pf Train ferry 45 25

1987

E2823 10pf Longboat 8 5

GHANA

West Africa
1957 12 pence = 1 shilling
20 shillings = 1 pound
1965 100 pesewas = 1 cedi
1967 100 new pesewas = 1 new cedi
1972 100 pesewas = 1 cedi

1957

182 2½d Viking ship
183 1s3d Galleon
184 5s *Volta River* (freighter)
                            Set of 3 1.10 2.00

1965

424† 60p *Shama* (trawler) 2.00 2.50

1967

469† 10np Freighter and tug, Tema 15 5

476† 12½np 15th-century British galleon 1.00 1.00
477† 20np 15th-century Portuguese galleon .. 1.40 1.75
478† 25np 15th-century Spanish galleon 1.75 2.25

1969

No. 469 *overprinted* **NEW CONSTITUTION 1969**
550† 10np Freighter and tug, Tema 20 20

1976

756† 30np Scout yachts 85 75

No. 756 overprinted **'INTERPHIL' 76 BICENTENNIAL EXHIBITION**

769† 30np Scout yachts 40 50

1978

838† 60p Fishing canoe 55 60

1981

955† 2c Royal Yacht *Britannia* 1.25 1.25
954† 3c Royal Yacht *Britannia* 1.25 1.40
950† 4c Royal Yacht *Britannia* 1.25 1.40

1982

993† 80p Sea scout sailing dinghy 65 45

1983

1050† 2c30 Cable ship 15 12

1984

Nos. 950 and 954 surcharged **C20 C20**
1068† 20c on 3c Royal Yacht *Britannia* 6.00 6.00
1069† 20c on 4c Royal Yacht *Britannia* 6.00 6.00

GIBRALTAR

South-west Europe
1931 12 pence = 1 shilling
20 shillings = 1 pound
1971 100 pence = 1 pound

1931

110 1d Liner and battleship
111 1½d Liner and battleship
112 2d Liner and battleship
113 3d Liner and battleship
Set of 4 8.50 10.00

1938

As Nos. 110/11, but with portrait of King George VI
122b† 1d Liner and battleship 40 55
123† 1½d Liner and battleship (red) 13.00 2.50
123b† 1½d Liner and battleship (violet) 25 60

1949

As No. 115 of Antigua
137† 3d Paddle-steamer 2.75 1.50

1953

147† 1½d Tunny fishing boat 90 45
149† 2½d Sailing yachts 1.00 25
150† 3d *Saturnia* (liner) 1.25 10
151† 4d Freighters at coaling wharf 1.25 75

1954

As No. 150, but inscribed "ROYAL VISIT 1954"
159† 3d *Saturnia* 15 25

1967

200 ½d H.M.S. *Victory* (Nelson)
201 1d *Arab* (early steamer)
202 2d H.M.S. *Carmania* (merchant cruiser)
203 2½d *Mons Calpe* (ferry)
204 3d *Canberra* (liner)
205 4d H.M.S. *Hood* (battle cruiser)
205a 5d *Mirror* (cable ship)
206 6d *Xebec* (sailing vessel)
207 7d *Amerigo Vespucci* (Italian cadet ship)
208 9d *Raffaello* (liner)
209 1s *Royal Katherine* (Henry VIII)
210 2s H.M.S. *Ark Royal* (Second World War aircraft carrier)
211 5s H.M.S. *Dreadnought* (nuclear submarine)
212 10s *Neuralia* (liner)
213 £1 *Mary Celeste* (sail merchantman)
Set of 15 38.00 35.00

1974

338† 20p *King George V* (Second World War battleship) 60 60

1980

438† 9p H.M.S. *Victory* (Nelson) 25 25
440† 40p H.M.S. *Victory* after Trafalgar 80 1.00

1982

475 ½p Crest of H.M.S. *Opossum* (frigate)
476 15½p Crest of H.M.S. *Norfolk* (cruiser)
477 17p Crest of H.M.S. *Fearless* (destroyer)
478 60p Crest of H.M.S. *Rooke* (shore base)
Set of 4 2.10 2.40

1983

493 4p Crest of H.M.S. *Faulknor* (destroyer)
494 14p Crest of H.M.S. *Renown* (battle cruiser)
495 17p Crest of H.M.S. *Ark Royal* (aircraft carrier)
496 60p Crest of H.M.S. *Sheffield* (cruiser)
Set of 4 1.75 2.10

1984

510 20p Crest of H.M.S. *Active* (destroyer)
511 21p Crest of H.M.S. *Foxhound* (destroyer)
512 26p Crest of H.M.S. *Valiant* (battleship)
513 29p Crest of H.M.S. *Hood* (battle cruiser)
Set of 4 1.75 1.90

1985

522 4p Crest of H.M.S. *Duncan* (destroyer)
523 9p Crest of H.M.S. *Fury* (destroyer)
524 21p Crest of H.M.S. *Firedrake* (destroyer)
525 80p Crest of H.M.S. *Malaya* (battleship)
Set of 4 2.10 2.50

1986

541 22p Crest of H.M.S. *Lightning* (destroyer)
542 29p Crest of H.M.S. *Hermione* (cruiser)
543 32p Crest of H.M.S. *Laforey* (destroyer)
544 44p Crest of H.M.S. *Nelson* (battleship)
Set of 4 2.75 2.75

1987

563† 22p Yachts in marina 50 50

STANLEY GIBBONS STAMP COLLECTING SERIES

Introductory booklets on *How to Start, How to Identify Stamps* and *Collecting by Theme.* A series of well illustrated guides at a low price.
Write for details.

565	18p Crest of H.M.S. *Wishart* (destroyer)		
566	22p Crest of H.M.S. *Charybdis* (cruiser		
567	32p Crest of H.M.S. *Antelope* (destroyer)		
568	44p Crest of H.M.S. *Eagle* (aircraft carrier)		
	Set of 4	2.50	2.50

1988

588†	22p *Canberra* (liner)	45	50
589†	22p Ferry	45	50

592	18p Crest of H.M.S. *Clyde* (submarine)		
593	22p Crest of H.M.S. *Foresight* (destroyer)		
594	32p Crest of H.M.S. *Severn* (submarine)		
595	44p Crest of H.M.S. *Rodney* (battleship)		
	Set of 4	2.10	2.25

GILBERT AND ELLICE ISLANDS

Pacific Ocean
1939 12 pence = 1 shilling
20 shillings = 1 pound
1966 100 cents = 1 dollar

1939

45†	1½d Canoe	30	75
46†	2d Canoe and canoe-house	20	65
49†	5d Ellice Islands canoe	1.75	90
51†	1s *Triona* (freighter), 1931	2.00	1.25
52†	2s *Nimanoa* (colonial schooner)	6.00	6.50
53†	2s6d Gilbert Islands canoe	8.00	8.50

1949

As No. 115 *of Antigua*

60†	2d Paddle-steamer	1.00	70

1956

As Nos. 45/6, 49, 51/3, *but with portrait of Queen Elizabeth II*

66†	2d Canoe and canoe-house	75	45
69†	5d Ellice Islands canoe	2.50	1.25
71†	1s *Triona*	55	50
72†	2s *Nimanoa*	7.00	3.25
73†	2s6d Gilbert Islands canoe	5.50	3.75
75†	10s Canoe (as stamp No. 45)	21.00	14.00

1960

76†	2d *Triona II* (freighter), 1943	35	15

STAMP MONTHLY

— finest and most informative magazine for all
collectors. Obtainable from your newsagent or by
postal subscription — details on request.

1967

132†	3c H.M.S. *Royalist* (screw corvette), 1892	10	5

1970

167†	10c *John Williams III* (missionary sailing ship)	30	15
169†	35c *John Williams VII* (missionary motor ship)	50	40

172†	35c Sailing canoes	40	30

1971

174†	2c Fishing canoe	15	10
177†	5c Gilbertese canoe	35	15
184†	35c Fishing canoes at night	2.00	65

192†	35c Outrigger canoe	45	40

1972

197†	10c South Pacific canoe types	10	15

1973

218†	10c Outrigger canoe	15	10

1974

227	3c "Te Mataaua" canoe crest		
228	10c "Te-Nimta-wawa" canoe crest		
229	35c "Tara-Tara-Venei-Na" canoe crest		
230	50c "Te Bou-uoua" canoe crest		
	Set of 4	1.25	95

232†	4c "Te Koroba" canoe	15	5
233†	10c *Kiakia* (sailing ship)	20	10

1975

259†	35c Fishing canoes	45	70

GILBERT ISLANDS

Pacific Ocean
100 cents = 1 dollar

1976

Nos. 174, 177 *and* 184 *of Gilbert and Ellice Islands overprinted*
THE GILBERT ISLANDS

4†	2c Fishing canoe	50	40
13†	5c Gilbertese canoe	60	45
20†	35c Fishing canoes at night	4.00	4.00

23†	1c *Teraaka* (training ship)	12	12
24†	3c *Tautunu* (freighter)	20	20
37†	$1 *Tabakea* (ferry)	2.50	2.75

1977

48†	8c Outrigger canoe	35	25
49†	20c Royal Yacht *Britannia*	45	35

51	5c H.M.S. *Dolphin* (frigate), 1765		
52	15c *Betsey* (American expedition ship), 1798		
53	20c *Vostok* (Russian expedition ship), 1820		
54	35c *Vincennes* (American expedition ship), 1838–42		
	Set of 4	9.00	12.00

Gilbert Islands

55†	8c H.M.S. *Resolution* and H.M.S. *Discovery* (Cook)	65	20
58†	40c H.M.S. *Resolution* and ship's boat, Christmas Island	2.50	1.40

63†	40c Scout outrigger canoe	85	1.00

1979

80†	10c H.M.S. *Endeavour* (Cook)	35	20

GOLD COAST

West Africa
12 pence = 1 shilling
20 shillings = 1 pound

1949

As No. 115 of Antigua

150†	2½d Paddle-steamer	1.50	2.00

GREAT BRITAIN

Western Europe
1951 12 pence = 1 shilling
20 shillings = 1 pound
1971 100 pence = 1 pound

1951

509†	2s6d H.M.S. *Victory* (Nelson)	12.00	75
510†	5s Yacht and Thames sailing barge, Dover	30.00	1.50

1963

639†	2½d Modern lifeboat	10	10
640†	4d 19th-century lifeboat	40	30

1966

703†	1s3d "SRN6" hovercraft	25	30

711†	6d Norman ship, 1066	10	10

1967

715†	9d Freighter at quay	8	10

751	1s9d *Gipsy Moth IV* (yacht) (Chichester)	12	12

1968

770†	1s9d H.M.S. *Endeavour* (Cook)	15	20

1969

778	5d *Queen Elizabeth 2* (liner)		
779	9d *Elizabeth Jonas* (Elizabethan galleon)		
780	9d *Earl of Balcares* (East Indiaman)		
781	9d *Cutty Sark* (clipper)		
782	1s *Great Britain* (steam/sail), 1843		
783	1s *Mauretania* (liner), 1906		
	Set of 6	75	90

1970

822†	1s6d *Mayflower* (Pilgrim Fathers), 1620	20	20

1972

902†	7½p Wreck of brig *President*	70	80

1974

954†	3½p *Peninsular* (packet steamer), 1888	8	8

COLLECT MAMMALS ON STAMPS

A Stanley Gibbons thematic catalogue on this popular subject. Copies available at £7.50 (p. + p. £2) from: Stanley Gibbons Publications Ltd, 5 Parkside, Christchurch Road, Ringwood, Hants BH24 3SH.

1975

980	7p Sailing dinghies		
981	8p Racing yachts		
982	10p Cruising yachts		
983	12p Multi-hulled yachts		
	Set of 4	90	1.00

1978

1050†	9p North Sea oil rig	25	20

1979

1103†	15p River Thames police launch	40	40

1981

1166†	14p Cockle dredger	35	35

1982

1187	15½p *Mary Rose* (Henry VIII)		
1188	19½p *Triumph* (Blake)		
1189	24p H.M.S. *Victory* (Nelson)		
1190	26p H.M.S. *Dreadnought* (battleship) (Fisher)		
1191	29p H.M.S. *Warspite* (battleship) (Cunningham)		
	Set of 5	2.50	2.75

1204†	19½p 18th-century galleons	60	65

1983

1217†	28p *Iolair* (oilfield emergency support vessel)	1.40	1.60

1985

1286	17p Lifeboat		
1287	22p Trawler		
1288	31p Liner		
1289	34p Yacht		
	Set of 4	2.75	2.75

1986

17 PENCE · INDUSTRY YEAR 1986

1308†	17p North Sea oil rig	45	45

1987

1368†	22p Great Eastern (liner), 1858	35	40

1988

1393†	26p Queen Elizabeth (liner)	40	45

1396†	26p Sailing clipper	30	35

ARMADA · LIZARD · 19 JULY 1588

1400	18p Spanish galeasse off the Lizard, 1588		
1401	18p English fleet leaving Plymouth, 1588		
1402	18p Engagement off Isle of Wight, 1588		
1403	18p Attack of English fire-ships, Calais, 1588		
1404	18p Armada in storm, North Sea, 1588		
	Set of 5	1.40	1.50

GREECE

South-east Europe
100 lepta = drachma

1927

410†	5lep Freighter in Corinth Canal	35	15
415†	50lep Freighter in Corinth Canal	1.75	10

416†	80lep Freighter in Corinth Canal	1.75	30
419†	3d Averoff (cruiser)	5.50	12

428†	4d Battle of Navarino, 1827	9.00	55

1933

475†	50d Averoff (cruiser)	45.00	3.75

1946

646†	50d Second World War convoy	40	8
647†	100d Helle (cruiser)	55	8
652†	2000d Hyacinth (torpedo-boat) and Perla (submarine)	12.00	2.75

1947

673†	800d Greek frigate, 1824	1.25	20

1958

778	50lep Michael Carras (tanker)		
779	1d Queen Frederika (liner)		
780	1d50 Full-rigged sailing ship, 1821		
781	2d Byzantine galley		
782	3d50 6th-century B.C. galley		
783	5d Argo (5th-century B.C.)		
	Set of 6	11.00	8.50

784†	10d Shipping, Piraeus	5.00	15
785†	15d Coasters, Salonika	1.40	20
786†	20d Fishing boats, Patras	5.00	15
787†	25d Fishing boats, Hermoupolis	1.40	55
789†	50d Shipping, Kavalla	2.25	50

1960

827	2d50 Brig in storm		
828	4d50 Brig in calm waters		
	Set of 2	1.50	1.10

COLLECT BIRDS ON STAMPS

Second revised edition of this Stanley Gibbons thematic catalogue – now available at £8.50 (p. + p. £2) from: Stanley Gibbons Publications Ltd, 5 Parkside, Christchurch Road, Ringwood, Hants BH24 3SH.

1961

849	2d50 Nirefs (Olympic yacht)	50	25

1967

1052†	20lep Lonchi (destroyer)	12	10
1053†	1d Eugene Eugenides (cadet ship)	12	10
1055†	3d Averoff (cruiser)	30	25
1056†	6d Australis (liner)	40	15

1969

1101	1d Yachts	15	5

1112	80lep 19th-century brig and steamship		
1113	2d Olympic Garland (tanker)		
1114	2d Themistocles and Karteria (warships), 1821		
1115	4d50 Velos (destroyer)		
1116	6d Battle of Salamis, 480 B.C.		
	Set of 5	2.50	1.25

1971

1168	20lep Leonidas (warship), 1821		
1169	1d Pericles (warship), 1821		
1170	1d50 Terpsichore (warship), 1821		
1171	2d50 Karteria (warship), 1821		
1172	3d Battle of Samos		
1173	6d Battle of Yeronda		
	Set of 6	2.25	1.10

1977

1387†	4d Battle of Navarino, 1827	12	8

1393†	4d Ancient galley, sailing ships and modern liner	10	5

1398†	1d50 Topsail schooner, Kalamata	5	5

1978

1411† 5d *Maximilianos* (passenger steamer)   15   5

1440	50lep Destroyer		
1441	1d Motor torpedo-boats		
1442	2d50 *Papanicolis* (submarine)		
1443	4d *Psara* (cruiser)		
1444	5d *Madonna of Hydra* (armed sailing caique)		
1445	7d Byzantine dromon		
1446	50d Athenian trireme		
	Set of 7	1.75	1.25

1980

1539† 20d Harbour tug 45   20

1981

1556† 12d Oil rig 35   8

1983

1609	11d Figurehead from Tsamados's *Ares*		
1610	15d Figurehead from Miaoulis's *Ares*		
1611	18d Figurehead of unknown vessel from Sphakia		
1612	25d Figurehead from *Spetses*		
1613	40d Figurehead from *Epameinondas*		
1614	50d Figurehead from *Carteria*		
	Set of 6	3.25	1.90

1620† 18d Outboard motor boat 40   20
1621† 27d Sailboard 55   30

1646† 32d Ancient galley 45   40

CHARITY TAX STAMPS

1941

К.П.
λεπτῶν
50

No. 410 *surcharged*
C561   50lep on 5lep Freighter in Corinth Canal   20   15

1942

✝
ΦΥΜ· Τ.Τ.Τ.
10 ⇌ ΔΡ.

No. 410 *surcharged*
C591†   10d on 5lep Freighter in Corinth Canal   20   15

GREENLAND

North Atlantic
100 ore = 1 krone

1945

15†   2k Eskimo kayak 30.00   27.00

No. 15 *overprinted* **DANMARK BEFRIET 5 MAJ 1945**
24†   2k Eskimo kayak 55.00   40.00

1950

33†	50ore *Gustav Holm* (polar ship)	27.00	12.00
34†	1k *Gustav Holm*	12.00	1.75
35†	2k *Gustav Holm*	5.50	1.75
36†	5k *Gustav Holm*	2.75	1.00

1958

No. 33 *surcharged* **30 + 10** *and Cross of Lorraine*
40   30 + 10ore on 50ore *Gustav Holm* (polar ship) 3.00   1.75

1971

77†	50ore Mail kayak	25	20
78†	70ore Umiak (women's boat)	40	25
81†	1k *Kununguak* (coaster) and *Dlik* (tug)	70	60
82†	1k30 *Sokongen* (schooner)	40	40
83†	1k50 *Karen* (sailing longboat)	40	40

1972

85   60ore + 10ore *Dannebrog* (Danish royal yacht) 1.25   1.50

1974

91†   1k Trawler and kayaks 55   5

1982

134   2k70 Kayak 50   50

135   2k + 40ore Eric the Red's ship, 900 90   90

136†   2k Whaleboat 40   40

1983

142†   4k50 16th-century ship 75   85

1985

152   2k80 *Hvalfisken* (brig) 1.00   1.00

GRENADA

West Indies
1898 12 pence = 1 shilling
20 shillings = 1 pound
1949 100 cents = 1 dollar

1898

56   2½d Flagship of Columbus, 1498 .... 10.00   7.00

1906

77	½d Flagship of Columbus, 1498		
78	1d Flagship of Columbus, 1498		
79	2d Flagship of Columbus, 1498		
80	2½d Flagship of Columbus, 1498		
84	3d Flagship of Columbus, 1498		
85	6d Flagship of Columbus, 1498		
86	1s Flagship of Columbus, 1498		
87	2s Flagship of Columbus, 1498		
88	5s Flagship of Columbus, 1498		
83	10s Flagship of Columbus, 1498		
	Set of 10	£110	£180

1934

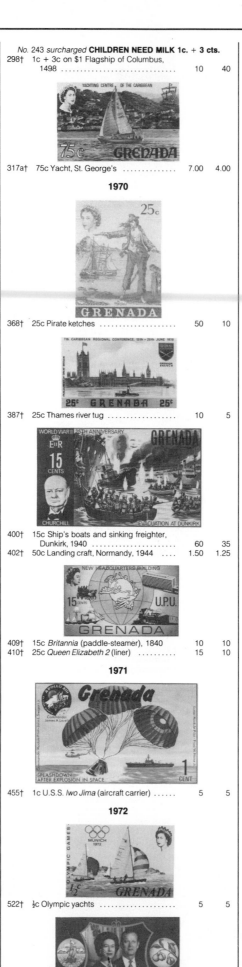

136†	1d Flagship of Columbus, 1498	80	1.00
138†	2d Flagship of Columbus, 1498	40	50
140†	3d Flagship of Columbus, 1498	35	1.00
141†	6d Flagship of Columbus, 1498	70	1.40
142†	1s Flagship of Columbus, 1498	1.00	3.00
143†	2s6d Flagship of Columbus, 1498	6.50	14.00
144†	5s Flagship of Columbus, 1498	20.00	27.00

1938

As Nos. 136, 138 and 140/4, but with portrait of King George VI or similar vert design with royal cyphers

154†	1d Flagship of Columbus, 1498	12	10
156†	2d Flagship of Columbus, 1498	15	10
158b†	3d Flagship of Columbus, 1498	25	70
159†	6d Flagship of Columbus, 1498	40	20
160†	1s Flagship of Columbus, 1498	30	20
161†	2s Flagship of Columbus, 1498	4.25	70
162†	5s Flagship of Columbus, 1498	2.50	2.00
163b†	10s Flagship of Columbus, 1498	7.00	7.00

1949

As No. 115 of Antigua

169†	6c Paddle-steamer	30	30

1951

181†	25c Flagship of Columbus, 1498	2.25	80
182†	50c Flagship of Columbus, 1498	3.00	60
183†	$1.50 Flagship of Columbus, 1498	7.50	5.00
184†	$2.50 Flagship of Columbus, 1498	4.75	5.00

1953

As Nos. 181/4, but with royal cypher of Queen Elizabeth II

201†	25c Flagship of Columbus, 1498	55	20
202†	50c Flagship of Columbus, 1498	80	40
203†	$1.50 Flagship of Columbus, 1498	4.00	3.50
204†	$2.50 Flagship of Columbus, 1498	7.50	3.50

1961

209†	8c Flagship of Columbus, 1498	12	5
210†	25c Solent (paddle-steamer)	20	15

1966

243†	$1 Flagship of Columbus, 1498	1.50	1.25

1967

No. 243 overprinted **expo67 MONTREAL CANADA** *and emblem*

260†	$1 Flagship of Columbus, 1498	20	20

1967

No. 243 overprinted **ASSOCIATED STATEHOOD**

274†	$1 Flagship of Columbus, 1498	70	70

1968

289†	10c Fishing boat, Antibes	10	5
292†	25c Fishing boat, Antibes	15	5

No. 243 surcharged **CHILDREN NEED MILK 1c. + 3 cts.**

298†	1c + 3c on $1 Flagship of Columbus, 1498	10	40
317a†	75c Yacht, St. George's	7.00	4.00

1970

368†	25c Pirate ketches	50	10
387†	25c Thames river tug	10	5
400†	15c Ship's boats and sinking freighter, Dunkirk, 1940	60	35
402†	50c Landing craft, Normandy, 1944	1.50	1.25
409†	15c Britannia (paddle-steamer), 1840	10	10
410†	25c Queen Elizabeth 2 (liner)	15	10

1971

455†	1c U.S.S. Iwo Jima (aircraft carrier)	5	5

1972

522†	½c Olympic yachts	5	5
530	8c Flagship of Columbus, 1498	12	12
531	$1 Flagship of Columbus, 1498	55	65

1973

552†	25c Class II racing yacht	35	20
554†	60c Bloodhound (yacht)	55	65
565†	¼c Racing yachts	5	5
566†	1c Cruising yacht	5	5
567†	2c Open-deck sloops	5	5
568†	35c Mermaid (sloop)	35	20
571†	$1 Boat-building	90	80
MS572†	$2 Racing yachts	1.60	2.00

1974

No. 317a overprinted **INDEPENDENCE 7TH FEB. 1974**

603†	75c Yacht, St. Georges	2.00	1.25

629†	1c Caesar (mailboat), 1839	5	5
634†	35c Queen Elizabeth 2 (liner)	50	40

1975

649†	¼c Yachts	5	5
650†	1c Racing yachts	5	5
651†	2c Harbour ferry	5	5
652†	3c Fishing boats	10	5
653†	5c Victoria (liner)	10	5
658†	15c Fishing boat	10	8
666†	$3 Sailing dinghy	1.25	2.00

699†	10c Bonhomme Richard and H.M.S. Serapis (frigate), 1779	10	5
714†	1c Scout sailing dinghy	5	5
MS720†	$1 Scouts building raft	90	20
MS744†	$1 Sailing dinghies	80	20

1976

771†	2c Southward (liner)	5	5
772†	35c Game fishing launch	40	20
MS776†	$2 Sailing dinghies	1.50	1.50

791†	$3 Rowing boat with canon, 1776	2.75	2.25

833	½c Geestland (freighter)
834	1c Federal Palm (freighter)
835	2c H.M.S. Blake (cruiser), 1961
836	25c Vistafjord (liner)
837	75c Canberra (liner)
838	$1 Regina (liner)
839	$5 Arandora Star (liner)

	Set of 7	6.50	5.00
MS840	$2 Santa Maria (Columbus)	2.00	2.50

1977

868†	1c Speedboats	5	5
871†	35c Sailing dinghies	35	35
873†	$2 Game fishing launch	1.60	1.60
MS874†	$3 Racing yachts	2.00	2.25

880†	2c Scout sailing dinghies	5	5

1978

973†	$3 H.M.S. Resolution (Cook)	2.00	1.75

1980

Nos. 651/2 and 666 overprinted **PEOPLE'S REVOLUTION 13 MARCH 1979**

1040†	2c Harbour ferry	5	5
1041†	3c Fishing boats	5	5
1052†	$3 Sailing dinghy	1.50	2.00

MS1059†	$4 Olympic yacht	1.25	1.40

1081	½c Carib canoes
1082	1c Boat building
1083	2c Fishing boat
1084	4c Santa Maria (Columbus)
1085	5c West Indiaman barque, c. 1840
1086	6c Orinoco (paddle-steamer)
1087	10c Schooner
1088	12c Trimaran
1089	15c Petite Amie (cruising yacht)
1090	20c Fishing pirogue
1091	25c Police launch
1092	30c Speedboat
1093	40c Seimstrand (freighter)
1094	50c Ariadne (sail-training schooner)
1095	90c Geestide (freighter)
1096	$1 Cunard Countess (liner)
1097	$3 Rum-runner (pleasure launch)
1098	$5 Statendam (liner)
1099	$10 Coastguard patrol boat

	Set of 19	16.00	12.00

1981

1116†	40c Crawfish boat	20	20
1117†	90c Cunard Countess (liner)	50	50

1166†	90c Queen Elizabeth 2 (liner) (on stamp No. 410)	50	50
1167†	$4 Solent (paddle-steamer) (on stamp No. 210)	2.00	2.00

1983

1245†	$3 Boat building	1.40	1.40

1246†	30c Freighter	15	15

1984

1342	40c Freighter
1343	70c Queen Elizabeth 2 (liner)
1344	90c Sailing sloops
1345	$4 Amerikanis (liner)

	Set of 4	4.50	4.25
MS1346	$5 16th-century Spanish galleonl	4.00	5.00

COLLECT MAMMALS ON STAMPS

A Stanley Gibbons thematic catalogue on this popular subject. Copies available at £7.50 (p. + p. £2) from: Stanley Gibbons Publications Ltd, 5 Parkside, Christchurch Road, Ringwood, Hants BH24 3SH.

1358†	$4 Australia II (yacht)	2.75	2.75

1985

1404†	$1.10 Sailboards	60	65
1405†	$4 Sailboards	2.10	2.25

1447†	$4 Royal Yacht Britannia	2.50	2.50

1987

1611	10c Columbia (yacht), 1958
1612	60c Resolute (yacht), 1920
1613	$1.10 Endeavour (yacht), 1934
1614	$4 Rainbow (yacht), 1934

	Set of 4	2.25	2.50
MS1615	$5 Weatherley (yacht), 1962	2.25	2.40

1616†	10c Flagship of Columbus, 1498	5	8
1617†	30c Santa Maria, Pinta and Nina	12	15
1621†	$1.10 Spanish caravel	50	55
1622†	$2 Carib sailing raft	90	95

1626†	15c Monitor and Merrimack (ironclad warships), 1862	8	10
1628†	50c Sirius (steamship), 1838	25	30
1630†	70c U.S.S. Enterprise (aircraft carrier), 1960	30	35
1632†	$1.50 U.S.S. Holland I (submarine), 1900	70	75
1633†	$2 Oceanic (liner), 1871	90	95

1647†	60c Statue of Liberty and small boats	25	30
1652†	$4 Queen Elizabeth 2 (liner)	1.75	1.90

OFFICIAL STAMPS

1982

Nos. 1085/97 and 1099 overprinted **P.R.G.**

O1†	5c West Indiaman barque, c. 1840	5	5
O2†	6c *Orinoco* (paddle-steamer)	5	5
O3†	10c Schooner	5	5
O4†	12c Trimaran	5	5
O5†	15c *Petite Amie* (cruising yacht)	5	8
O6†	20c Fishing pirogue	8	10
O7†	25c Police launch	10	10
O8†	30c Speedboat	12	12
O9†	40c *Seimstrand* (freighter)	15	20
O10†	50c *Ariadne* (sail-training schooner)	20	25
O11†	90c *Geestide* (freighter)	40	35
O12†	$1 *Cunard Countess* (liner)	40	40
O13†	$3 Rum-runner (pleasure launch)	1.25	1.25
O14†	$10 Coastguard patrol boat	4.25	3.75

GRENADINES OF GRENADA

West Indies
100 cents = 1 dollar

1974

Design as No. 629 of Grenada inscribed "GRENADA GRENADINES"

25†	8c *Caesar* (mailboat), 1839	10	8

1975

98†	75c Boarders in rowing boat, Boston Tea Party	65	8
99†	$2 Naval engagement, American War of Independence	1.50	8

As Nos. 649/53, 658 and 666 of Grenada, but inscribed "GRENADA GRENADINES"

111†	½c Yachts	5	5
112†	1c Racing yachts	5	5
113†	2c Harbour ferry	5	5
114†	3c Fishing boats	5	5
115†	5c *Victoria* (liner)	5	5
120†	15c Fishing boat	5	5
128†	$3 Sailing dinghy	1.75	2.00

1976

155	½c Game fishing launch	
156	1c Schooner	
157	2c Racing yachts	
158	18c Boat building	
159	22c Sailing sloops	
160	75c Cruising yacht	
161	$1 Speedboat	
	Set of 7	1.10	1.25
MS162	$2 Sailing dinghies	90	1.25

176	½c *South Carolina* (American frigate), 1777	
177	1c *Lee* (American schooner), 1775	
178	2c H.M.S. *Roebuck* (frigate), 1774	
179	35c *Andrea Doria* (American brig), 1775	
180	50c *Providence* (American sloop), 1775	
181	$1 *Alfred* (American frigate), 1775	
182	$2 *Confederacy* (American frigate), 1779	
	Set of 7	6.00	5.50
MS183	$3 *Revenge* (American cutter), 1777	3.50	4.00

MS198†	$3 Olympic yacht	1.00	1.40

1977

249†	$3 Scout yachts	1.75	2.25

1978

307†	18c H.M.S. *Resolution* (Cook)	25	10
MS311†	$4 H.M.S. *Resolution*	2.50	3.00

1979

333†	$1 Cargo liner	45	35

1980

Nos. 120 and 128 overprinted **PEOPLE'S REVOLUTION 13 MARCH 1979**

366†	15c Fishing boat	10	5
374†	$3 Sailing dinghy	1.60	1.60

No. 333 overprinted **LONDON 1980**

393†	$1 Cargo liner	55	35

1981

426†	10c H.M.S. *Temeraire* (ship of the line) and paddle-tug	8	8

1982

480†	$2.50 *Queen Elizabeth 2* (liner) and sailing clipper	1.50	90

484†	90c Scout sailing dinghies	55	30

1984

581†	$4 Olympic yachts	1.75	1.90

609	30c *Geeststar* (cargo liner)		
610	60c *Daphne* (liner)		
611	$1.10 *Southwind* (schooner)		
612	$4 *Oceanic* (liner)		
	Set of 4	3.75	3.75
MS613	$5 Pirate ship	3.25	3.50

1985

657†	$1.10 Sailing dinghy	65	70

668†	$4 Guide sailing dinghy	2.40	2.25

710†	$4 Royal Yacht *Britannia*	2.10	2.25

1986

733†	70c Rowing boats, Central Park, New York, 1894	35	40
734†	$4 Rowing boats, Central Park, New York, 1986	2.00	2.10

805	50c + 20c Olympic yacht	35	40

1987

859	25c *Defender* (yacht), 1895	
860	45c *Caletea* (yacht), 1886	
861	70c *Azzurra* (yacht), 1981	
862	$4 *Australia II* (yacht), 1983	
	Set of 4	2.10	2.40
MS863	$5 *Columbia* and *Shamrock* (yachts), 1899	2.25	2.40

866†	50c *Santa Maria* (Columbus)	25	30
867†	60c Spanish galleon	25	30
871†	$3 Spanish galley	1.40	1.50
MS872†	Two sheets. (a) $5 Carib canoes; (b)		
	$5 *Santa Maria*	Set of 2 sheets	4.50	4.75

873†	10c "SR-N1" (hovercraft), 1959	5	8
876†	50c *Hunley* (Confederate submarine),		
	1864	25	30
881†	$2 *Great Britain* (liner), 1843	90	95

899†	70c Small boat flotilla	30	35
902†	$2 Modern frigate	90	95

1988

943†	70c Scout canoe	30	35

GRENADINES OF ST. VINCENT

West Indies
100 cents = 1 dollar

1974

34	5c Boat building
31	30c Careening, Port Elizabeth
32	35c Yachts, Admiralty Bay
33	$1 Fishing boat race
	Set of 4	50	60

1975

68†	45c Schooner, Petit St. Vincent	25	10
69†	$1 Sailing dinghies	60	40

COLLECT BIRDS ON STAMPS

Second revised edition of this Stanley Gibbons thematic catalogue – now available at £8.50 (p. + p. £2) from: Stanley Gibbons Publications Ltd, 5 Parkside, Christchurch Road, Ringwood, Hants BH24 3SH.

1976

74†	5c Yachts at anchor, Union Island	5	5
77†	$1 Mail schooner, Union Island	35	35

1977

91†	45c Cruising yacht, Mayreau	15	5
92†	$1 Yachts, Mayreau	25	20

101†	35c Sailing dinghies and motor boat	10	5
102†	45c Cruising yacht and sailing dinghies	15	10
103†	$1 Sailing dinghies	40	40

107†	35c Cruising yacht, Canouan	10	5
108†	45c Mail schooner, Canouan	15	5

1979

145	5c Racing yachts
146	40c Racing yachts
147	50c Racing yachts
148	$2 Racing yachts
	Set of 4	1.40	1.00

1980

172†	50c Racing yacht	15	15

No. 172 *surcharged* **HURRICANE RELIEF 50c**

176†	50c + 50c Racing yacht	25	35

1981

187†	$1.50 Fishing boats, Bequia	50	50
188†	$2 *Friendship Rose* (cruising yacht)	65	65

195†	50c Royal Yacht *Mary*	15	15
197†	$3 Royal Yacht *Alexandra*	65	65
199†	$3.50 Royal Yacht *Britannia*	75	75

1982

208	1c H.M.S. *Experiment* (frigate)
209	3c *Lady Nelson* (cargo liner)
210	5c *Daisy* (brig)
211	6c Carib canoe
212	10c *Hairoun Star* (freighter)
213	15c *Jupiter* (liner)
214	20c *Christina* (steam yacht)
215	25c *Orinoco* (paddle-steamer)
216	30c H.M.S. *Lively* (frigate)
217	50c *Alabama* (Confederate warship)
218	60c *Denmark* (freighter)
219	75c *Santa Maria* (Columbus)
220	$1 *Baffin* (cable ship)
221	$2 *Queen Elizabeth 2* (liner)
222	$3 Royal Yacht *Britannia*
223	$5 *Geeststar* (cargo liner)
224	$10 *Grenadines Star* (ferry)
	Set of 17	8.75	9.50

1983

243†	60c Yachts, Union Island	20	20
245†	$2 Fishing boats	70	70

246†	45c 18th-century British warship	15	15
247†	60c 18th-century American warship	20	20

256†	60c *Mary Rose* and Henry VIII	35	35
263†	$2.50 *Mary Rose*	75	75

1985

386†	35c Sailboards	20	25
389†	$3 Game fishing launch	1.50	1.60

Nos. 199 *and* 222 *overprinted or surcharged* **CARIBBEAN ROYAL VISIT 1985**

424†	$1.50 on $3.50 Royal Yacht *Britannia*	3.00	3.00
426†	$3 Royal Yacht *Britannia*	5.50	5.00

1986

467† $3 Model sailing dinghy 1.50 1.60

1988

547 50c *Australia IV* (yacht)
548 65c *Crusader II* (yacht)
549 75c *New Zealand K27* (yacht)
550 $2 *Italia* (yacht)
551 $4 *White Crusader* (yacht)
552 $5 *Stars and Stripes* (yacht)
　　　　　　　　　　　 Set of 6 5.25 5.50
MS553 $1 *Champosa V* (yacht) 45 50

OFFICIAL STAMPS

1982

Nos. 195, 197 and 199 overprinted **OFFICIAL**
O1 50c Royal Yacht *Mary* 15 20
O3 $3 Royal Yacht *Alexandra* 75 1.00
O5 $3.50 Royal Yacht *Britannia* 1.00 1.25

APPENDIX

The following stamps have either been issued in excess of postal needs, or have not been made available to the public in reasonable quantities at face value. Miniature sheets, imperforate stamps etc., are excluded from this section.

Bequia
1984
Grenadines of St. Vincent 1982 Ships definitives (Nos. 208/24) overprinted **BEQUIA.** 1, 3, 5, 6, 10, 15, 20, 25, 30, 50, 60, 75c, $1, $2, $3, $5, $10

1985
Leaders of the World. Warships of the Second World War. Two designs for each value, the first showing technical drawings and the second the ship at sea. 15, 50c, $1, $1.50, each x 2

Union Island
1984
Grenadines of St. Vincent 1982 Ships definitives (Nos. 208/24) overprinted **UNION ISLAND.** 1, 3, 5, 6, 10, 15, 20, 25, 30, 50, 60, 75c, $1, $2, $3, $5, $10

GUADELOUPE
West Indies
100 centimes = 1 franc

1928

128† 1f Fishing boats, Pointe-a-Pitre (blue and red) 2.00 1.10
129† 1f Fishing boats, Pointe-a-Pitre (orange and red) 40 40
130† 1f Fishing boats, Pointe-a-Pitre (brown and blue) 15 10
131† 1f05 Fishing boats, Pointe-a-Pitre 50 50
132† 1f10 Fishing boats, Pointe-a-Pitre 1.25 1.10
133† 1f25 Fishing boats, Pointe-a-Pitre (brown and blue) 15 10
134† 1f25 Fishing boats, Pointe-a-Pitre (red) 35 35
135† 1f40 Fishing boats, Pointe-a-Pitre 20 20
136† 1f50 Fishing boats, Pointe-a-Pitre 15 10
137† 1f60 Fishing boats, Pointe-a-Pitre 20 20
138† 1f75 Fishing boats, Pointe-a-Pitre (brown and mauve) 1.75 1.25
139† 1f75 Fishing boats, Pointe-a-Pitre (blue) 2.50 1.75

140† 2f Fishing boats, Pointe-a-Pitre 15 10
141† 2f25 Fishing boats, Pointe-a-Pitre 30 30
142† 2f50 Fishing boats, Pointe-a-Pitre 35 35
143† 3f Fishing boats, Pointe-a-Pitre 15 10
144† 5f Fishing boats, Pointe-a-Pitre 30 20
145† 10f Fishing boats, Pointe-a-Pitre 35 25
146† 20f Fishing boats, Pointe-a-Pitre 40 40

1931
As No. 109 of Cameroun
150† 1f50 Liner 1.40 1.60

1937
As Nos. 110/11 of Cameroun
157† 20c Liner 30 30
158† 30c Sailing ships 30 30
MS162a† 3f Sailing ships 1.00 1.00

1947

211† 10c Brigantine and fishing boat 5 5
212† 30c Brigantine and fishing boat 5 5
213† 50c Brigantine and fishing boat 5 5
230† 200f Fishing boats 6.00 2.50

GUATEMALA
Central America
100 antavos de quetzal = 1 quetzal

1935

291 10c *Agamemnon* (freighter) 3.50 3.25

299† 3c Liner, Puerto Barrios 40 20
315† 30c Freighters, Puerto Barrios (green) . 5.00 3.50
315a† 30c Freighters, Puerto Barrios (red) 1.50 20

1956

591 30c Freighter, Champerico 2.25 1.00

1959

623 6c *Quetzaltenango* (freighter) and caravel of 1532 .... 50 15

1971
No. 623 overprinted **FERIA INTERNACIONAL "INTERFER—71"**
30 Oct. al 21 Nov.
916 6c *Quetzaltenango* (freighter) and caravel of 1532 .... 20 12

1984

1251† 4c Lighter 10 5
1255† 25c Freighter 50 8

GUERNSEY
Western Europe
1969 12 pence = 1 shilling
20 shillings = 1 pound
1971 100 pence = 1 pound

1969

27† 10s Fishing boats, Alderney 42.00 32.00
28a† £1 Yachts, St. Peter Port 2.75 3.00

1970

33† 4d Royal Navy landing craft 35 40
34† 5d British warships off Guernsey, 1945 .. 35 40

1971
As No. 27 but currency changed
58† 50p Fishing boats, Alderney 2.50 3.25

1972

67 2p *Earl of Chesterfield* (mail packet), 1794
68 2½p *Dasher* (mail packet), 1827
69 7½p *Ibex* (mail packet), 1891
70 9p *Alberta* (mail packet), 1900
　　　　　　　　　　　 Set of 4 1.90 2.00

1973

80 2½p *St. Julien* (mail packet), 1925
81 3p *Isle of Guernsey* (mail packet), 1930
82 7½p *St. Patrick* (mail packet), 1947
83 9p *Sarnia* (mail packet), 1961
　　　　　　　　　　　 Set of 4 1.40 1.50

1974

94 2½p *John Lockett* (lifeboat), 1875
95 3p *Arthur Lionel* (lifeboat), 1912

96 8p *Euphrosyne Kendal* (lifeboat), 1954
97 10p *Arun* (lifeboat), 1972

              Set of 4   60   60

1977

159† 11p *Flying Christine II* (marine
     ambulance)   30   35

1980

223† 13½p Fishing boats, *c.* 1850   30   30

1981

230† 12p Yacht   30   30

240† 8p Sark launch   15   15
242† 18p Hydrofoil   45   45
243† 22p Herm catamaran   55   60
244† 25p *Sea Trent* (Alderney coaster)   65   70

1982

254† 13p Norman ships, 1066   40   45
255† 20p H.M.S. *Crescent* (frigate), 1793   50   55

1983

274† 13p Ferry, St Peter Port   35   35

282 9p *Star of the West* (brigantine), 1869
283 13p *Star of the West*

---

284 26p *Star of the West*
285 28p *Star of the West*
286 31p *Star of the West*

              Set of 5   3.00   3.00

1984

297† 2p Dinghies   5   5
300† 5p *Royal Odyssey* (liner)   8   10
304† 9p Fishing boats   15   20
309† 15p Yachts   25   30
313† 50p Yachts and motor cruisers   90   95

331† 34p Alderney mail boat, 1812 . . . .   1.10   1.10

1986

360 9p H.M.S. *Victory* and H.M.S. *Rose*
     (sloop), 1809
361 14p H.M.S. *Orion* (ship of the line) at
     Battle of the Nile, 1798
362 29p H.M.S. *Orion* engaging *Santissima*
     Trinidad at Battle of St Vincent, 1797
363 31p H.M.S. *Crescent* (frigate) and
     Reunion, 1793
364 34p H.M.S. *Russell* (ship of the line)
     engaging *Ville de Paris* at Battle of the
     Saints, 1782

              Set of 5   3.25   3.25

1987
As No. 309, but smaller, 17 × 21 mm
399† 15p Yachts   25   30

1988

415 11p *Golden Spur* (full-rigged ship) off St.
     Sampson
416 15p *Golden Spur* and junk, Hong Kong
417 29p *Golden Spur*, Macao
418 31p *Golden Spur* in China tea race
419 34p *Golden Spur*, 1872

              Set of 5   2.10   2.40

420† 16p Lihou Island mail-carrying rowing
     boat   30   35
421† 16p Lihou Island mail-carrying rowing
     boat   30   35
     Nos. 420/1 form a composite design

429† 16p Powerboats   30   35
430† 30p Powerboats   60   65
431† 32p Powerboats and hydrofoil   65   70

POSTAGE DUE STAMPS
1977

D18 ½p Motor launches
D19 1p Motor launches
D20 2p Motor launches
D21 3p Motor launches
D22 4p Motor launches
D23 5p Motor launches
D24 6p Motor launches
D25 8p Motor launches
D26 10p Motor launches
D27 14p Motor launches
D28 15p Motor launches
D29 16p Motor launches

              Set of 12   2.00   2.10

1982

D33† 4p Brig at quay, 1892   8   10
D40† 50p Brig at quay, 1892   90   95

Alderney
1983

A5† 11p Yachts   20   25
A12† 18p *Royalist* (training ship) in Old
     Harbour   30   35

1987

A32 11p Wreck of *Liverpool* (full-rigged ship),
     1902
A33 15p Wreck of *Petit Raymond* (schooner),
     1906
A34 29p Wreck of *Maina* (yacht), 1910
A35 31p Wreck of *Burton* (steamer), 1911
A36 34p Wreck of *Point Law* (oil tanker), 1975

              Set of 5   5.25   5.25

GUINEA

West Africa
1959 100 centimes = 1 franc
1973 100 caury = 1 syli
1986 100 centimes = 1 franc

1959

201† 1f Local fishing boats   5   5
202† 2f Local fishing boats   8   5
203† 3f Local fishing boats   8   5
204† 5f Dhow   8   5
205† 10f Pirogue   10   8

1974

843† 4s Bulk carrier loading bauxite 30 15

861† 10s Liner 75 60
MS862† Two sheets. (a) 10s Pirogue (other
sheet shows space satellite)
Price for 2 sheets 10.00 10.00

1982

1049† 7s River craft 60 45

1984

1136† 5s Congo river steamer and canoe 50 30

1985

1152† 10s "Flying Dutchman" class yacht 85 55

1172† 10s Fleet of Columbus 85 55

1217 10s *Pinta* (Columbus)
1218 20s *Santa Maria* (Columbus)

1219 30s *Nina* (Columbus) (air)
1220 40s *Santa Maria* (Columbus)
Set of 4 7.50 5.00
MS1221 50s *Nina* (Columbus) 3.75 4.00

1986

*Nos. 1217/***MS***1221 surcharged*

1242† 5f on 10s *Pinta* 5 5
1243† 35f on 20s *Santa Maria* 15 8
1244† 70f on 30s *Nina* (air) 30 20
1245† 200f on 40s *Santa Maria* 85 65
MS1246† 500f on 50s *Nina* 2.40 2.50

GUINEA-BISSAU

West Africa
100 centavos = 1 peso

1981

676 3p Viking ship (Eric the Red)
677 5p *Sao Gabriel* (Vasco da Gama)
678 6p *Victoria* (Magellan)
679 30p *Emerillon* (Cartier)

680 35p *Golden Hind* (Drake) (air)
681 40p H.M.S. *Endeavour* (Cook)
Set of 6 5.00 3.50
MS682 50p *Santa Maria* (Columbus)
.... 3.00 3.25

1982

701† 35p Scout canoes 1.60 1.00

1983

MS775 50p Portuguese caravel 3.00 3.25

779† 5p Cable ship 40 5

1984

845† 15p Olympic yachts 25 5
MS850† 100p Sailboard 5.00 5.50

1985

933† 80p Red Cross rescue boat 90 25

950 8p *Santa Maria* (Columbus)
951 15p 16th-century Dutch carrack
952 20p *Mayflower* (Pilgrim Fathers)
953 30p *St Louis* (French galleon)
954 35p *Royal Sovereign* (British royal yacht)
955 45p *Soleil Royal* (17th-century French
warship)
956 80p 18th-century British naval brig
Set of 7 2.75 1.25

1987

992† 50p *Santa Maria* (Columbus) 10 5
993† 50p Galley, Seville, 1492 .... 10 5
995† 50p Shipping, Seville, 1492 .... 10 5
MS996† 150p 15th-century galleon, Lisbon .. 30 15

GUYANA

South America
100 cents = 1 dollar

1966

No. 344 of British Guiana overprinted **GUYANA INDEPENDENCE**

1966

406† $2 Gold dredger 50 75

1969

502† 30c Building *Independence* (World's first
aluminium ship) 10 10

1974

606† 8c *Sandbach* (on British Guiana stamp No. 78) 5 5
608† 40c *Sandbach* (on British Guiana stamp No. 78) 20 20

1983

1071 $4.80 *Sandbach* (sail merchantman) 22.00 12.00

1127 30c *Kurupukari* (river vessel)
1128 60c *Makouria* (river vessel)
1129 120c *Powis* (river vessel)
1130 130c *Pomeroon* (river vessel)
1131 150c *Lukanani* (river vessel)
Set of 5 2.50 2.40

1985

1550† 150c *Den Arendt* (slave ship), 1627 .... 60 55

1986

1744† 320c *Sandbach* (on British Guiana stamp No. 253) 40 45

EXPRESS LETTER STAMPS

1986

As No. 1744 in miniature sheet surcharged **EXPRESS $20.00**
E3† $20 on $6.40 *Sandbach* (on British Guiana stamp No. 253) 2.50 2.75

GWALIOR

Indian sub-continent
12 pies = 1 anna
16 annas = 1 rupee

1938

No. 256 of India overprinted **GWALIOR** in English and Hindi
111† 6a *Strathnaver* (liner) 2.25 3.50

HAITI

West Indies
100 centimes = 1 gourde

1943

358 3c *Crete-a-Pierrot* (gunboat), 1902
359 5c *Crete-a-Pierrot*

360 10c *Crete-a-Pierrot*
361 25c *Crete-a-Pierrot*
362 50c *Crete-a-Pierrot*
363 5g *Crete-a-Pierrot*
364 60c *Crete-a-Pierrot* (air)
365 1g25 *Crete-a-Pierrot*
Set of 8 12.00 6.50

1950

443† 30c Fleet of Columbus 1.25 45

1956

541† 50c Liner 50 15
543† 75c Liner 70 45

1961

764† 20c Pirate ships attacking galleon 25 10
765† 50c Galleon 45 20
766† 20c Pirate ships attacking galleon (air, inscr "AVION") 25 5
767† 50c Galleon (inscr "AVION") 45 15

No. 543 overprinted **Dr. F. Duvalier President 22 Mai 1961**
775† 75c Liner 35 30

1965

929 10c Freighters in port
930 50c Freighters in port
931 50c Freighters in port (air)
932 1g50 Freighters in port
Set of 4 1.25 75

1978

1383† 5g Olympic yachts 2.50 1.50

COLLECT RAILWAYS ON STAMPS
A Stanley Gibbons thematic catalogue on this popular subject. Copies available at £7.50 (p. + p. £2) from: Stanley Gibbons Publications Ltd, 5 Parkside, Christchurch Road, Ringwood, Hants BH24 3SH.

1982

1453 25c Freighter in port
1454 50c Freighter in port
1455 1g Freighter in port
1456 1g25 Freighter in port
1457 2g Freighter in port
1458 5g Freighter in port
Set of 6 3.75 2.50

Nos. 1453 and 1455/7 overprinted **1957 - 1982 25 ANS DE REVOLUTION**
1459 25c Freighter in port
1460 1g Freighter in port
1461 1g25 Freighter in port
1462 2g Freighter in port
Set of 4 1.40 1.25

1983

1465† 25c Fishing boats 15 5
1467† 75c Fishing boats (air) 40 25
1469† 1g25 Fishing boats 60 40

1986
No. 1467 surcharged **G.O.25**
1549† 25c on 75c Fishing boats 10 5

HAWAII

South Pacific
100 cents = 1 dollar

1894

81 12c *Arawa* (early steamer) 8.00 8.00

HONDURAS

Central America
1931 100 centavos = 1 peso
1933 100 centavos = 1 lempira

1931

321† 5c Steamer on Lake Yojoa 40 10

No. 321 overprinted **T. S. de C**
330† 5c Steamer on Lake Yojoa 40 25

1972

808† 1l Fishing boat, Trujillo Bay 1.75 90

1976

898† 5c Continental Navy warships, 1776 .... 20 15

1986

1052† 85c Yacht 85 40

HONG KONG

South-east coast of China
100 cents = 1 dollar

1941

164† 4c *Empress of Japan* (liner) and junk 1.50 1.00
168† $1 Clipper ship 8.50 3.50

1949

As No. 115 *of Antigua*

174† 20c Paddle-steamer 3.75 80

1968

247 10c *Iberia* (liner)
248 20c Pleasure launch
249 40c Car ferry
250 50c Passenger ferry
251 $1 Sampan
252 $1.30 Junk
               Set of 6 16.00 7.00

1972

278 $1 Junk 1.75 1.75

1975

332† $1 Dragon boat 1.25 1.75

1977

365† 60c Ferry boat 70 90
367† $2 Junk and sampan 1.10 1.75

1982

407 20c Junks, Victoria harbour, 1855
408 $1 Junks at West Point, 1847
409 $1.30 Junks
410 $2 *Queen Elizabeth 2* (liner)
               Set of 4 1.60 1.90

1983

439† $1 *Liverpool Bay* (container ship) 35 40

445† $5 *Jumbo* (floating restaurant) 1.50 2.00

1984

454 40c 19th-century sail frigate
455 $1 Topsail schooner
456 $1.30 Sailing clipper
457 $5 19th-century sail frigate
               Set of 4 2.40 2.75

1985

488 40c Dragon boat prow
489 $1 Dragon boat drummer and rowers
490 $1.30 Dragon boat rowers
491 $5 Dragon boat stern
               Set of 4 1.50 2.00

1986

519† $1.70 Container ship 45 45

521 50c Fishing sampan
522 $1 Stern trawler
523 $1.70 Fishing junk
524 $5 Junk trawler
               Set of 4 2.00 2.25

1987

535† $1.30 Boat dwellings, Kowloon, 1838 .... 30 35

HUNGARY

Central Europe
1926 100 filler = 1 pengo
1946 100 filler = 1 forint

1926

471† 32f Danube steamer 80 12
472† 40f Danube steamer 1.50 12

1928

502 30f Danube steamer
503 32f Danube steamer
504 40f Danube steamer
505 46f Danube steamer
506 50f Danube steamer
               Set of 5 4.75 1.60

1941

705† 20f River steamer, Straits of Kazan 12 5
707† 40f River steamer, Straits of Kazan 45 12

1947

988† 20fi Paddle-steamer, Esztergom 12 5

993† 3fo *Falcone* (racing yacht) 2.25 25

1948

1028†	2fi *Santa Maria* (Columbus)	20	15
1029†	4fi *Clermont* (paddle-steamer) and *Queen Mary* (liner)	20	15
1034†	12fi *Fram* (Amundsen)	60	30

1949

1078	50fi Paddle-steamer	3.50	3.00

1950

1092†	3fo Freighter	2.50	20

1136†	1fo60 Freighter	60	10

1953

1287†	1fo Sailing dinghies, Lake Balaton	35	15

1955

1447†	2fo *Beke* (freighter)	1.40	65

1958

1547†	2fo Paddle-steamer, tug and barges, Budapest	40	10

1959

1553†	20fi Oceanographic research ship	35	8

1569†	2fo *Kisfaludy* (Lake Balaton steamer) ..	70	15

1590†	30fi *Kek Madar* (yacht)	12	5
1594†	2fo *Beloiannis* (Lake Balaton steamer)	75	15
1596†	70fi *Tihany* (water bus) (air)	20	5
1598†	1fo70 *Saturnus* (yacht)	70	30

1961

1757†	2fo + 1fo Racing yachts	65	60

1963

1899†	10fi *Snow White* (Danube steamer)	5	5

1921	20fi Lake passenger launch		
1922	40fi *Beloiannis* (lake steamer)		
1923	60fi Yacht		
	Set of 3	1.25	40

1964

2026†	60fi Paddle-steamer, Budapest	25	5
2027†	1fo River steamer, Budapest	45	5
2028†	1fo50 Paddle-steamer, Budapest	65	15
2029†	2fo River freighter, Budapest	90	25
2030†	2fo50 Paddle-tug and barges, Budapest	1.75	1.00
MS2030a†	10fo *Sirali I* (hydrofoil)	4.50	5.00

1965

2103	1fo + 50fi Flood rescue boat	50	30

1966

2182	1fo *Johann Baptist* (paddle-tug)	50	15
2183	2fo *Rakoczi* (river ferry)	90	35

1967

2275	30fi *Ferenc Deak* (Danube paddle-steamer)		
2276	60fi *Revfulop* (river bus)		
2277	1fo *Hunyadi* (Danube passenger vessel)		
2278	1fo50 *Szekszard* (tug)		
2279	1fo70 *Miscolc* (tug)		
2280	2fo *Tihany* (freighter)		
2281	2fo50 *Sirali I* (hydrofoil)		
	Set of 7	14.50	5.75

1968

2365†	2fi Lake Balaton steamer	5	5
2365a†	40fi Lake Balaton steamer	5	5
2367†	1fo Yachts	15	5

1972

2719†	1fo 19th-century river steamer	15	5
2720†	1fo Hydrofoil	15	5

2743†	4fo River steamer, Esztergom	65	12

1973

2806†	4fo Paddle-steamer, tug and barges, Budapest (on stamp No. 1547)	70	35

1975

2937†	80fi Canoe	20	5
2938†	1fo20 Freighter	25	5

MS2983	2fo + 1fo Galley, Visegrad, 1480 (sheet also contains three other designs)	8.00	9.00

1977

MS3160   2fo × 11 Various Danube ships 12.00 12.00

1978

MS3197   Two sheets. (a) 2fo × 4 Viking longship (Leif Eriksson); *Santa Maria* (Columbus); *Sao Gabriel* (Vasco da Gama); *Victoria* (Magellan). (b) 2fo × 4 *Golden Hind* (Drake); *Discoverie* (Hudson); H.M.S. *Resolution* (Cook); *Roosevelt* (Peary)
Set of 2 sheets   6.50   6.50

1979

3263   3fo *Calypso* (research vessel)   65   15

1980

3305†   3fo Galley, Rhodes   55   10
3306†   4fo Pharaonic ship, Alexandria   75   15
3307†   5fo Nile river boat, Egypt 1.40   60

3350†   40fi Harbour steamer, New York   10   5

1981

3367†   2fo *Malygin* (icebreaker)   30   10

3399   1fo *Franz I* (paddle-steamer), 1830, and *Ferenc Deak* (on stamp No. 2275)
3400   1fo *Arpad* (paddle-steamer), 1834, and *Revfulop* (on stamp No. 2276)
3401   2fo *Szechenyi* (paddle-steamer), 1855, and *Hunyadi* (on stamp No. 2277)

3402   2fo *Grof Szechenyi Istvan* (paddle-steamer), 1896, and *Szekszard* (on stamp No. 2278)
3403   4fo *Zsofia* (paddle-steamer), 1914, and *Miscolc* (on stamp No. 2279)
3404   6fo *Felszabadulas* (paddle-steamer), 1917, and *Tihany* (on stamp No. 2280)
3405   8fo *Rakoczi* (passenger vessel), 1964, and *Sirali I* (on stamp No. 2281)
Set of 7   5.50   4.50
MS3406   20fo *Solyom* (hydrofoil) and *Hunyadi* (on stamp No. 2277) 5.00   5.00

1983

3516†   4fo + 2fo Danube houseboats 1.25   1.25

3532†   1fo Yacht, Zanka   20   5

1984

3577†   2fo Danube river boat   40   20
3578†   4fo River tanker   60   30
3581†   8fo Tug and barges 1.25   50

1985

3608†   1fo Danube river steamer   20   10
3609†   1fo Danube passenger launch   20   10
3610†   2fo Hydrofoil   40   15
3611†   2fo River launch   40   15
3612†   4fo River launch   70   30
3613†   6fo River launch   95   50

1986

3707   2fo *Vasa* (Swedish warship), 1628 ...... 1.50   1.50

1987

3777†   5fo Cabin cruisers, Toronto 1.10   65

3783†   2fo H.M.S. *Resolution* (Cook)   60   30
3787†   4fo *Terra Nova* (Scott)   80   45

ICELAND

North Atlantic
100 aurar = 1 krona

1930

159†   5a Viking longship 1.50   4.25
161†   10a Viking longship 6.00   8.00

175†   20a Icelandic fishing boat 20.00 40.00

1933

201†   10a + 10a Shipwreck and breeches-buoy 1.25   3.25
203†   35a + 25a Shipwreck and breeches-buoy 1.25   3.25

1939

239†   35a Viking longship 2.00   4.00

1940
No. 239 overprinted **1940**
258†   35a Viking longship 7.00 17.00

1949

291†   75a + 25a Freighter and ship's lifeboat   35   70

1950

297†   10a *Ingolfur Arnarson* (trawler)   5   10
299†   25a *Ingolfur Arnarson*   10   5

304† 1k25 *Ingolfur Arnarson* 14.00 5
305† 1k50 *Ingolfur Arnarson* 11.00 5

1961

384 2k50 *Gullfoss* (cargo liner)
385 4k50 *Gullfoss*
Set of 2 50 20

1963

401 5k *Huni* (herring trawler)
402 7k50 *Huni*
Set of 2 80 40

1964

408 10k *Gullfoss* (cargo liner) 1.10 1.00

1973

506† 20k *Esja* (mail steamer) 10 10

1978

567 60k Wrecked trawler and breeches-buoy 15 10

1983

630† 1100a Stern trawler 70 90

1986

679† 10k Rowing boat, Stykkisholmur 50 50

1987

692 50k *Svanur* (19th-century ketch) 2.00 1.50

MS706 30k Schooner, Djupivogur, 1836 ...... 1.40 1.40

OFFICIAL STAMPS

1930

Nos. 159 *and* 161 *overprinted* **Pjonustumerki**
O175† 5a Viking longship 8.50 26.00
O177† 10a Viking longship 8.50 26.00

IFNI

North-west Africa
100 centimos = 1 peseta

1959

149† 50c + 10c Moroccan fishing boats 10 5

1961

182† 25c + 10c Freighter at wharf 5 5
184† 1p + 10c Freighter at wharf 10 5

1967

227 1p50 Bulk carrier and floating crane 15 8

INDIA

Southern Asia
1937 12 pies = 1 anna
16 annas = 1 rupee
1957 10 naye paisa = 1 rupee
1964 100 paisa = 1 rupee

1937

256† 6a *Strathnaver* (liner) 5.00 10

1954

350† 4a Liner 1.90 15

1965

498 15p *Jalausha* (freighter) 15 5

518† 2r Kashmiri boat, Lake Dal 2.00 5

1966

527 15p *Mysore* (cruiser) 15 10

1968

577 20p *Nilgiri* (frigate) 25 10

1969

591 20p 19th-century sail warships 10 5

599 20p *Ajanta* (tanker) 20 10

1970

622 20p Dredger and pilot vessel 5 5

1972

663 20p Liner 25 10

1977

844 25p *Loyalty* (liner) 15 15

862 3r Liner at wharf, Bombay 1.25 1.75

1978

876   1r Kashmiri boat, Lake Dal 75   75

1981

1029   35p *Taragiri* (frigate) 15   5

1982

1049   1r *Sagar Samrat* (oil rig) 20   12

1065   2r Yachts 25   30

1983

1085   2r H.M.S. *Beagle* (Charles Darwin) 40   45

1984

1115†   1r *Vikrant* (aircraft carrier) 20   15
1116†   1r *Vela* (submarine) 20   15
1117†   1r Destroyer 20   15

1986

1184   2r *Vikrant* (aircraft carrier) 35   35

1987

1227   6r50 *Trishna* (yacht), 1985 75   80

INDIAN FORCES IN INDO-CHINA

South-east Asia
100 paisa = 1 rupee

1968
No. 518 of India overprinted **ICC** *in English and Devanagari*
N57   2r Kashmiri boat, Lake Dal 1.00   3.25

INDO-CHINA

South-east Asia
100 cents = 1 piastre

1931

163†   1/10c Junk 5   5
164†   1/5c Junk 5   5
165†   2/5c Junk 5   5
166†   ½c Junk 5   5
167†   4/5c Junk 5   5
168†   1c Junk 5   5
169†   2c Junk 5   5

INDONESIA

South-east Asia
100 sen = 1 rupiah

1961

852†   10s Ambonese boat 15   10

1963

981†   25r Yachts 15   8

1964

999†   1r75 *Hadju Agus Salim* (freighter) 10   5
1001†   2r50 Buginese sailing boat 10   5
1006†   15r *Sam Ratulangi* (freighter) 15   5

1019   20r *Sandjaja* and *Siliwanghi* (destroyers)
1020   30r *Nanggala* (submarine)
1021   40r *Matjan Tutul* (torpedo-boat)
                                 Set of 3   55   30

1965
No. 1006 overprinted **'65 Sen**
1075†   (15)s on 15r *Sam Ratulangi* (freighter)   25   5

COLLECT RAILWAYS ON STAMPS

1966

1121†   1r50 Madurese sailing boat 25   5
1124†   3r Liner in dry dock 40   12

1968

1210†   7r50 Olympic yachts (face value bottom right) 10   5
1211†   7r50 Olympic yachts (face value top right) 10   5

1973

1346   40r Motor torpedo-boat, Battle of Arafura   85   35

1974

1389†   100r East Indies galley 1.75   60

1975

1398†   130r Tanker 1.00   70
1400†   200r Oil rig 1.75   1.00

1980

1562   60r Pinisi sailing ship
1563   125r Schooner
1564   150r Madurese sailing boat
                                 Set of 3   1.75   85
MS1565   300r Schooner 1.75   1.75

MS1578 500r Pinisi sailing ship 2.75 2.75

1984

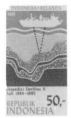

1736† 110r Hull on slipway 35 12

1985

1772 50r *Tyro* (oceanographic survey ship)
1773 100r *Tyro*
1774 275r *Tyro*
　　　　　　　　　　Set of 3 70 25

1796† 350r Sailboards 60 25

1798† 140r Tanker 25 8
1800† 350r Oil rig 45 15

1986

1814† 75r Pinisi sailing ship 15 5

IRAN

Western Asia
100 dinars = 1 rial

1935

735† 90d *Palang* (gunboat) 3.00 30

1949

905† 50d Freighters, Bandar Shahpur 1.60 30

1954

1053† 10r Ancient Persian galley 40.00 19.00

1969

1583 8r Oil rig 50 15

1970

1613 8r Tankers *Yowa Maru, Bergetun, Beau, Japan Jasmin, Barbara, Isomeria, Esso Newcastle, British Glory, Katrine Maersk*, and one unidentified, Kharg Island 80 20

1974

1917 10r *Palang* (destroyer) 55 15

1986

2355† 10r *Paykan* (missile boat) 30 15

STAMP MONTHLY

— finest and most informative magazine for all collectors. Obtainable from your newsagent or by postal subscription — details on request.

1987

2397 10r Freighter 30 15

2406† 25r Armed launch 45 40

IRAQ

Western Asia
1918 16 annas = 1 rupee
1931 1000 fils = 1 dinar

1918

No. 508 *of Turkey surcharged* **IRAQ IN BRITISH OCCUPATION 6An.**
8† 6a on 2pi *Hamidiye* (cruiser) 90 1.25

1923

42† 1a Gufas, River Tigris 20 10

1963

620† 1f Gufas, River Tigris 12 12
622† 3f Gufas 12 12

1965

672 10f Oil tanker 35 12

1969

852 15f *Antara* (floating crane)
853 20f *Al-Walid* (harbour tender)
854 30f *Al-Rashid* (pilot boat)
855 35f *Hillah* (dredger)
856 50f *Al-Faq* (survey ship)
　　　　　　　　　　Set of 5 3.25 1.25

1971

940† 5f Marsh canoe 20 8

1976

1268†	10f *Rumaila* (tanker)		25	10
1269†	15f *Rumaila*		35	15

1981

1507	50f Freighter			
1508	120f Freighter			
		Set of 2	2.25	1.40

1987

1753	50f *Al Alwah* (freighter)			
1754	100f *Khaled Ibn Al Waleed* (container ship)			
1755	150f *Al Alwah*			
1756	250f *Khaled Ibn Al Waleed*			
		Set of 4	2.50	2.00
MS1757	200f *Khaled Ibn Al Waleed* at wharf		1.40	1.60

1763†	40f Missile boat		15	12
1765†	100f Missile boat		40	30

OFFICIAL STAMPS

1920
No. 8 overprinted **ON STATE SERVICE**

O25†	6a on 2pi *Hamidiye* (cruiser)		1.75	80

1923
No. 42 overprinted **ON STATE SERVICE** *in English only*

O55†	1a Gufas, River Tigris		30	10

1924
No. 42 overprinted **ON STATE SERVICE** *in English and Arabic*

O76†	1a Gufas, River Tigris		30.00	22.00

OBLIGATORY TAX

دفاع وطنی
ه فلوس

No. 620 surcharged

T931†	5f on 1f Gufas, River Tigris		1.50	1.50

COLLECT MAMMALS ON STAMPS
A Stanley Gibbons thematic catalogue on this popular subject. Copies available at £7.50 (p. + p. £2) from: Stanley Gibbons Publications Ltd, 5 Parkside, Christchurch Road, Ringwood, Hants BH24 3SH.

IRELAND
Western Europe
1970 12 pence = 1 shilling
20 shillings = 1 pound
1971 100 pence = 1 pound

1970

279	4d 18th-century yachts		10	10

1974

336	5p Daunt Island lightship and Ballycotton lifeboat, 1936		25	20

1976

398	15p Lobster boat		60	60

1979

457†	13p *William Cory* (cable ship), 1866		25	60

1981

477†	25p Holland submarine, 1878		45	60

1982

524	22p Galway hooker			
525	22p Currach			
526	22p *Asgard II* (cadet ship)			
527	22p "Howth" 17-foot yacht			
		Set of 4	2.00	2.40

1985

606†	26p 18th-century fishing boats, Cork		35	25

1986

639†	24p Canal barges, Robertstown		70	70
641†	30p Motor cruiser on Lough Derg		90	1.25

642	24p *Severn* (19th-century paddle-steamer)			
643	28p *Leinster* (modern ferry)			
		Set of 2	1.60	1.40

1988

696†	24p *Sirius* (paddle-steamer), 1838		45	50

ISLE OF MAN
North-west Europe
100 pence = 1 pound

1973

12†	½p Motor cruisers, Castletown		8	8
18†	3½p Fishing boats, Port St. Mary		12	12
27†	9p Ferries in Douglas Bay		30	35
33†	£1 Viking longship		3.25	3.75

34	15p Viking longship, 938		70	65

1974

43†	3½p Wreck of *St. George* (paddle-steamer), 1830		12	15
44†	8p *Manchester* and *Salford* (lifeboat), 1868		60	65
45†	10p *Osman Gabriel* (lifeboat)		60	65

51†	4½p King Edgar's royal barge, *c.* 970		10	12
52†	8p Viking fleet, 974		30	30

1975

62† 10p *William T. Graves* (19th-century steamship) 35 40

12p *River steamer on Niger* 30 35

70†

1978

107† 6p H.M.S. *Ben-my-Chree*, 1915 .... 15 15
108† 7p H.M.S. *Vindex*, 1915 .... 20 20

123† 16p Ferry passing Douglas Head 65 65
127† £1 Viking longship 2.50 2.50

1979

158 15p *Odin's Raven* (replica Viking ship) 40 40

159† 6p 18th-century frigate 15 15
161† 13p H.M.S. *Spencer* (ship of the line) 30 40

1980

170 7p *Mona's Isle I* (paddle-steamer)
171 8p *Douglas I* (paddle-steamer)
172 11½p H.M.S. *Mona's Queen* (paddle-steamer) sinking U-boat
173 12p H.M.S. *King Orrey III* leading German destroyers, surrender of High Seas Fleet, 1918
174 13p *Ben-my-Chree IV* (ferry)
175 15p *Lady of Man II* (ferry)
           Set of 6 1.50 1.60

179 12p Sail-training ships 35 35

183† 7p *Robert Quayle* (brig), 1819 .... 20 20

1981

190 8p Luggers, Douglas
191 9p *Wanderer* (lugger) rescuing survivors from *Lusitania*
192 18p Nickey (fishing boat), Port St. Mary
193 20p Nobby (fishing boat), Ramsey
194 22p *Sunbeam* and *Zebra* (Nickey fishing boats), Port Erin
           Set of 5 1.75 1.75

196† 18p Fishing lugger 40 45

198† 20p 18th-century British warship, Madras 50 50

1982

208† 20p *Tynwald* (ferry), Dunkirk, 1940 ...... 45 50

223 12p *Mona I* (paddle-steamer)
224 19½p *Manx Maid II* (ferry)
           Set of 2 95 1.00

1983

251† 10p *Three Legs of Man III* (trimaran) 30 30

1984

259 10p *Manx King* (full-rigged sailing ship)
260 13p *Hope* (barque)
261 20½p *Rio Grande* (brig)

262 28p *Lady Elizabeth* (barque)
263 31p *Sumatra* (barque)
           Set of 5 3.00 3.00
MS264 28p *Lady Elizabeth* (as stamp No. 262), 31p As wreck (on Falkland Islands stamp No. 417) 2.50 2.00

275† 22p *Anna* (full-rigged sailing ship), 1852 60 60

1986

313 26p Model of Viking longship 70 70

315† 2p Viking longship 5 5

322† 15p *Mayflower* (Pilgrim Fathers) 45 45
323† 31p *Mayflower* (Pilgrim Fathers) 90 90

1987

334† 2p Brigantine, North Quay, Douglas 5 5
336† 10p 19th-century yachts, Douglas Bay .. 20 25

340 12p Brig, Douglas, 1899
341 26p Fishing boats, Douglas, 1900
342 29p Brigantine, Peel, 1906
343 34p Fishing boats, Peel, 1909
           Set of 4 2.90 2.90

1988

368† 5p Ferry, Douglas 8 10

STAMP MONTHLY
— finest and most informative magazine for all collectors. Obtainable from your newsagent or by postal subscription — details on request.

381† 13p *Flex Service 3* (cable ship) and
cable 25 30
382† 13p *Flex Service 3* 25 30

385 16p *Euterpe* (full-rigged ship), 1863
386 29p *Vixen* (topsail schooner), 1853
387 31p *Ramsey* (full-rigged ship), 1870
388 34p *Star of India* (barque) (ex *Euterpe*),
1976
Set of 4 1.75 2.00

ISRAEL

Western Asia
1958 1000 prutot = 1 pound
1960 100 agorot = 1 pound
1980 100 agorot = 1 shekel

1958

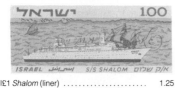

143 10p Ancient Hebrew ship
144 20p *Nirit* (immigration ship), 1948
145 30p *Shomron* (freighter)
146 1000p *Zion* (liner)
Set of 4 50 40

1963

269 I£1 *Shalom* (liner) 1.25 1.00

1964

286 25a Immigrant ship, 1948 .... 15 15

1967

362 40a *Dolphin* (freighter) 12 12

1969

405 30a Freighters and tug, Elat
406 60a Freighters, Ashod
407 I£1 *Theodor Herzl* (liner), Haifa
Set of 3 60 60

411† 80a *Elat* (destroyer) 20 20

1970

451 15a "420" class yachts
452 30a "420" class yachts
453 80a "420" class yachts
Set of 3 50 50

1971

505apa† 80a Sailing dinghy, Elat 10 10
509p† I£2 Pleasure launches, Coral Island .. 25 25

1980

MS783 2s 17th-century ships, Haifa; 3s Xebec 1.50 1.60

1983

914† 18s *Reshef* (missile vessel) 35 25

ITALIAN COLONIES

GENERAL ISSUES
Africa
100 centesimi = 1 lira

1934

75 25li Pirogue 5.50 18.00

COLLECT MAMMALS ON STAMPS
A Stanley Gibbons thematic catalogue on this popular
subject. Copies available at £7.50 (p. + p. £2) from:
Stanley Gibbons Publications Ltd, 5 Parkside, Christchurch Road, Ringwood, Hants BH24 3SH.

ITALIAN EAST AFRICA

East Africa
100 centesimi = 1 lira

1923

44† 5c Ethiopian canoe 5 15
47† 50c Ethiopian canoe 10 50

ITALY

Southern Europe
100 centisimi = 1 lira

1923

157† 30c Ferry boat 25 5.00

1931

312† 50c *Amerigo Vespucci* (cadet ship) 25 5
313† 1li25 *Trento* (cruiser) 90 40

1932

360† 1li Liners 80 50

1934

400† 2li55 + 2li *Brindisi* (cruiser), 1924 ...... 45 7.00
402† 25c Lugger, Klume (air) 15 50

436† 50c Naval launch 40 75
437† 75c Naval launch 55 1.00

1937

513† 1li25 Roman galleys 60 50

1952

820   25li Fishing boat, Trieste 1.10   25

827†   60li Motor torpedo boat 3.00   1.25

1957

960   25li 16th-century ship 30   5

1958

970   110li Goats in rowing boat 35   8

1965

1133   30li "Flying Dutchman" class yachts
1134   70li "5.5 S.1" class yachts
1135   50li "Lightning" class yachts
                                Set of 3   40   35

1968

1234†   40li *Andrea Doria* (battleship), *Grillo*
         (submarine), *Pullino* (submarine) and
         Zeffiro (destroyer) 10   5

1971

1303   25li *Tirrenia* (liner) 10   5

1977

1525   170li *Ferdinando Primo* (paddle-
         steamer), 1818
1526   170li *Carracciolo* (sail corvette), 1869
1527   170li *Saturnia* (liner), 1927
1528   170li *Sparviero* (hydrofoil missile boat)
                                Set of 4   80   20

1978

1552   170li *Fortuna* (19th-century brigantine)
1553   170li *Benedetto Brin* (cruiser), 1901
1554   170li *Lupo* (frigate), 1976
1555   170li *Africa* (container ship), 1976
                                Set of 4   1.00   20

1979

1621   170li *Cosmos* (full-rigged sailing ship),
         1865
1622   170li *Dandolo* (cruiser), 1878
1623   170li *Deledda* (ferry), 1978
1624   170li *Carlo Fecia di Cossato*
         (submarine), 1977
                                Set of 4   1.00   35

1980

1634†   170li 15th-century ship 25   5

1691   200li *Gabbiano* (corvette), 1942
1692   200li *Audace* (destroyer), 1971
1693   200li *Italia* (barque), 1903
1694   200li *Castoro Sei* (floating dock)
                                Set of 4   1.25   35

1981

1728†   200li *Amerigo Vespucci* (cadet ship) ..   35   5

STAMP MONTHLY
— finest and most informative magazine for all
collectors. Obtainable from your newsagent or by
postal subscription — details on request.

IVORY COAST
West Africa
100 centimes = 1 franc

1913

43	1c River canoe		
44	2c River canoe		
45	4c River canoe		
46	5c River canoe (green)		
61	5c River canoe (brown and chocolate)		
47	10c River canoe (red and orange)		
62	10c River canoe (green)		
63	10c River canoe (red on blue)		
48	15c River canoe		
49	20c River canoe		
50	25c River canoe (blue)		
64	25c River canoe (violet and black)		
51	30c River canoe (brown and chocolate)		
65	30c River canoe (red and orange)		
66	30c River canoe (red and blue)		
67	30c River canoe (green)		
52	35c River canoe		
53	40c River canoe		
54	45c River canoe (brown and orange)		
68	45c River canoe (purple and red)		
55	50c River canoe (lilac and black)		
69	50c River canoe (blue)		
70	50c River canoe (blue and green)		
71	60c River canoe		
72	65c River canoe		
56	75c River canoe (red and brown)		
73	75c River canoe (blue)		
74	85c River canoe		
75	90c River canoe		
57	1f River canoe (black and yellow)		
76	1f10 River canoe		
77	1f50 River canoe		
78	1f75 River canoe		
58	2f River canoe		
79	3f River canoe		
59	5f River canoe (brown and blue)		
	Set of 36	32.00	25.50

1915
*No. 47 surcharged +**5c***
60   10c + 5c River canoe (red and orange)   25   30

1922
Nos. 48, 56, 68, 73, 75 and further colour of 75c surcharged
80   50c on 45c River canoe (purple and red)
81   50c on 75c River canoe (blue)
82   50c on 90c River canoe
83   60c on 75c River canoe (violet on red)
84   65c on 15c River canoe
85   85c on 75c River canoe (red and brown)
                                Set of 6   3.25   2.40

1924
*Nos. 58, 59 and other values from 1913 issue with colours
changed surcharged*
86   25c on 2f River canoe
87   25c on 5f River canoe (brown and blue)
88   90c on 75c River canoe (red)
89   1f25 on 1f River canoe (blue)
90   1f50 on 1f River canoe (blue)
91   3f on 5f River canoe (green and red)
92   10f on 5f River canoe (mauve and red)
93   20f on 5f River canoe (red and green)
                                Set of 8   13.50   13.50

1931
As No. 109 of Cameroun
97†   1f50 Liner 1.75   2.00

1937
As Nos. 110/11 of Cameroun
155†   20c Liner 30   30
156†   30c Sailing ships 30   30

1965

257   30f River steamer, 1900 35   30

1967

286   30f Mail launch, 1937 55   35

1968

297†   500 Pirogues, Tiegba 7.00   3.00

1969

317†   200f River canoe (on stamp No. 59) 3.75   3.75

319   30f *Villa de Maranhao* (mail steamer),
1889 50   25

327†   30f Game fishing launch 35   20

1970

337†   50f Freighters under construction 60   25

1972

397   200f Pirogues, Bletankoro 2.50   95

1976

479†   100f *Ranger* (John Paul Jones), 1777   85   35
481†   150f 18th-century French warships 1.25   55

1977

515   65f *Yamoussoukro* (container ship)   45   20

1978

556†   60f Oil exploration ship   40   20

1980

662   60f *Sotra* (ferry)   35   20

1982

721†   80f Scout dinghy   45   40
722†   100f Scout yacht   55   50
723†   150f Scout dinghy   70   65
MS725†   500f Scout yacht 2.00   2.40

1984

816   100f Container ship
817   125f Cargo liner
818   350f *Queen Mary* (liner)
819   500f *France* (liner)

Set of 4   5.00   4.50

1985

835   100f *Adjame* (river steamer)   50   30

COLLECT RAILWAYS ON STAMPS

A Stanley Gibbons thematic catalogue on this popular subject. Copies available at £7.50 (p. + p. £2) from: Stanley Gibbons Publications Ltd, 5 Parkside, Christchurch Road, Ringwood, Hants BH24 3SH.

865†   250f Container ship 1.25   95

1986

899   125f *Stephan* (cable ship), 1910   65   45

1987

944   155f "Soling" class yachts
945   195f Sailboards
946   250f "470" class yachts
947   550f Sailboard

Set of 4   4.25   3.50
MS948   650f "470" class yachts 2.50   2.00

JAMAICA

West Indies
1919 12 pence = 1 shilling
20 shillings = 1 pound
1969 100 cents = 1 dollar

1919

82a†   2½d Troopship, 1919   80   1.40
96a†   3d Fleet of Columbus, 1494   40   15
98a†   6d Sailing ships, Port Royal, 1853 ......   9.00   75

1938

126†   3d *Highland Monarch* (liner) (blue &
green)   30   30
126a†   3d *Highland Monarch* (green & blue) ..   95   55
126b†   3d *Highland Monarch* (green & red)   70   25

1949

As No. 115 of Antigua
146†   2d Paddle-steamer   55   55

1955

155†   2d 18th-century warship, Port Royal   20   5

1956

169† 1s6d Raft, Rio Grande 35 10

1960

178† 2d *City of Berlin* (liner), 1860 .... 15 5

1962

198† 6d Sailing dinghies 10 5

1964

225† 9d Bulk carrier loading gypsum 45 5
229† 3s Game fishing boat 1.00 80
230† 5s *Sea Diver* (diving vessel) 1.10 65

1969

Nos. 225 and 229/30 surcharged **C-DAY 8th SEPTEMBER 1969**
and new value
285† 8c on 9d Bulk carrier loading gypsum .. 10 5
289† 30c on 3s Game fishing boat 1.50 2.00
290† 50c on 5s *Sea Diver* (diving vessel) 1.50 2.00

1970

As Nos. 225 and 229/30, but with face values in cents
312† 8c Bulk carrier loading gypsum 30 5
316† 30c Game fishing boat 1.50 60
317† 50c *Sea Diver* (diving vessel) 1.50 2.00

320† 3c *Dacia* (cable ship), 1870 .... 15 10

1971

332† 3c 18th-century ships, Port Royal 30 10
334† 30c Pirate schooner attacking
merchantman 1.60 2.00

1972

356† 50c River raft 60 40

No. 356 overprinted **TENTH ANNIVERSARY INDEPENDENCE**
1962-1972
361† 50c River raft 50 1.25

1974

380 5c *Mary* (sailing packet), 1808–15
381 10c *Queensbury* (sailing packet),
1814–27
382 15c *Sheldrake* (sailing packet), 1829–34
383 50c *Thames* (steam packet), 1842
Set of 4 2.40 2.75

1979

474† 75c Game fishing boat 25 20
476† $2 Yachts and cruise liner 50 45

1981

527† $2 *Highland Monarch* (liner) 1.50 1.40

1983

579 15c Freighter at wharf
580 20c *Veendam* (cruise liner)
581 45c Container ship
582 $1 Tanker
Set of 4 1.75 1.40

586† 20c Yacht 15 20

1987

701† $5 *Alene* (liner), 1887 .... 1.25 1.40

STANLEY GIBBONS
STAMP COLLECTING SERIES

Introductory booklets on *How to Start, How to Identify Stamps* and *Collecting by Theme*. A series of well illustrated guides at a low price.
Write for details.

JAPAN

Eastern Asia
100 sen = 1 yen

1921

206 1½s *Katori* and *Kashima* (warships), 1921
207 3s *Katori* and *Kashima*
208 4s *Katori* and *Kashima*
209 10s *Katori* and *Kashima*
Set of 4 £100 65.00

1935

276† 1½s *Hiyei* (cruiser) 2.00 1.60
278† 6s *Hiyei* 12.00 7.50

1937

316† ½s *Goshuin-sen* (16th-century trading
ship) 1.50 70

1942

393† 2s Shipbuilding 80 45

410† 5s + 2s Attack on Pearl Harbour, 1941 2.25 3.25

1948

MS477 2y × 2 Sampans, Seto Inland Sea
(green border and inscriptions) 9.00 4.50
MS478 2y × 2 Sampans, Seto Inland Sea
(blue border and inscriptions) 9.00 9.00
MS479 2y × 2 Sampans, Seto Inland Sea
(turquoise border and inscriptions) 9.00 9.00

1949

519 2y *Koan Maru* (ferry)
520 5y *Koan Maru*
Set of 2 7.50 2.75

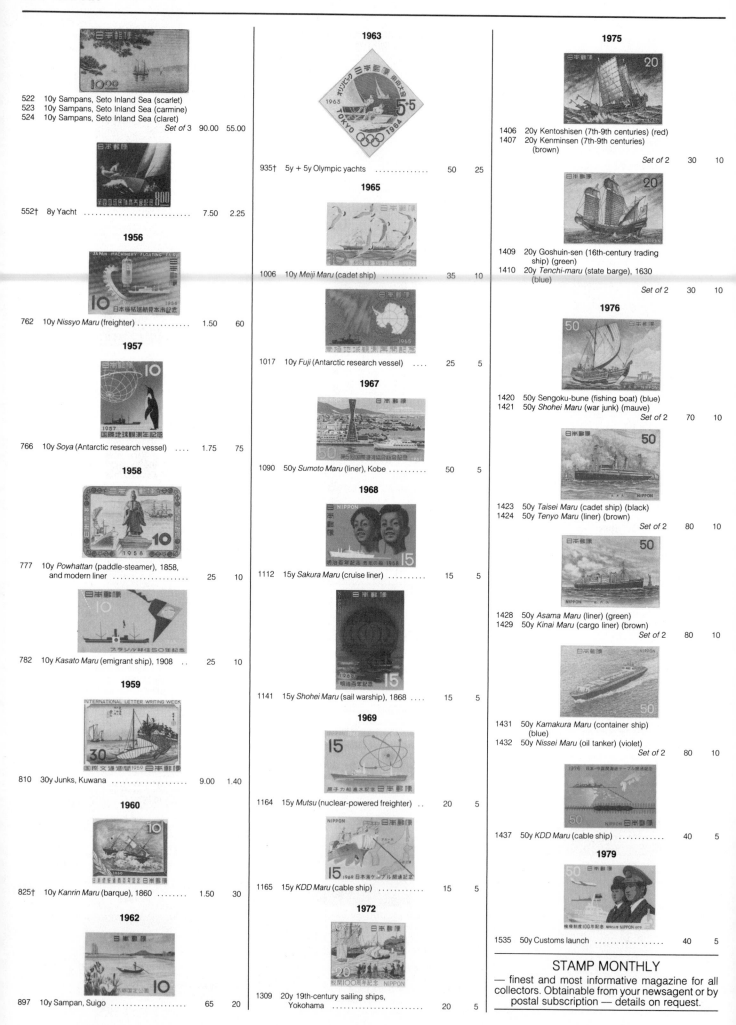

522 10y Sampans, Seto Inland Sea (scarlet)
523 10y Sampans, Seto Inland Sea (carmine)
524 10y Sampans, Seto Inland Sea (claret)
     Set of 3 90.00 55.00

552† 8y Yacht 7.50 2.25

1956

762 10y *Nissyo Maru* (freighter) 1.50 60

1957

766 10y *Soya* (Antarctic research vessel) 1.75 75

1958

777 10y *Powhattan* (paddle-steamer), 1858,
     and modern liner   25 10

782 10y *Kasato Maru* (emigrant ship), 1908 .. 25 10

1959

810 30y Junks, Kuwana 9.00 1.40

1960

825† 10y *Kanrin Maru* (barque), 1860 .... 1.50 30

1962

897 10y Sampan, Suigo 65 20

1963

935† 5y + 5y Olympic yachts 50 25

1965

1006 10y *Meiji Maru* (cadet ship) 35 10

1017 10y *Fuji* (Antarctic research vessel) 25 5

1967

1090 50y *Sumoto Maru* (liner), Kobe 50 5

1968

1112 15y *Sakura Maru* (cruise liner) 15 5

1141 15y *Shohei Maru* (sail warship), 1868 .... 15 5

1969

1164 15y *Mutsu* (nuclear-powered freighter) .. 20 5

1165 15y *KDD Maru* (cable ship) 15 5

1972

1309 20y 19th-century sailing ships,
      Yokohama 20 5

1975

1406 20y Kentoshisen (7th-9th centuries) (red)
1407 20y Kenminsen (7th-9th centuries)
      (brown)
       Set of 2 30 10

1409 20y Goshuin-sen (16th-century trading
      ship) (green)
1410 20y *Tenchi-maru* (state barge), 1630
      (blue)
       Set of 2 30 10

1976

1420 50y Sengoku-bune (fishing boat) (blue)
1421 50y *Shohei Maru* (war junk) (mauve)
       Set of 2 70 10

1423 50y *Taisei Maru* (cadet ship) (black)
1424 50y *Tenyo Maru* (liner) (brown)
       Set of 2 80 10

1428 50y *Asama Maru* (liner) (green)
1429 50y *Kinai Maru* (cargo liner) (brown)
       Set of 2 80 10

1431 50y *Kamakura Maru* (container ship)
      (blue)
1432 50y *Nissei Maru* (oil tanker) (violet)
       Set of 2 80 10

1437 50y *KDD Maru* (cable ship) 40 5

1979

1535 50y Customs launch 40 5

STAMP MONTHLY
— finest and most informative magazine for all
collectors. Obtainable from your newsagent or by
postal subscription — details on request.

1980

1556† 50y Fishing boats 40 20

1569 50y *Nippon Maru* (cadet ship) 40 20

1982

1682 60y 16th-century Portuguese galleon 55 25

1983

1721 60y *Shirase* (Antarctic research ship) 80 35

1986

1846 60y *Nippon Maru* (cadet ship) 70 30

JAPANESE OCCUPATION OF BURMA

South-east Asia
12 pies = 1 anna
16 annas = 1 rupee

1942

No. O23 of Burma overprinted
J44 80a Sailing craft on River Irrawaddy 38.00

JAPANESE OCCUPATION OF CHINA

Eastern Asia
100 cents = 1 dollar (yuan)

NORTH CHINA
1945

206† $20 River boat, Tientsin 30 50

JAPANESE OCCUPATION OF MALAYA

South-east Asia
100 cents = 1 dollar

1943

J274† 4c Tin-dredger 12 12

JAPANESE OCCUPATION OF NORTH BORNEO

South-east Asia
100 cents = 1 dollar

1942

南政国本日大

No. 313 of North Borneo overprinted
J11† 25c Malay prau £110 £150

1944

本 日 大
使 郵 國 帝

才 平 ル 沢 北

No. 313 of North Borneo overprinted
J30† 25c Malay prau 8.50 13.00

JAPANESE OCCUPATION OF THE PHILIPPINES

South-east Asia
100 centavos = 1 peso

1943

Nos. 566 and 569 of Philippine Islands surcharged with native characters, 1-23-43 and value
J13 2c on 8c Filipino prau
J14 5c on 1p Filipino prau

                                    Set of 2   75   75

J21† 12c Morro vinta (sailing canoe) 70 70
J22† 16c Morro vinta (sailing canoe) 5 5
J27† 2p Morro vinta (sailing canoe) 1.40 1.25
J28† 5p Morro vinta (sailing canoe) 4.75 4.00

J29 2c Japanese battleship
J30 5c Japanese battleship

                                    Set of 2   40   40

No. J21 surcharged BAHA 1943 +21
J36† 12c + 21c Morro vinta (sailing canoe) .. 12 12

1944

Nos. 567/8 of Philippine Islands surcharged REPUBLIKA NG PILIPINAS 5-7-44 and value
J43 5c on 20c Filipino prau
J44 12c on 60c Filipino prau

                                    Set of 2   1.40   1.40

OFFICIAL STAMPS

No. 569 of Philippine Islands overprinted REPUBLIKA NG PILIPINAS (K. P.)
JO47 1p Filipino prau 85 90

JERSEY

North-west Europe
1969 12 pence = 1 shilling
20 shillings = 1 pound
1970 100 pence = 1 pound

1969

15† ½d Sailing dinghies, Elizabeth Castle 10 45

1970

37† 1s9d *Vega* (Red Cross supply ship) 2.75 2.00

As No. 15, but face value in new currency
42† ½p Sailing dinghies, Elizabeth Castle 5 8

1971

66† 2½p 18th-century English warships 20 20

1974

110† 20p *Aquila* (paddle-steamer), 1874 .... 60 60

115 3½p 18th-century royal yacht
116 5½p 18th-century French warship
117 8p 18th-century Dutch vessel
118 25p H.M.S. *Britannia* (ship of the line) at Battle of La Hague, 1692

                                    Set of 4   1.00   1.00

1976

160† 5p Ship's boat, 1584 .... 10 10
162† 11p H.M.S. *Phoenix*, H.M.S. *Rose* and H.M.S. *Rainbow* (frigates), Long Island, 1776 .... 30 35

165† 7p Sampan, River Yangtze 15 15

1977

175† 5p *Santa Anna* (carrack), 1530 .... 10 12

179† 7p Paddle-steamer, 1846 .... 20 20

1978

192† 10½p *Century* (brigantine) 25 25

197 6p Mail cutter, 1778–1827
198 8p *Flamer* (packet steamer), 1831–37
199 10½p *Diana* (packet stemer), 1877–90
200 11p *Ibex* (packet steamer), 1891–1925
201 13p *Caesarea* (packet steamer), 1960–75
                              Set of 5 1.25 1.25

1980

238† 7p *Eye of the Wind* (brigantine) 20 20
239† 9p Inflatable dinghy 25 25
241† 14p *Discovery* (Scott) 35 35
243† 17½p *Eye of the Wind* 45 45

1983

304† 8p H.M.S. *Tamar* (sloop) and H.M.S. *Dolphin*, (frigate) Falkland Islands, 1765 .... 25 25
305† 11p H.M.S. *Dolphin* and H.M.S. *Swallow* (frigate) Magellan Strait, 1767 .... 35 35
307† 24p H.M.S. *Swallow* careened, New Britain, 1768 .... 75 75
308† 26p H.M.S. *Swallow* and pirate ship, 1768 .... 80 80
309† 29p H.M.S *Endymion* (frigate), 1781 .... 90 90

316† 24p *Chesterfield* (sailing packet) and French privateer, 1810 .... 70 70
318† 29p Mail steamer, St. Helier, 1827 ...... 90 90

1984

334 9p *Sarah Bloomshoft* (lifeboat), 1906
335 9p *Hearts of Oak* (lifeboat) and *Maurice Georges*, 1949
336 12p *Elizabeth Rippon* (lifeboat) and *Hanna*, 1949
337 12p *Elizabeth Rippon* (lifeboat) and *Santa Maria*, 1951
338 20½p *Elizabeth Rippon* (lifeboat) and *Bacchus*, 1973
339 20½p *Thomas James King* (lifeboat) and *Cythara*, 1983
                              Set of 6 2.40 2.40

352† 9p *Hebe* (brig), 1874 .... 30 30
353† 12p *Gaspe* (schooner) and *Diomede* (American privateer) 40 40
354† 22p *London* (paddle-steamer), 1856 .... 70 70
355† 31p *Rambler* (barque), 1840 .... 90 90

1985

363† 31p *Sir Winston Churchill* (cadet ship) .. 95 95

373† 13p Full-rigged sailing ship in Russian port 35 35
375† 22p British fleet's attack on Viborg, 1855 55 55

377† 13p *Westward* (racing schooner) 40 40

1987

405 10p *Westward* (racing schooner)
406 14p Racing yacht
407 31p *Westward* and *Britannia* (Royal racing yacht), 1935
408 34p *Westward* fitting out
                              Set of 4 2.10 2.10

417 11p H.M.S. *Racehorse* (bomb ketch) in Arctic, 1773

418 15p H.M.S. *Alarm* (galley) on fire, Rhode Island, 1778
419 29p H.M.S. *Arethusa* (frigate) wrecked, 1779
420 31p H.M.S. *Rattlesnake* (sloop) beached, 1782
421 34p Fishing boats and Mont Orgueil, 1792
                              Set of 5 3.00 3.00

423† 15p Norman ship, 1030 .... 40 40

431† 31p Fishing boat, St. Helier 60 65

1988

445† 22p Hydrofoil 45 50

457† 34p *Zebu* (cadet brigantine) 70 75

POSTAGE DUE STAMPS

1982

D42† 10p Ferry, St. Helier 20 25
D44† 30p Cruising yachts, La Collette 50 55
D46† £1 Motor cruisers and yacht, St. Helier 1.75 1.90

JIND

Indian sub-continent
12 pies = 1 anna
16 annas = 1 rupee

1937

No. 256 of India overprinted **JIND STATE**
118 6a *Strathnaver* (liner) 85 3.75

JOHORE

South-east Asia
100 cents = 1 dollar

1944

As No. 115 of Antigua
149† 15c Paddle-steamer 60 1.00

1960

161† 20c Malay fishing prau 15 5

JORDAN

Middle East
1949 1000 milliemes = 1 pound
· 1950 1000 fils = 1 dinar

1949

285†	1m Liner	10	15
286†	4m Liner	15	25
287†	10m Liner	15	25
288†	20m Liner	30	45

1962

512	15f *Rida* (freighter), Aqaba		
513	35f *Rida*		
	Set of 2	45	20

1964

624†	35f Scout sailing dinghy	2.00	85

1967

798†	2f Fishing canoes, Lake Patzcuaro, Mexico	5	5

1976

1136†	60f Freighter, Aqaba	75	25

1984

1410†	25f Naval patrol boat	35	15

1985

1458†	60f Sailing dinghies, Aqaba	60	30

JORDANIAN OCCUPATION OF PALESTINE

Middle East
1000 milliemes = 1 pound

1949
Nos. 285/8 of Jordan overprinted **PALESTINE** *in English and Arabic*

P30†	1m Liner	15	30
P31†	4m Liner	20	40
P32†	10m Liner	25	50
P33†	20m Liner	35	70

KAMPUCHEA

South-east Asia
100 cents = 1 riel

1985

655	10c River launch, 1942		
656	40c River launch, 1948		
657	80c Tug, 1913		
658	1r Dredger		
659	1r20 Tug		
660	2r River freighter		
661	2r50 River tanker		
	Set of 7	4.00	1.75

1986

734	20c English kogge of Richard II's reign		
735	50c Kogge		
736	80c Knarr		
737	1r Galley		
738	1r50 Norman ship		
739	2r Mediterranean usciere		
740	3r French kogge		
	Set of 7	3.25	1.10

KEDAH

South-east Asia
100 cents = 1 dollar

1949
As No. 115 of Antigua

73†	15c Paddle-steamer	50	1.25

1957

98†	20c Malay fishing prau	30	45

1959

110†	20c Malay fishing prau	20	10

KELANTAN

South-east Asia
100 cents = 1 dollar

1949
As No. 115 of Antigua

58†	15c Paddle-steamer	60	1.25

1957

90†	20c Malay fishing prau	20	25

1961

102†	20c Malay fishing prau	30	30

KENYA

East Africa
100 cents = 1 shilling

1963

6†	40c Fishing boats	15	20
13†	10s *Europa* (liner), 1952	4.75	1.25

1980

170†	3s Speedboat, Mombasa	15	10

1981

209†	5s Royal Yacht *Britannia*	75	45

1983

252†	70c Container barge and tugs	20	5
254†	3s50 Container barge loading	75	65

279† 10s Customs patrol boat 1.40 1.40

282† 3s50 Modern mail steamer 45 50

284† 70c Freighters at quay, Kilindi 25 5
286† 3s50 Freighters, Mombasa 65 35

1986

388† 7s Container ship 90 80

394 1s Mashua dhow
395 3s Mtepe dhow
396 5s Dau La Mwao dhow
397 10s Jahazi dhow
                          Set of 4   2.25 2.25
MS398 25s Lamu dhow 3.00 3.50

1988

459† 4s H.M.S. *Sirius* (frigate), 1788 .... 30 35

KENYA, UGANDA AND TANGANYIKA

East Africa
100 cents = 1 shilling

1935

111† 5c Dhow, Lake Victoria 25 5
116† 50c Dhow, Lake Victoria 90 15

1938

As Nos. 111 and 116, but with portrait of King George VI
132† 5c Dhow, Lake Victoria 15 5
140† 25c Dhow, Lake Victoria 1.25 75
144† 50c Dhow, Lake Victoria 65 5

1941

No. 115 of South Africa surcharged **5c. KENYA TANGANYIKA UGANDA**. *Alternate stamps inscribed in English or Afrikaans*
151† 5c on 1d *Dromedaris* (Van Riebeeck) 60 1.50

1949

As No. 115 of Antigua
160† 30c Paddle-steamer 50 30

1966

226† 2s50 Game fishing launch 80 50

1969

256 30c *Umoja* (train ferry)
257 50c *Harambee* (lake freighter)
258 1s30 *Victoria* (lake ferry)
259 2s50 *St. Michael* (car ferry)
                          Set of 4   1.60 1.10

263† 2s50 Freighters at wharf 20 30

KHOR FAKKAN

Arabian peninsula
100 naye paise = 1 rupee

Appendix

The following have either been issued in excess of postal needs, or have not been made available to the public in reasonable quantities at face value. Miniature sheets, imperforate stamps etc, are excluded from this section.

1965

New York World's Fair. No. 81 of Sharjah overprinted **KHOR FAKKAN** *in English and Arabic. Air 20np Oil rig*
I.T.U. Centenary. As No. 166 of Sharjah. 1np *Monarch* (cable ship)

KIAUTSCHOU

China
1901 100 pfennige = 1 mark
1905 100 cents = 1 dollar

1901

As Nos. K7/19 of Cameroun, but inscribed "KIAUTSCHOU"
11 3pf *Hohenzollern* (German Imperial yacht)
12 5pf *Hohenzollern*
13 10pf *Hohenzollern*
14 20pf *Hohenzollern*
15 25pf *Hohenzollern*
16 30pf *Hohenzollern*
17 40pf *Hohenzollern*
18 50pf *Hohenzollern*
19 80pf *Hohenzollern*
20 1m *Hohenzollern*
21 2m *Hohenzollern*
22 3m *Hohenzollern*
23 5m *Hohenzollern*
                          Set of 13   £350 £650

1905

As Nos. 11/23, but face values in Chinese currency
34 1c *Hohenzollern* (German Imperial yacht)
35 2c *Hohenzollern*
36 4c *Hohenzollern*
37 10c *Hohenzollern*
38 20c *Hohenzollern*
39 40c *Hohenzollern*

---

40 ½dol *Hohenzollern*
41 1dol *Hohenzollern*
42 1½dol *Hohenzollern*
43 2½dol *Hohenzollern*
                          Set of 10   38.00 £550

KIRIBATI

Pacific Ocean
100 cents = 1 dollar

1979

86† 1c *Teraaka* (training ship) 10 5
87† 3c *Tautunu* (inter-island freighter) 10 8
98† $1 *Tabakea* (lagoon ferry) 10 10

101† 20c Gilbert Islands canoe (on Gilbert
     and Ellice Islands stamp No. 73) 20 25

1980

112† 12c *Teraaka* (training ship) 12 12

1981

148† $1 H.M.S. *Resolution* (Cook) 1.10 1.10

149† 12c Royal Yacht *Katherine* 15 15
151† 50c Royal Yacht *Osborne* 45 45
153† $2 Royal Yacht *Britannia* 1.50 1.50

161† 50c *Nei Manganibuka* (tuna-fishing boat) 60 60

1982

190† 25c Scouts repairing dinghy 30 30

194†	25c Outrigger canoe	30	30

1983

199†	50c Container ship off Betio	40	45
201†	12c Outrigger canoe	15	20
209†	50c Lighter and launches, Betio	50	55
214†	$1 U.S.S. *Tarawa* (aircraft carrier)	1.00	1.10
215†	12c *Betsey* (American full-rigged ship), 1798	15	15

1984

219	12c *Riki* (tug)
220	35c *Nei Nimanoa* (ferry)
221	50c *Nei Tebaa* (ferry)
222	$1 *Nei Momi* (inter-island ship)

	Set of 4	2.00	2.00
225†	30c *Nouamake* (game fishing boat)	30	30

1985

250†	40c *Moanaraoi* (freighter)	55	55

1986

259†	40c Whaling ship, 1844	50	50
260†	55c *Vostok* (Russian warship), 1820	70	70
267†	$1.50 *Australia II* (yacht), 1983	1.25	1.40

1987

268†	30c *Moamoa* (freighter)	25	30

1988

290†	$1 18th-century Australian brig	90	95
MS292†	$2 *Logistic Ace* (container ship)	1.75	1.90

OFFICIAL STAMPS

1981

Nos. 86/7 and 98 overprinted **O.K.G.S.**

O1†	1c *Teraaka* (training ship)	5	5
O2†	3c *Tautunu* (inter-island freighter)	5	5
O13†	$1 *Tabakea* (lagoon ferry)	5	5

KOREA

Eastern Asia

South Korea

1946 100 cheun = 1 won
1955 100 weun = 1 hwan
1962 100 chon = 1 won

1946

92†	50w 16th-century "turtle" ship	14.00	5.00

1952

196	1200w Freighter
197	1800w Freighters
198	4200w Freighters

	Set of 3	2.50	90

1953

As Nos. 196/8 but face values in hwan

210	12h Freighters
211	18h Freighters
212	42h Freighters

	Set of 3	3.25	90

1955

256	20h 16th-century "turtle" ship	3.00	1.50

1959

336	40h Marine landing-craft	70	25

1961

404	40h Destroyer	90	30

1962

433	2w 16th-century 20-oared "turtle" ship
434	4w 16th-century 16-oared "turtle" ship

	Set of 2	2.25	1.50
449	4w Trawler	75	25

1964

509†	40w Freighter	1.60	35
528†	4w Trawlers	90	25

1965

593†	4w *Korea* (freighter)	75	25

1969

782	7w 16th-century "turtle" ship	75	25

1974

1103   10w Container ships, Inchon 40   12

1977

1272†   20w Tanker 40   5

1311   20w Freighter 25   5

1978

1334   20w Destroyer 20   5

1980

1459   30w Cable ship 30   5

1981

1465	30w Korea Sun (tanker)		
1466	90w Asia Yukho (freighter)		
	Set of 2	55	15

1470	30w Saturn (bulk carrier)		
1471	90w Hanjin Seoul (container ship)		
	Set of 2	60	15

1482	40w Chung Ryong No. 3 (tug)		
1483	100w Soo Gong No. 71 (trawler)		
	Set of 2	70	15

1484	40w Al Debaran (log carrier)		
1485	100w Hyundai No. 1 (car carrier)		
	Set of 2	70	15

1501	40w Stolt Hawk (chemical carrier)		
1502	100w Passenger ferry		
	Set of 2	45	15

1982

1537†   60w Battle of Hansan, 1592 40   5

1986

1740†   30w Excursion launch, River Han 10   5
1741†   60w Excursion launch, River Han 15   5

1988

1826†   80w + 20w Olympic yachts 15   5

North Korea
100 cheun = 1 won

1959

N209†   10ch Chungnyon-ho (freighter) 1.25   50

1961

N328†   10ch Trawler 50   15

1962

N367†   10ch Trawler 60   12

1963

N445†   40ch Trawlers 1.50   40

N448†   10ch Motor torpedo-boat 55   10

1964

N506	5ch Whale-catcher		
N507	5ch Trawler		
N508	10ch Trawler		
N509	10ch Trawler		
	Set of 4	1.10	40

N535†   10ch Tobolsk (passenger ship) 50   10

1965

N638	10ch Whale-catcher		
N639	10ch Fishing fleet service vessel		
	Set of 2	95	20

N667	2ch "Finn" class yachts		
N668	10ch "5.5m" class yacht		
N669	10ch "Dragon" class yacht		
N670	40ch "Star" class yachts		
	Set of 4	2.75	1.25

1967

N802   10ch Chollima (freighter) 35   10

1968

N852†   5ch September 2 (dredger) 15   5

1969

N939   10ch Taesungsan (freighter) 40   12

1971

N1021†   10ch Freighter 40   10

N1041†   5ch *Ponghwasan* (refrigerated
         freighter) 20   5

1972

N1086†   5ch Dredger 15   5

N1112†   10ch Freighter 30   10

1974

N1225†   10ch Whale-catcher and factory ship   30   10

N1324   2ch *Chilbosan* (fish factory ship)
N1325   5ch *Paekdusan* (trawler support ship)
        and trawler
N1326   10ch *Moranbong* (freighter)
N1327   20ch Whale-catcher
N1328   30ch Trawlers
N1329   40ch Stern trawler
                    Set of 6   2.00   1.10

1976

N1496†   40ch Cable-laying barge 75   20

N1555†   25ch Junk 45   15

1977

N1623†   2ch River launch 45   5
N1625†   30ch Freighters 60   20

1978

N1699   15ch Modern mail steamer 40   10

N1718   2ch *Mangyongbong* (freighter)
N1719   5ch *Hyoksin* (freighter)
N1720   10ch *Chongchongang* (gas carrier)
N1721   30ch *Sonbong* (tanker)
N1722   50ch *Taedonggang* (freighter) (air)
                    Set of 5   2.00   1.25

1979

N1863†   20ch Olympic yachts 40   15

1980

N1958†   10ch Red Cross ship 45   10
N1961†   10ch Hospital ship 1.90   40

N1966†   40ch *Calypso* (research ship) 1.50   55

N2016   10ch *Malygin* (ice-breaker) (on Russia
        stamp No. 584)
N2017   20cn *Malygin* (on Russia stamp No.
        585)
N2018   30ch *Malygin* (on Russia stamp No.
        586)
                    Set of 3   3.50   1.25
MSN2019   50ch *Malygin* (on Russia stamp No.
        587) 3.00   2.50

1983

N2312   20ch *Colourful Cow* (kogge), 1402
N2313   20ch "Turtle" ship, 1592
N2314   35ch *Great Harry* (warship), 1555
N2315   35ch "Turtle" ship
N2316   50ch *Eagle of Lubeck* (galleon), 1567
N2317   50ch *Merkur* (full-rigged sailing ship),
        1847
N2318   50ch *Duchess Elizabeth* (cadet ship)
                    Set of 7   12.00   4.25
MSN2319   80ch *Cristoforo Colombo* (cadet
        ship) 4.50   3.50

N2334   40ch *Gorch Foch* (cadet ship) and
        Mangyongbong (on stamp No.
        N1718) 2.50   1.25

N2351†   40ch Freighter 3.50   1.10

1984

MSN2404 80ch *Gorch Foch* (cadet ship) and
"Turtle" ship (on stamp No. N2313) 4.25 3.50

N2418 5ch Trawler
N2419 10ch Trawler
N2420 40ch Game fishing launch
                        Set of 3   2.50   1.25

1986

N2467† 10ch Oil tanker and barrage 12 5

Appendix
The following stamps have either been issued in excess of
postal needs or have not been made available to the public in
reasonable quantities at face value. Miniature sheets, imperforate
stamps etc. are excluded from this section.

1984
Container ships. 10, 20, 30ch
Russian Icebreakers. 20, 30ch
European Royal History. 10ch x 6, various historical scenes
    1571–1844

1985
Ships and Lighthouses. 10, 20, 30, 40ch

1986
"Stockholmia 86" International Stamp Exhibition. 10ch. Icebreaker

---

KOUANG TCHEOU (KWANGCHOW)

South China
100 cents = 1 piastre

1937
Nos. 163/9 of Indo-China overprinted **KOUANG-TCHEOU**
98† 1/10c Junk 5 10
99† 1/5c Junk 5 10
100† 2/5c Junk 5 10
101† ½c Junk 5 10
102† 4/5c Junk 5 10
103† 1c Junk 5 10
104† 2c Junk 5 10

KUWAIT

Arabian Peninsula
1939 12 pies = 1 anna
16 annas = 1 rupee
1957 100 naye paise = 1 rupee
1961 1000 fils = 1 dinar

1939
No. 256 of India overprinted **KUWAIT**
44† 6a *Strathnaver* (liner) 8.50 5.50

1951
Nos. 509/10 of Great Britain surcharged **KUWAIT** *and value*
90† 2r on 2s6d H.M.S. *Victory* (Nelson) 8.00 4.00
91† 5r on 5s Yacht and Thames sailing barge,
       Dover 15.00 5.50

1958

137† 40np Dhow 45 10
141† 2r Dhow 2.50 25

1961

154† 30f Dhow 60 8
156† 40f Dhow 60 15
158† 75f Dhow 85 35
161† 250f Dhow 6.50 1.50

1964

244 8f Dhow
245 15f Dhow
246 20f Dhow
247 30f Dhow
                        Set of 4   1.25   55

1966

324 20f *British Fusilier* (tanker)
325 45f *British Fusilier*
                        Set of 2   1.40   80

330 4f Dhow
331 25f Dhow
                        Set of 2   1.75   75

1969

453 20f *Al Sabahian* (tanker)
454 45f *Al Sabahiah*
                        Set of 2   2.25   1.25

1970

480 8f Shoue (dhow)
481 10f Sambuk (dhow)
482 15f Baggala (dhow)
483 20f Battela (dhow)
484 25f Bum (dhow)
485 45f Baggala (dhow)
486 50f Dhow-building
                        Set of 7   1.50   1.75

513 20f *Medora* (tanker)
514 45f *Medora*
                        Set of 2   2.50   90

1972

555 5f Fishing boat
556 10f Fishing boat
557 20f Fishing boat
                        Set of 3   1.40   45

1978

761† 5f Dhows 10 5
764† 5f Dhows 10 5

1981

894 30f Tanker
895 80f Tanker
                        Set of 2   2.25   1.25

1982

939 30f Container ship
940 80f Freighter
                        Set of 2   1.50   90

1983

1009 15f Dhow
1010 30f Dhow
1011 80f Dhow
                        Set of 3   2.00   90

1985

1088 30f Dhow
1089 80f Dhow
                        Set of 2   1.75   95

1986

1109 20f *Al Mirqab* (container ship)
1110 70f *Al Mubarakiah* (container ship)
                                        Set of 2   65   35

1987

1139 25f Container ship
1140 50f Container ship
1141 150f Container ship
                                        Set of 3   80   50

LABUAN

Off North coast of Borneo
100 cents = 1 dollar

1894

As No. 74 of North Borneo, with colours changed, overprinted
LABUAN
69† 8c Malay prau 1.75   6.50

1896

No. 69 further overprinted **1846 JUBILEE 1896**
88† 8c Malay prau 8.50   6.50

1897

As No. 102b of North Borneo, with colours changed, overprinted
LABUAN
94a† 8c Malay prau 5.00   4.25

1899

No. 94a surcharged **4 CENTS**
104a† 4c on 8c Malay prau 7.50 12.00

1904

No. 94a surcharged **4 cents**
129† 4c on 8c Malay prau 8.00 13.00

POSTAGE DUE STAMPS

1901

No. 94a overprinted **POSTAGE DUE**
D6† 8c Malay prau 11.00

LAOS

South-east Asia
1951 100 cents = 1 piastre
1955 100 cents = 1 kip

1951

1† 10c Pirogue, River Mekong   5   5
2† 20c Pirogue, River Mekong   8   8
3† 30c Pirogue, River Mekong   65   55

1965

176† 25k Pirogue race   45   30

1967

202† 60k + 15k Pirogue on flooded airport 1.10   1.10

1971

315† 70k Pirogue building   45   30

1974

395† 25k Car ferry, River Mekong   45   20
397† 250k House boat, River Mekong (air) 2.00 1.25

1979

475† 5k River pirogues   15   10
478† 500k River pirogues 2.25 1.25

1982

559 50c River raft
560 60c River sampan
561 1k River house boat
562 2k River passenger steamer
563 3k River ferry
564 8k Self-propelled barge
                                        Set of 6   2.75   1.40

1983

MS667 10k Pirogues and sampan, River
Tachin 2.40   1.60

COLLECT RAILWAYS ON STAMPS

A Stanley Gibbons thematic catalogue on this popular subject. Copies available at £7.50 (p. + p. £2) from: Stanley Gibbons Publications Ltd, 5 Parkside, Christchurch Road, Ringwood, Hants BH24 3SH.

674 1k *Victoria* (Magellan)
675 2k *Grande Hermine* (Cartier)
676 3k *Santa Maria* (Columbus)
677 4k *El Ray* (Cabral)
678 5k H.M.S. *Resolution* (Cook)
679 6k *Pourquois Pas?* (Charcot) (inscr
      "CABOT" in error)
                                        Set of 6   4.50   2.00

1984

795† 1k River house boat   30   10

1985

852† 1k *Pinta* (Columbus)   10   5
853† 2k *Nina* (Columbus)   15   5
854† 3k *Santa Maria* (Columbus)   20   5

1987

981 50c Schooner
982 1k Schooner
983 2k Full-rigged ship
984 3k Early screw-steamer
985 4k Early screw-steamer
986 5k Early paddle-steamer
987 6k River paddle-steamer
                                        Set of 7   75   30
MS988 10k *Matthew* (Cabot), 1497 (on
      Canada stamp No. 412)   40   20

POSTAGE DUE STAMPS

1952

D28† 10p Sampans   80   80

Appendix
The following stamps have either been issued in excess of postal needs or have not been available to the public in reasonable quantities at face value. Miniature sheets, imperforate stamps etc, are excluded from this section.

1975

Centenary of Universal Postal Union. 10k Junk and modern liner

LATVIA

Eastern Europe
100 santimi (centimes) = 1 lat

1925

119† 6-12s Freighters, Libau 1.00 3.00

1928

162† 50s Tug and freighters, Riga 1.75 1.75

LEBANON

Middle East
100 centimes = 1 piastre

1930

167† 1p Fishing boat, Saida (green) 30 20
167a† 1p Fishing boat, Saida (purple) 30 20
174† 6p Fishing boats, Tyre 70 50

1947

355† 50p Phoenician galley 2.75 75
356† 75p Phoenician galley 3.50 1.25
357† 100p Phoenician galley 4.75 2.50

1961

694† 70p Tourist punt 1.25 70

713† 5p Fishing boats, Tyre 10 5
714† 10p Fishing boats, Tyre 25 5
715† 15p Fishing boats, Tyre 30 5
716† 20p Fishing boats, Tyre 30 8
717† 30p Fishing boats, Tyre 40 12

1962

As No. 713, but with larger figures of value

733† 5p Fishing boats, Tyre 15 5

1966

938† 15p Phoenician sailing ship 20 10

942† 5p Rowing boat 10 5

1967

962† 20p Fishing boat, Sidon 20 5

980† 20p Tourist punt, Jeita 25 10

1968

1013† 17p50 Feluccas, Beirut 30 15

1969

1060† 30p Yacht 50 25
1061† 40p Racing yacht 60 40

1971

1108† 70p *Tarablous* (naval patrol boat) 2.00 65

1973

1155† 25p Phoenician galley 45 15

1975

1226† 35p Phoenician galley 35 25

POSTAGE DUE STAMPS

1931

D192† 1p Phoenician galley 35 35

LEEWARD ISLANDS

West Indies
12 pence = 1 shilling
20 shillings = 1 pound

1949

As No. 115 of Antigua
120† 3d Paddle-steamer 50 45

LESOTHO

Southern Africa
100 lisente = 1 maloti

1986

742† 35s Rowing boat 35 30

1987

779† 4m Sailboard 2.25 2.50

788 9s Fleet of Columbus, 1492
789 15s Fleet of Columbus, 1492
790 35s Caravel, 1492
791 5m Fleet of Columbus, 1492
Set of 4 2.75 3.00
MS792 4m *Santa Maria* (Columbus) 2.25 2.40

LIBERIA
West Africa
100 cents = 1 dollar

1886

29†	32c *Alligator* (first settlers' ship), 1822	12.00	12.00

1909

252†	5c *Lark* (gunboat)	1.50	35
259†	50c *Canoe*	2.50	60

1913

Nos 252 and 259 surcharged

323†	2c on 5c *Lark*	2.25	3.50
283†	10c on 50c *Canoe* (surch **1914 10 CENTS**)	9.00	9.00
301†	10c on 50c *Canoe* (surch **10** and ornaments)	6.50	6.00

1918

351†	5c *Alligator* (first settlers' ship), 1822	45	10

1921

404†	10c *Alligator* (first settlers' ship), 1822 ..	60	10
408†	30c *Canoe*	1.00	15
409†	50c *Kru canoe*	1.00	25
413†	$5 *Canoe*	23.00	1.50

Nos. 404, 408/9 and 413 overprinted **1921**

418†	10c *Alligator*	5.50	50
422†	30c *Canoe*	3.50	50
423†	50c *Kru canoe*	3.00	70
427†	$5 *Canoe*	23.00	3.50

1923

466	1c *Alligator* (first settlers' ship), 1822	
467	2c *Alligator*	
468	5c *Alligator*	
469	10c *Alligator*	
470	$5 *Alligator*	
	Set of 5 38.00	2.50

1936

No. 351 surcharged **1936 3 1936 3**

537†	3c on 5c *Alligator*	30	45

No. O364 surcharged **1936 3 1936 3** *with star*

548†	3c on 5c *Alligator*	25	50

1940

575†	3c *Immigrant ships, 1839*	30	10

1941

No. 575 overprinted **POSTAGE STAMP CENTENNIAL 1840-1940 ROWLAND HILL** *with portrait of Rowland Hill (No. 581 additionally overprinted* **AIR MAIL** *with airplane)*

578†	3c *Immigrant ships, 1839*	1.75	1.75
581†	3c *Immigrant ships, 1839 (air)*	1.40	1.40

No. 575 surcharged **RED CROSS TWO CENTS** *with Red Cross (No. 587 additionally overprinted* **AIR MAIL** *with airplane)*

584†	3c *Immigrant ships, 1839*	1.40	1.40
587†	3c *Immigrant ships, 1839 (air)*	1.40	1.40

1949

704†	3c *Alligator* (first settlers' ship), 1822	75	1.25
707†	50c *Alligator*	2.50	2.75

1953

730†	25c *African Glen* (freighter), Monrovia (purple)	50	30

1954

As No. 730, but colour changed and inscribed "COMMEMORATING PRESIDENTIAL VISIT U.S.A.—1954"

751†	25c *African Glen* (blue)	60	20

1960

833†	10c *Pirogue*	40	75

1969

1001†	20c *Yachts, Argenteuil*	50	20

1971

1062†	20c *Inflatable dinghy*	45	15

1972

MS1073†	30c Olympic yachts, Kiel (sheet contains one other design)	1.25	1.25

1099†	3c *Elizabeth* (emigrants' ship), at Providence Island, 1822	25	30
1101†	20c *Elizabeth* (emigrants' ship), at Providence Island, 1822	60	45
MS1103†	50c *Elizabeth* crossing the Atlantic	2.25	1.75

1125	3c H.M.S. *Ajax* (ship of the line) and figurehead, 1809		
1126	5c H.M.S. *Hogue* (screw ship of the line) and figurehead, 1848		
1127	7c H.M.S. *Ariadne* (frigate) and figurehead, 1816		
1128	15c H.M.S. *Royal Adelaide* (ship of the line) and figurehead, 1828		
1129	25c H.M.S. *Rinaldo* (screw sloop) and figurehead, 1860		
1130	25c H.M.S. *Nymphe* (screw sloop), 1888		
	Set of 6	3.00	1.75
MS1131	50c H.M.S. *Victory* (Nelson), 1765	2.25	2.00

1974

1187†	2c *Thomas Coutts* (full-rigged sailing ship), 1817, and *Aureol* (liner), 1974	10	5
1188†	3c *Modern liner*	15	5

1221†	15c "Liberty" ship, 1944	40	15

1975

1238†	50c *Santa Maria* (Columbus) (and on U.S.A. stamp No. 236)	1.50	55
MS1239†	75c *Mayflower* (Pilgrim Fathers) (and on U.S.A. stamp No. 556) (air)	2.75	1.60

1240† 1c Canoes, Lambarene 10 5

1976

1273† 25c Olympic yachts 65 35

1280† 25c *Dominia* (cable ship), 1926 . . . . 75 30

1284† 1c Canoe, River Mano 5 5
1289† 55c Game fishing launch 1.00 30

1979

1382† 25c *John Penn* (paddle-steamer), 1860 . . 60 25

1388 5c *World Peace* (tanker)
1389 $1 *World Peace*

Set of 2 2.00 1.75

1431† 35c Indian canoe 80 45

1981
As Nos. 1284 and 1289, but smaller, 33 × 20mm
1504a† 1c Canoe, River Mano 5 5
1509a† 80c Game fishing launch 1.75 1.25

1984

1588† 31c Bulk carrier, Buchanan 80 65

1987

1659† 15c Schooner, New York 20 15
1660† 15c *Bay Queen* (harbour ferry), New
         York 20 15
1662† 15c Tug and schooner 20 15
1670† 60c Yachts and cabin cruisers 70 60

OFFICIAL STAMPS

1909
As Nos. 252 and 259, but colours changed, overprinted **OS**
O264† 5c *Lark* (gunboat) 75 15
O271† 50c Canoe 1.75 40

1915
Nos. O264 and O271 surcharged with new value
O326† 2c on 5c *Lark* (gunboat) 2.50 3.00
O314† 10c on 50c Canoe 6.50 7.50

1918
As No. 351, but with colour changed, overprinted **OS**
O364† 5c *Alligator* 45 10

1921
As Nos. 404, 408/9 and 413, but colours changed, overprinted **OS**
O432† 10c *Alligator* 1.25 15
O436† 30c Canoe 1.40 15
O437† 50c Kru canoe 1.50 25
O441† $5 Canoe 17.00 1.75

Nos. O432, O436/7 and O441 overprinted **1921**
O446† 10c *Alligator* 1.75 25
O450† 30c Canoe 1.75 30
O451† 50c Kru canoe 3.50 40
O455† $5 Canoe 16.00 3.00

REGISTRATION STAMPS

Each inscribed with the name of a different town

1919

R388 10c *Quail* (patrol boat) (Buchanan)
R389 10c *Quail* (Grenville)
R390 10c *Quail* (Harper)
R391 10c *Quail* (Monrovia)
R392 10c *Quail* (Robertsport)

Set of 5 3.75 25.00

1923

R499 10c Sailing skiff (Buchanan)
R500 10c Lighter (Grenville)
R501 10c Full-rigged sailing ship (Harper)
R502 10c *George Washington* (liner)
         (Monrovia)
R503 10c Canoe (Robertsport)

Set of 5 32.00 2.25

LIBYA

North Africa
1912 100 centesimi = 1 lira
1961 1000 milliemes = 1 pound
1982 1000 dirhams = 1 dinar

1921

54† 30c Roman galley 5 12
55† 50c Roman galley 5 5
30† 55c Roman galley 95 95
59† 1li25 Roman galley 8 10

1961

263 15m *Esso Canterbury* (tanker)
264 50m *Esso Canterbury*
265 100m *Esso Canterbury*

Set of 3 2.00 90

1967

392 60m Tanker 70 25

1969

Face values in white

444 5m Destroyer
445 10m Destroyer
446 15m Destroyer
447 25m Destroyer
448 45m Destroyer
449 60m Destroyer

Set of 6 2.75 1.60

1970
As Nos. 444/9 but face values in black
457 5m Destroyer
458 10m Destroyer
459 15m Destroyer
460 25m Destroyer
461 45m Destroyer
462 60m Destroyer

Set of 6 2.75 1.60

1978

828† 30dh Frigate 20 5

1980

994† 20dh Italian landings at El Hani, 1911 .... 20 5
995† 35dh Italian landings at El Hani, 1911 .... 35 12

1014† 25dh Liner 25 8

1982

1227† 30dh Modern naval vessels 35 25
MS1231† 200dh Modern naval vessels 2.50 2.75

1983

1303 100dh Phoenician galley
1304 100dh Ancient Greek galley
1305 100dh Ancient Egyptian ship
1306 100dh Roman sailing ship
1307 100dh Viking longship
1308 100dh Libyan xebec
Set of 6 4.00 3.00

1353† 100dh Sailboard 65 45

1984

1432† 25dh Sailboards 20 10
1433† 25dh Sailing dinghy (orange and red sails) 20 10
1434† 25dh Sailing dinghy (mauve sails) 20 10
1437† 25dh Rowing boat 20 10
1438† 25dh Motor boat 20 10

1552† 100dh Sailboards 70 40

1573† 25dh Liner at quay 20 10

1985

1713† 50dh Burning of U.S.S. *Philadelphia*, 1804 .... 35 12
1715† 100dh Felucca 60 35

1986

1873† 50d American aircraft carrier 20 20
1874† 100d Capture of U.S.S. *Philadelphia* (frigate), 1801 .... 40 30

LIECHTENSTEIN

Central Europe
100 rappen = 1 franc

1928

82† 20r + 10r Pontoon 14.00 13.00

LITHUANIA

Eastern Europe
100 centu = 1 litas

1923

219† 1li Paddle-tug and freighter, Memel 2.50 2.50

LOURENCO MARQUES

East Africa
100 centavos = 1 escudo

1913

Nos. 1/2, 5 and 7 of Portuguese Colonies surcharged **REPUBLICA LOURENCO MARQUES** *and value*
107† ½c on 2½r Departure of Vasco da Gama's fleet 50 45
108† ½c on 5r Vasco da Gama's fleet at Calicut 50 45
111† 5c on 50r *Sao Gabriel* (flagship) 50 45
113† 10c on 100r *Sao Gabriel* 65 45

Nos. 104/5, 108 and 110 of Macao surcharged **REPUBLICA LOURENCO MARQUES** *and value*
115† ½c on ½a Departure of Vasco da Gama's fleet 60 45
116† ½c on 1a Vasco da Gama's fleet at Calicut 60 45
119† 5c on 8a *Sao Gabriel* (flagship) 60 45
121† 10c on 16a *Sao Gabriel* 75 45

Nos. 58/9, 62 and 64 of Timor surcharged **REPUBLICA LOURENCO MARQUES** *and value*
123† ½c on ½a Departure of Vasco da Gama's fleet 60 45
124† ½c on 1a Vasco da Gama's fleet at Calicut 60 45
127† 5c on 8a *Sao Gabriel* (flagship) 60 45
129† 10c on 16a *Sao Gabriel* 75 45

LUXEMBOURG

Western Europe
100 centimes = 1 franc

1964

743 3f Barge, Moselle Canal 25 12

1967

807† 3f Barges, River Moselle 20 10

1971

876† 3f Yachts 25 12

1975

948† 4f River barge, Remich 50 12

1988

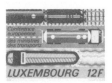

1223† 12f Canal barge 30 35

MACAO

South-east coast of China
1898 78 avos = 1 rupee
1913 100 avos = 1 pataca

1898

As Nos. 378/9, 382 and 384 of Portugal, but inscribed "MACAU"

104†	½a Departure of Vasco da Gama's fleet	60	45
105†	1a Vasco da Gama's fleet at Calicut	60	45
108†	8a *Sao Gabriel* (flagship)	1.75	1.25
110†	16a *Sao Gabriel*	2.25	1.50

1913

*Nos. 104/5, 108 and 110 overprinted **REPUBLICA***

256†	½a Departure of Vasco da Gama's fleet	55	25
257†	1a Vasco da Gama's fleet at Calicut	55	25
260†	8a *Sao Gabriel* (flagship)	70	40
262†	16a *Sao Gabriel*	95	40

1934

338	½a Galeasse
339	1a Galeasse
340	2a Galeasse
341	3a Galeasse
342	4a Galeasse
343	5a Galeasse
344	6a Galeasse
345	7a Galeasse
346	8a Galeasse
347	10a Galeasse
348	12a Galeasse
349	14a Galeasse
350	15a Galeasse
351	20a Galeasse
352	30a Galeasse
353	40a Galeasse
354	50a Galeasse
355	1p Galeasse
356	2p Galeasse
357	3p Galeasse
358	5p Galeasse

Set of 21 42.00 18.00

1936

*Nos. 340/1, 344/6 and 350 overprinted **Aviao** and Greek characters, 6a also surcharged **5 avos***

359	2a Galeasse
360	3a Galeasse
361	5a on 6a Galeasse
362	7a Galeasse
363	8a Galeasse
364	15a Galeasse

Set of 6 9.00 6.00

1940

Nos. 344/6 and 352/4 surcharged

391†	1a on 6a Galeasse	1.50	60
394†	2a on 6a Galeasse	50	20
395†	3a on 6a Galeasse	50	20
396†	5a on 7a Galeasse	50	35
397†	5a on 8a Galeasse	50	25
398†	8a on 30a Galeasse	1.25	65
399†	8a on 40a Galeasse	1.40	65
400†	8a on 50a Galeasse	1.40	65

1951

447†	1p Sampan	1.50	30
448†	3p Junk	8.50	1.25
449†	5p Junk	18.00	3.50

1967

504	10a *Vega* (fast patrol boat)	55	30
505	20a *Don Fernando* (sail frigate)		

Set of 2 55 30

1981

542	10a Junk		
543	30a Junk		
544	1p Junk		
545	3p Junk		

Set of 4 1.60 1.25

1983

585	4p 16th-century Portuguese galleon		
586	4p 16th-century Portuguese galleon and emblem		

Set of 2 2.00 1.40

1984

598	20a Hok Lou T'eng (local fishing boat)		
599	60a Tai T'ong (local fishing boat)		
600	2p Tai Mei Chai (local fishing boat)		
601	5p Ch'at Pong T'o (local fishing boat)		

Set of 4 2.25 1.60

1985

605	1p50 Junk	35	15

617	50a Tou (sailing barge)		
618	70a *Veng Seng Lei* (motor junk)		
619	1p *Tong Heng Long No. 2* (motor junk)		
620	6p *Fong Vong San* (container ship)		

Set of 4 1.75 1.25

1986

630	10a Hydrofoil		
631	40a Hovercraft		
632	3p Jetfoil		
633	7p50 High speed ferry		

Set of 4 2.50 1.60

COLLECT BIRDS ON STAMPS

Second revised edition of this Stanley Gibbons thematic catalogue – now available at £8.50 (p. + p. £2) from: Stanley Gibbons Publications Ltd, 5 Parkside, Christchurch Road, Ringwood, Hants BH24 3SH.

635†	2p Sampan, Sao Paulo da Monte	50	20
637†	2p Junk, Guia	50	20

1987

645	50a Dragon boat
646	5p Dragon boat figurehead

Set of 2 1.00 60

POSTAGE DUE STAMPS

1949

*Nos. 342, 344, 346/8 and 352/3 surcharged **PORTEADO** and new value*

D424	1a on 4a Galeasse
D425	2a on 6a Galeasse
D426	4a on 8a Galeasse
D427	5a on 10a Galeasse
D428	8a on 12a Galeasse
D429	12a on 30a Galeasse
D430	20a on 40a Galeasse

Set of 7 6.00 5.50

MADAGASCAR AND DEPENDENCIES

Indian Ocean off East Africa
100 centimes = 1 franc

1931

As No. 109 of Cameroun

152†	1f50 Liner	70	35

1937

As Nos. 110/11 of Cameroun

187†	20c Liner	30	30
188†	30c Sailing ships	30	30
MS192a†	3f Liner	70	70

1954

As No. 264 of Cameroun

330	15f Landing craft, Normandy, 1944	75	60

1956

335†	10f Dredger	20	5
336†	15f Pirogue	55	15

MADEIRA

Atlantic Ocean, north-west of Africa
100 centavos = 1 escudo

1898

Nos. 378/9, 382 and 384 of Portugal, but inscribed "MADEIRA"

134†	2½r Departure of Vasco da Gama's fleet	65	30
135†	5r Vasco da Gama's fleet at Calicut	70	30
138†	50r *Sao Gabriel* (flagship)	2.25	90
140†	100r *Sao Gabriel*	2.25	1.50

1980

177†	30e Local fishing boat	80	35

1981

180† 8e50 Portuguese caravel, 1418 .... 25 10

1984

213† 51e Local sailing boat 70 35

1985

60

221† 60e Tourist launch 75 40

1986

224 68e50 Tanker 80 45

1988

238 80e Motor fishing boat 70 40

MALACCA

South-east Asia
100 cents = 1 dollar

1949

As No. 115 of Antigua
19† 15c Paddle-steamer 60 1.75

1957

45† 20c Malay fishing prau 25 50

1960

*As No. 45, but with tree and deer emblem instead of Queen
Elizabeth II*
56† 20c Malay fishing prau 20 5

COLLECT BIRDS ON STAMPS

Second revised edition of this Stanley Gibbons thematic
catalogue – now available at £8.50 (p. + p. £2) from:
Stanley Gibbons Publications Ltd, 5 Parkside, Christchurch Road, Ringwood, Hants BH24 3SH.

MALAGASY REPUBLIC

Indian Ocean off East Africa
100 centimes = 1 franc

1962

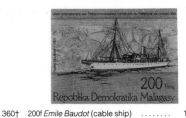

42† 50f Pirogue 45 25

51† 15f *Gasikara* (tanker) 25 15

1965

105† 12f Pirogue 20 15
109† 65f *Porthos* (hydrofoil) 75 35

1971

205† 5f Outrigger canoe 10 10

1974

272† 300f Scout canoe 2.50 1.50

1975

305 40f *Randolph* (American frigate), 1777
306 50f *Lexington* (American brigantine) and
     H.M.S. *Edward* (sloop), 1776
307 100f *Languedoc* (French ship of the line),
     1778 (air)
308 200f *Bonhomme Richard* (American
     frigate) and H.M.S. *Serapis* (frigate),
     1779
309 300f *Millern* (sail merchantman) and
     Montgomery (American brig)
     Set of 5 4.50 2.75
MS310 500f *Hannah* (American schooner),
     1775 .... 3.75 4.00

336 8f Sailing pirogue
337 45f Malagasy schooner
     Set of 2 45 35

1976

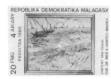

360† 200f *Emile Baudot* (cable ship) 1.50 1.00

     Nos. 305/10 overprinted **4 JUILLET 1776—1976**
371 40f *Randolph*
372 50f *Lexington* and H.M.S. *Edward*
373 100f *Languedoc* (air)
374 200f *Bonhomme Richard* and H.M.S.
     Serapis
375 30f *Millern* and *Montgomery*
     Set of 5 4.00 2.75
MS376 500f *Hannah* 3.50 4.00

1985

554† 20f Fishing boats, Saintes-Maries 10 5

1987

617 60f *Sarimanok* (early dhow)
618 150f *Sarimanok* (early dhow)
     Set of 2 20 15

642† 60f Fleet of Dias, 1492 .... 8 5
643† 150f Portuguese galleon 15 10
647† 450f *Nina* (Columbus) 45 35

659† 10f Ship's boat 5 5

MALAWI

Central Africa
1964 12 pence = 1 shilling
20 shillings = 1 pound
1970 100 tambalas = 1 kwacha

1964

219† 4d Fishing pirogue 25 15

1967

277 4d *Ilala I* (lake steamer), 1875
278 9d *Dove* (lake paddle-steamer), 1892
279 1s *Chauncy Maples I* (lake steamer), 1901
280 3s *Gwendolen* (lake steamer), 1899
                                    Set of 4   2.00   1.60

1975

486 3t *Mpasa* (lake vessel)
487 8t *Ilala II* (lake vessel), 1949
488 15t *Chauncy Maples II* (lake vessel)
489 30t *Nkwazi* (lake vessel)
                                    Set of 4   1.25   1.00

1977

549† 20t *Ilala II* (lake vessel), 1949   80   30

1983

682† 1k Pirogue 1.10   1.25

1985

727 1k Trawler   95   1.25

728 7t *Ufulu* (lake tanker)
729 15t *Chauncy Maples II* (lake vessel)
730 20t *Mtendere* (lake vessel)
731 1k *Ilala II* (lake vessel)
                                    Set of 4   2.25   2.00

MALAYAN FEDERATION

South-east Asia
100 cents = 1 dollar

1957

3† 25c Tin dredger   40   5

MALAYSIA

South-east Asia
100 cents = 1 dollar

1974

127† 50c Tin dredger 1.50   1.75

1983

254† 20c *Tenaga Satu* (liquid gas tanker)   35   20

268† 20c Missile boat   20   20

1985

325† 15c Oil rig   10   10

1987

381 40c *Misc* (container ship)   20   25

MALDIVE ISLANDS

Indian Ocean
100 larees = 1 rupee

1950

21 2la Dhow
22 3la Dhow
23 5la Dhow
24 6la Dhow
25 10la Dhow
26 15la Dhow
27 25la Dhow
28 50la Dhow
29 1r Dhow
                                    Set of 9   13.00   13.00

1968

268 50la Punt
269 1r Ancient Greek galley

270 2r Yacht, Argenteuil
271 5r Fishing boats, Les Saintes-Maries
                                    Set of 4   3.25   3.25

298† 10la Local fishing dhow   25   5

1971

368† 1r Inflatable dinghy   40   40

1973

439† 2la Scout rowing boat   5   5
443† 1r Scout rowing boat 1.25   55

1974

477† 3la *Nomad* (weather ship)   5   5
481† 3r *Nomad* 2.25   1.50

508† 2la Paddle-steamer and modern mail ship   5   5
511† 2r50 Paddle-steamer and modern mail ship 1.60   1.60

537† 3la H.M.S. *Conqueror* (battleship)   5   5
538† 4la H.M.S. *Indomitable* (aircraft carrier)   5   5
MS543† 10r H.M.S. *Indomitable* (aircraft carrier) 8.00   8.50

1975

579† 7la Motor cruisers, Mahe   5   5

No. 443 overprinted **14th Boy Scout Jamboree July 29— August 7, 1975**
582† 1r Scout rowing boat   30   30

586   1la Madura prau
587   2la Ganges patela
588   3la Indian palla
589   4la Odhi (dhow)
590   5la Maldivian schooner
591   25la *Cutty Sark* (tea clipper)
592   1r Maldivian bagala
593   5r *Maldive Courage* (freighter)

Set of 8   4.75   4.50
MS594   10r Madura prau 6.00   7.00

619†   5la Tourist launch and outboard motor
            boats   5   5
620†   7la Yachts   5   5
623†   10r Motor cruisers 4.00   4.00

1976

647†   1r *Salernum* (cable ship)   70   55

1977

MS720†   7.50r German "Helgoland" class
            battleship, 1914 ....   5.00   6.00

721†   6la Boat building   10   5

1978

746   1la Mas odi (fishing boat)
747   2la Battela (dhow)
748   3la Bandu odi (fishing boat)
749   5la *Maldive Trader* (freighter)
750   1r *Fath-hul Baaree* (brigantine)
751   1r25 Mas dhoni (dhow)
752   3r Baggala (dhow)
753   4r Baggala (dhow)

Set of 8   3.50   2.10
MS754   1r Battela (dhow), 4r Mas dhoni (dhow)   2.25   2.50

764†   3la H.M.S. *Endeavour* (Cook)   5   5
766†   75la H.M.S. *Resolution* and H.M.S.
            Discovery (Cook)   85   85
MS769†   5r H.M.S. *Endeavour* 7.00   7.50

785†   1la Fishing boat   5   5
791†   1r25 Dhow at night   50   35
MS794†   3r Fishing boats 1.25   1.50

1981

950†   5la Fishing boat   5   5
951†   15la Fishing boats   10   10

1983

1011†   2r Motor fishing boat   40   45

1025†   6r Fishing dhows 1.50   1.50

1984

1047†   15la Dhow   5   5
1049†   2r Sailboard   35   40
1051†   6r Fishing launch 1.00   1.25
1052†   8r Game fishing launch 1.40   1.50

1985

1091†   2r Coastguard cutter   55   45

1108   3la Mas odi (fishing boat)
1109   5la Battela (dhow)
1110   10la Addu odi (dhow)
1111   2r60 Modern dhoni (fishing boat)
1112   2r70 Mas dhoni (fishing boat)
1113   3r Batheli dhoni (fishing boat)
1114   5r *Inter I* (inter-island ferry)
1115   10r Dhoni-style yacht

Set of 8   2.25   2.50

1116†   6r Sailboards 1.10   1.25

1986

1213†   2r Boat building   40   45
MS1216†   15r Diving bell 2.75   3.25

1987

1245   15la *Intrepid* (yacht), 1970
1246   1r *France II* (yacht), 1974
1247   2r *Gretel* (yacht), 1962
1248   12r *Volunteer* (yacht), 1887

Set of 4   2.40   2.75

MALI

West Africa
100 centimes = 1 franc

1966

125†   3f Fishing pirogue   8   5
127†   20f Fishing pirogue   20   10
128†   25f Fishing pirogue   25   12
130†   85f Fishing pirogue   70   35

1970

262†   10f Scout canoes   60   25

1971

271†   200f America's Cup yacht   95   50

288 100f *Santa Maria* (Columbus), 1492
289 150f *Mayflower* (Pilgrim Fathers), 1620
290 200f *Potemkin* (Russian battleship), 1905
291 250f *Normandie* (French liner), 1935
Set of 4   3.00   2.25

1972

312† 130f Gondolas, Venice 50   35
313† 270f Gondolas, Venice 90   60

1974

439† 80f Full-rigged sailing ship and modern
liner 55   25

No. 439 surcharged **9 OCTOBRE 1974 250F**
463† 250f on 80f Full-rigged sailing ship and
modern liner 1.25
1.00

1975

503† 370f Battle of the Chesapeake, 1781 .... 1.25   80

1976

535† 400f 18th-century warships 2.25   1.00

554 200f Freighter 65   45

563 160f Muscat fishing boat
564 180f Cochin-China junk
565 190f *Ruytingen* (Dunkirk lightship)
566 200f Nile felucca
Set of 4   2.50   1.40

1978

622† 300f Captain Cook's ship 90   60

1979

723 300f H.M.S. *Resolution* (Cook), Kerguelen,
1776
724 480f H.M.S. *Resolution* (Cook), Hawaii,
1778
Set of 2   2.25   1.75

1980

752† 300f Racing yachts 85   50

782† 420f French fleet, Rhode Island, 1780 .. 1.25   75

No. 752 overprinted **FINN RECHARDT (Fin.) MAYRHOFER
(Autr.) BALACHOV (Urss)**
792† 300f Racing yacht 75   55

808† 120f Freighter 1.40   45

1981

862 180f Fleet of Columbus, 1492 (also on
U.S.A. stamp No. 238)
863 200f *Nina* (also *Santa Maria* on Spain
stamp No. 593)
864 260f *Pinta* (also *Santa Maria* on Spain
stamp No. 597)
865 30f *Santa Maria* (also on U.S.A. stamp
No. 237)
Set of 4   2.00   1.75

1982

947 200f Sailboard
948 270f Sailboard
949 300f Sailboard
Set of 3   1.75   1.50

1983

956† 300f Sailboards 70   50

968† 700f Container ship 3.00   2.25

981 240f Liner 65   45

1984

MS1003† 700f Olympic yacht 1.90   2.25

No. 981 surcharged **120F**
1006† 120f on 240f Liner 60   50

No. **MS1003** *surcharged* **350F VOILE 470 1. ESPAGNE 2.
ETATS-UNIS 3. FRANCE**
MS1050† 350f on 700f Olympic yacht 1.00   1.25

MALTA

Mediterranean
1899 12 pence = 1 shilling
20 shillings = 1 pound
1972 10 mils = 1 cent
100 cents = 1 pound

1899

57†	4½d Gozo fishing boat (brown)	17.00	8.00
58†	4½d Gozo fishing boat (orange)	3.50	3.75
59†	5d Galley of Knights of St. John (red)	15.00	4.50
60†	5d Galley of Knights of St. John (green)	3.50	5.00

1926

166†	1s Local felucca	3.00	2.50
169†	2s6d Gozo fishing boat	13.00	18.00

1928
Nos. 166 *and* 169 *overprinted* **POSTAGE AND REVENUE**

186†	1s Local felucca	2.50	2.50
189†	2s6d Gozo fishing boat	13.00	23.00

1930
As Nos. 166 *and* 169, *but inscribed* **"POSTAGE AND REVENUE"**

203†	1s Local felucca	5.00	7.50
206†	2s6d Gozo fishing boat	15.00	27.00

1949
As No. 115 *of Antigua*

252†	3d Paddle-steamer	1.00	45

1958

290†	3d German E-boats (motor torpedo-boats), 1941	10	5

1965

337†	4½d Galleys of Knights of St. John	30	20

354†	6d Turkish fleet, 1565	50	5

1973

489†	8m Freighter at wharf	5	5
490†	1c Fishing boats	10	5
494†	4c Yachts	15	10
496†	7c5m Luzzu regatta	30	10
500b†	£2 Luzzu	14.00	16.00

1974

528†	5c *Washington* (paddle-steamer) and *Royal Viking Star* (liner)	25	10

1976

560†	5c Olympic yachts	30	15

1977

585†	20c Canal barge	45	65

1979

619†	2c Maltese luzzu and aircraft carrier	5	5
622†	8c Maltese luzzu and aircraft carrier	45	50

625†	7c Speronara (fishing boat)	20	15

1981

669†	2c Building a galleon	5	8
672†	6c Trawler	20	25
676†	12c Modern shipyard	30	40
681†	£1 *Dwejra* (freighter) and container ship	3.00	3.25

1982

688†	13c *Chenna Selvan* (tanker under construction)	55	55

701	3c *Ta' Salvo Serafino* (oared brigantine), 1531		
702	8c *La Madonna del Rosaria* (tartane), 1740		
703	12c *San Paola* (xebec), 1743		
704	20c *Ta' Pietro Saliba* (xprunara), 1798		
	Set of 4	1.75	1.60

1983

725	2c *Strangier* (full-rigged sailing ship), 1813		
726	12c *Tigre* (topsail schooner), 1839		
727	13c *La Speranza* (brig), 1844		
728	20c *Wignacourt* (barque), 1844		
	Set of 4	1.75	1.60

1985

772	3c *Scotia* (paddle-steamer), 1844		
773	7c *Tagliaferro* (screw steamer), 1882		
774	15c *Gleneagles* (screw steamer), 1885		
775	23c *L'Isle Adam* (screw steamer), 1886		
	Set of 4	2.40	2.40

1986

792	7c *San Paul* (freighter), 1921		
793	10c *Knight of Malta* (cargo liner), 1930		
794	12c *Valetta City* (freighter), 1948		
795	20c *Saver* (freighter), 1959		
	Set of 4	2.50	2.50

1987

809	2c *Medina* (freighter), 1969		
810	11c *Rabat* (container ship), 1974		
811	13c *Ghawdex* (passenger ferry), 1979		
812	20c *Pinto* (car ferry), 1987		
	Set of 4	1.50	1.60

1988

827†	10c Harbour ferry	35	40

MANAMA

Arabian peninsula
100 dirhams = 1 riyal

1967

Nos. 140 and 148 of Ajman overprinted **MANAMA** *in English and Arabic*

5†	15d *Yankee* (sail training and cruise ship)		10	5
13†	10r *Brasil* (liner)		6.50	6.50

Appendix

The following stamps have either been issued in excess of postal needs, or have not been made available to the public in reasonable quantities at face value. Miniature sheets, imperforate stamps etc. are excluded from this section.

1966

New currency surcharges. No. 35 of Ajman surcharged **Manama 3 Riyals** *in English and Arabic. 3r on 3r Sailing yacht.*

1971

18th and 19th-century Ships Paintings. Postage 15, 20, 25, 30, 50d; Air 60d, 1, 2r.

MARIANA ISLANDS

Pacific Ocean
100 pfennig = 1 mark

1901

As Nos. K7/19 of Cameroun, but inscribed "MARIANEN"

13	3pf *Hohenzollern* (German Imperial yacht)	
14	5pf *Hohenzollern*	
15	10pf *Hohenzollern*	
16	20pf *Hohenzollern*	
17	25pf *Hohenzollern*	
18	30pf *Hohenzollern*	
19	40pf *Hohenzollern*	
20	50pf *Hohenzollern*	
21	80pf *Hohenzollern*	
22	1m *Hohenzollern*	
23	2m *Hohenzollern*	
24	3m *Hohenzollern*	
25	5m *Hohenzollern*	
	Set of 13 £100 £600	

MARSHALL ISLANDS

North Pacific
100 cents = 1 dollar

1901

As Nos. K7/19 of Cameroun, but inscribed "MARSHALL INSELN"

G11	3pf *Hohenzollern* (German Imperial yacht)	
G12	5pf *Hohenzollern*	
G13	10pf *Hohenzollern*	
G14	20pf *Hohenzollern*	
G15	25pf *Hohenzollern*	
G16	30pf *Hohenzollern*	
G17	40pf *Hohenzollern*	
G18	50pf *Hohenzollern*	
G19	80pf *Hohenzollern*	
G20	1m *Hohenzollern*	
G21	2m *Hohenzollern*	
G22	3m *Hohenzollern*	
G23	5m *Hohenzollern*	
	Set of 13 £100 £650	

1984

22†	40c *Hohenzollern* (on stamp No. G11)		50	25
24†	40c *Hohenzollern* (on stamp No. G23)		50	25

33	20c Sailing canoe			
34	20c Container ship			
35	20c Aircraft carrier			
36	20c Freighter			
	Set of 4		1.25	75

1985

58	14c *Morning Star I* (missionary brigantine), 1856			
59	22c Launch of *Morning Star I*			
60	33c *Morning Star I* leaving Honolulu			
61	44c *Morning Star 1* entering Ebon lagoon			
	Set of 4		1.60	95

66†	22c Satellite communications ship		40	15

1986

80†	22c Outrigger canoe		40	20
81†	22c Amphibious dukw		40	20
82†	22c LST 1108 (tank landing ship)		40	20
MS84†	44c U.S.S. *Saratoga* (aircraft carrier) ..		70	80

1987

107	22c *James Arnold* (whaling ship), 1854			
108	22c *General Scott* (whaling ship), 1859			
109	22c *Charles W. Morgan* (whaling ship), 1865			
110	22c *Lucretia* (whaling ship), 1884			
	Set of 4		1.40	75

118†	44c *Itasca* (U.S. coastguard cutter), 1937		50	25
120†	44c *Koshu* (Japenese patrol boat), 1937		50	25

MARTINIQUE

West Indies
100 centimes = 1 franc

1931

As No. 109 of Cameroun

133†	1f50 Liner		1.00	1.00

1937

As Nos. 110/11 of Cameroun

180†	20c Liner		40	40
181†	30c Sailing ships		45	45
MS185a†	3f Liner		90	90

1947

234†	60c Local fishing boats		15	10
235†	1f Local fishing boats		15	10
236†	1f50 Local fishing boats		20	15

MAURITANIA

West Africa
1931 100 centimes = 1 franc
1973 5 khoum = 1 ouguiya (um)

1931

As No. 109 of Cameroun

70†	1f50 Liner		1.25	1.25

1937

As Nos. 110/11 of Cameroun

71†	20c Liner		35	35
72†	30c Sailing ships		35	35

1960

139†	15f Fishing boat		20	10

1963

164†	200f Bulk carrier, Port-Etienne		2.75	1.75

1965

223†	10f Freighters and lighters, Nouakchott		10	5

1969

348†	15f Fishing boats, Nouadhibou		15	10

1972

398	45f 18th-century sailing ships, Venice			
399	100f Gondolas, Venice			
400	250f Gondolas, Venice			
	Set of 3		2.75	1.50

416	35f Freighter		25	20

1975

478 60u Canoe, River Ogowe 2.25 1.50

1979

614 12u *Sirius* (paddle-steamer)
615 14u *Great Republic* (paddle-steamer)
616 55u *Mauretania* (liner)
617 60u *Stirling Castle* (liner)
Set of 4 3.50 2.25

1981

708† 81um Battle of the Chesapeake, 1781 . . 1.50 1.50

709 19um *Pinta* (Columbus)
710 55um *Santa Maria* (Columbus)
Set of 2 1.40 1.40

1982

720† 19um Scout rowing boat 90 80
721† 22um Scout rowing boat 1.00 85
722† 92um Scout yacht 2.50 2.50

1984

790† 18um Building fishing boat 70 50

810 14um Sail boards
811 18um "Finn" class yachts
812 19um "470" class yachts
813 44um "Soling" class yacht
Set of 4 2.75 2.25
MS814 100um "Flying Dutchman" class yachts 2.75 3.00

1987

859† 2um *Santa Maria* (Columbus) 10 10
860† 22um *Nina* (Columbus) 55 35
861† 35um *Pinta* (Columbus) 75 65

MAURITIUS

Indian Ocean
100 cents = 1 rupee

1949

As No. 115 of Antigua
273† 20c Paddle-steamer 70 45

1950

277† 2c Local rowing boat 15 10

1953

As No. 277, but with portrait of Queen Elizabeth II
293† 2c Local rowing boat 5 5

1970

423† 2r50 *Heros* (settlers' ship), 1783 . . . . 70 90

1971

429† 60c Sailing dinghies 30 5

1972

459† 15c Pirate dhow 25 5
461† 1r *L'Hirondelle* (pirate brig) 65 15
462† 2r50 18th-century British frigate 3.00 4.75

1974

470 60c Capture of the *Kent*, 1800 . . . . 40 30

1976

501 10c *Pierre Loti* (packet steamer), 1953
502 15c *Secunder* (mail ship), 1907
503 50c *Hindoostan* (paddle-steamer), 1842
504 60c *St. Geran* (French sailing packet),
1740
505 2r50 *Maen* (Dutch merchantman), 1638
Set of 5 2.75 3.50

1978

538† 90c Battle of Grand Port, 1810 . . . . 8 10

1980

592 25c *Emirne* (French steam packet)
593 1r *Boissevain* (cargo liner)
594 2r *La Boudeuse* (18th-century French
frigate)
595 5r *Sea Breeze* (English clipper)
Set of 4 1.10 90

1982

642† 10r H.M.S. *Beagle* (Darwin) 1.40 1.75

1983

656† 10r Freighters, Port Louis 1.10 1.40

666† 1r Fishing boat 15 12

1984

682 25r Wreck of *Tayeb* (freighter)
683 1r *Taher* (freighter)
684 5r *Triton* (East Indiaman)
685 10r *Astor* (modern liner)

			Set of 4	2.25	2.50

694† 10r Indian immigrant ship, 1834 .... 1.25 1.75

1985

707† 10r Sailboards 1.25 1.50

715† 10r Sailing canoe, Coin de Mire Island 1.10 1.25

1987

768† 1r50 Racing yachts 25 20
770† 5r *Svanen* (cadet barquentine) 65 70

MEMEL

LITHUANIAN OCCUPATION

Eastern Europe
1920 100 pfennig = 1 mark
1923 100 centi = 1 litas

1923

28† 40m Liner, Memel 2.00 5.50
29† 50m Liner, Memel 2.00 5.50
30† 80m Liner, Memel 2.00 5.50
31† 100m Liner, Memel 2.00 5.50

Nos. 28/31 surcharged with new value

70† 15c on 40m Liner, Memel 2.75 6.50
71† 30c on 50m Liner, Memel 2.25 5.00
72† 30c on 80m Liner, Memel 2.75 6.50
73† 30c on 100m Liner, Memel 2.25 5.00

Nos. 29 and 31 surcharged with new value and bars

87† 15c on 50m Liner, Memel 75.00 £250
88† 25c on 100m Liner, Memel 50.00 £150

MEXICO

Central America
100 centavos = 1 peso

1940

662† 20c 17th-century pirate galleon 1.25 35

1950

1012a† 5p 17th-century galleon 3.50 25

1964

1086† 80c 16th-century Spanish galleon 2.25 25

1968

1165† 80c Olympic yachts 30 10

1972

1253 40c *Zaragoza* (cadet sail corvette) 15 5

1975

1331 80c *Acali* (trans-Atlantic balsa raft) 15 5

1977

1416 1p60 *Rio Yaqui* (freighter) 15 5

1978

1428† 4p30 Oil rig 20 5

1979

MS1535 10p 16th-century Spanish galleon 85 85

1983

1669 16p *Nauticas Mexico* (container ship) .. 40 15

1987

1851 150p *Santa Maria* (Columbus) 8 5

1853† 150p Fishing canoes, Michoacan 8 5

MICRONESIA

Pacific Ocean
100 cents = 1 dollar

1984

14a† 22c *Senyavin* (full-rigged sailing ship) .. 30 15
19† $2 Outrigger canoes, Kosrae 2.50 1.25

25†	28c *Hohenzollern* (on Caroline Islands stamp No. 13)	35	15
27†	28c *Hohenzollern* (on Careoline Islands stamp No. 25)	55	25

1985

32	22c U.S.S. *Jamestown* (sail warship), 1870		
33	33c *L'Astrolabe* (D'Urville), 1826 (air)		
34	39c *La Coquille* (Duperrey), 1822		
35	44c *Shenandoah* (Confederate warship), 1865		
	Set of 4	2.00	1.10

1986

54†	44c *Trienza* (cargo liner), 1946	65	35

MIDDLE CONGO

Central Africa
100 centimes = 1 franc

1931
As No. 109 *of Cameroun*

68†	1f50 Liner	1.00	80

MONACO

Southern Europe
100 centimes = 1 franc

1924

102†	2f 18th-century sailing ships, Monaco	70	60
103†	3f 18th-century sailing ships, Monaco	10.00	6.50
104†	5f 18th-century sailing ships, Monaco	5.00	3.25
105†	10f 18th-century sailing ships, Monaco	11.00	10.00

1926
No. 102 *surcharged* **1f50**

112†	1f50 on 2f 18th-century sailing ships, Monaco	2.00	2.00

1933
No. 104 *surcharged* **1F50** *and airplane*

143	1f50 on 5f 18th-century sailing ships, Monaco	22.00	15.00

1939

182†	70c *Hussar* (steam yacht)	25	15
183†	75c *Hussar* (green)	25	15
189†	3f *Hussar* (red)	30	15

1940
As Nos. 183 *and* 189, *with colours changed, and surcharged with Red Cross and* +1f

221†	75c + 1f *Hussar* (black)	1.90	1.90
225†	3f + 1f *Hussar* (blue)	7.50	7.50

1941
As 1939 *issue, but new values*

258†	1f20 *Hussar*	15	15
260†	2f *Hussar*	10	10
394†	10f *Hussar*	60	10
268†	15f *Hussar*	20	15
270†	25f *Hussar* (green)	90	60
374†	25f *Hussar* (black)	17.00	7.50

1944

301†	20f + 60f 4th-century fishing boat	2.75	3.25

1948

351†	15f + 25f Yachts	15.00	15.00

1949

375†	2f *Hirondelle I* (Prince Albert I's schooner), 1870	15	15
378†	5f *Princess Alice* (Prince Albert's steam yacht), 1906	30	25
380†	10f *Hirondelle II* (Prince Albert's steam yacht), 1914	65	55
381†	12f Whaleboat	95	75

1953

465†	3f Olympic yachts	25	20

475	2f *Princess Alice* (Prince Albert's steam yacht)		
476	5f *Princess Alice*		
477	15f *Princess Alice*		
	Set of 3	1.50	1.10

1955

530†	2f Paddle-steamer	10	10
534†	8f Fishing boats, River Orinocco	35	35
538†	30f U.S.S. *Nautilus* (submarine)	3.50	3.25

1956

549†	30f Fleet of Columbus, 1492	1.10	90
552†	100f Paddle-steamer, River Mississippi	1.40	1.40

1960

691†	50c *Hirondelle I* (schooner) and *Princess Alice* (steam yacht)	1.40	1.00

1962

741†	10c Galeazzi's diving turret	10	10
742†	25c *Trieste* (bathyscape)	10	10
745†	85c *Nautilus* (submarine), 1800	50	50
746†	1f Beebe's bathysphere	70	70

1965

828†	95c *Great Eastern* and *Alsace* (cable ships)	40	40

1966

861	1f *Hirondelle I* (schooner) and *Princess Alice* (steam yacht)	50	45

865	1f *Precontinent III* (underwater research craft)	30	30

1972

1028   1f Battle of Lepanto, 1571   60   40

1037   90c Tanker   50   30

1043†   30c Gondolas, Venice   25   20
1044†   60c Gondolas, Venice   35   25

1974

1116   40c Destroyer   20   10

1977

1285†   10c *Hirondelle I* (Prince Albert I's
  schooner)   10   10
1288†   80c Ship's boat   35   20
1290†   1f25 Ship's boat   60   40
1291†   1f40 Ship's boat   90   60
1293†   2f50 Ship's boat 1.60   1.40

1298   2f Yachts, Deauville 1.25   1.10

1305   10c *Princess Alice* (Prince Albert's steam
  yacht)   10   10
1307†   30c *Princess Alice*   20   15
1312†   1f90 Ship's steam launch in ice 1.25   85
1313†   3f *Princess Alice* 1.75   1.25

1978

1343†   80c *Ramoge* (research vessel)   35   30

1979

1396†   1f50 18th-century felucca   55   40

1981

1495   2f50 Hydrographic research ship   80   60

1530   1f50 17th-century ship in Arctic ice   65   35

1982

1599   1f60 Viking longships, Greenland, 982 ..   45   35

1600   1f80 Roman war galley   50   40

1983

1643   5f Oil rig 1.00   80

COLLECT RAILWAYS ON STAMPS

A Stanley Gibbons thematic catalogue on this popular subject. Copies available at £7.50 (p. + p. £2) from: Stanley Gibbons Publications Ltd, 5 Parkside, Christchurch Road, Ringwood, Hants BH24 3SH.

1984

1659†   4f Bathyscaphe (Piccard)   80   65

1665†   30c Barge and rowing boat   5   5
1667†   50c Sailing ships in harbour   10   5
1671†   90c Paddle-steamer   15   15
1673†   2f Fishing boats   35   15

1692†   2f Medieval ship   40   30

1738   2f10 *Hirondelle* (schooner) and *Denise*
  (midget submarine)   45   30

MS1749   4f Catamaran; 4f Single-hull yacht; 4f
  Trimaran 3.00   3.00

1985

1763†   4f Yacht and fishing boats, 1912   80   80

1986

1778†   2f20 *Ramoge* (research vessel)   55   35

1987

1824† 5f Sailing dinghies and sailboard 1.00 75

POSTAGE DUE STAMPS

1953

D480† 2f Brig 10 10
D481† 2f *United States* (liner) 10 10

1960

D698† 1c 18th-century felucca 45 45
D699† 2c *La Palmaria* (paddle-steamer) 15 15
D703† 30c *Charles III* (paddle-steamer), 1866 35 35

MONGOLIA

Central Asia
100 mung = 1 tugrik

1965

356† 5m Marine exploration ship and
bathysphere 20 5
362† 20m Antarctic research vessel 2.25 45

1971

622† 1t *Sukhe Bator* (lake steamer) 1.75 70

1973

755† 30m Medieval kogge (on Russia stamp
No. 3194) 45 15

1974

820† 50m *Sukhe Bator* (lake steamer) 1.75 40

1975

Тээвэр—50
1975—7—15.

No. 622 overprinted
924† 1t *Sukhe Bator* 3.25 3.25

1976

999† 30m Steamer, Lake Khobsogol 40 15

1977

1066† 30m *Gagarin* (Russian satellite-tracking
ship) 40 15

1088† 50m *Aurora* (Russian cruiser) 45 15

1978

1147 1t Liner 65 20

1979

1214† 1t *Hindostan* (paddle-steamer) 1.50 1.00

COLLECT MAMMALS ON STAMPS
A Stanley Gibbons thematic catalogue on this popular
subject. Copies available at £7.50 (p. + p. £2) from:
Stanley Gibbons Publications Ltd, 5 Parkside, Christchurch Road, Ringwood, Hants BH24 3SH.

1980

1317† 40m Bathysphere (Cousteau) 65 25

1981

1367 10m 15th-century B.C. Pharonic ship
1368 20m 9th-century Mediterranean sailing
ship
1369 40m 12th-century Hanse kogge
1370 50m 13th-century Venetian felucca
1371 60m *Santa Maria* (Columbus)
1372 80m H.M.S. *Endeavour* (Cook)
1373 1t *Poltava* (18th-century Russian
warship)
1374 1t20 19th-century American schooner
Set of 8 5.50 2.00

1394† 50m *Malygin* (Russian ice-breaker) (on
Russia stamp No. 584) 50 25
1395† 60m *Malygin* (on Russia stamp No.
585) 75 30
1396† 80m *Malygin* (on Russia stamp No.
586) 85 40
1397† 1t20 *Malygin* (on Russia stamp No.
587) 1.25 55
MS1398† 4t *Malygin* (on Russia stamp No.
584) 4.00 4.00

1478† 20m Motor fishing boat 30 10

MONTENEGRO

ITALIAN OCCUPATION
100 para = 1 dinar

1941

Montenegro

Црна Гора

17-IV-41-XIX

AL .13926

Nos. 360 and 364 of Yugoslavia overprinted
15† 50p Yacht 2.50 4.50
19† 5d Yacht 20.00 30.00

MONTSERRAT

West Indies
1949 12 pence = 1 shilling
20 shillings = 1 pound
1951 100 cents = 1 dollar

1949

As No. 115 of Antigua
118† 3d Paddle-steamer 35 35

1967

190† 5c Sailing dinghies 5 5

1969

233† 25c Game fishing launch 35 15

1973

315† 60c Carrack (Columbus), 1493 .... 2.25 2.50

1975

346† 70c Carib canoe 30 50

1976

361† $1.10 *Antelope* (sailing packet), 1786 .. 1.00 1.00

391 15c *Esmeralda* (cadet ship)
392 40c *Raleigh* (American frigate), 1776
393 75c H.M.S. *Druid* (frigate), 1776
394 $1.25 *Gloria* (cadet ship)
Set of 4 2.75 1.50

1977

396† 30c Royal Yacht *Britannia* 20 25

405† 40c *Statesman* (freighter) 30 25
407† $1.50 *Statesman* unloading 1.10 1.00

414† 55c Local dinghies 25 15

1980

460† 40c *Marquess of Salisbury* (sailing
       packet), 1817 .... 20 20
462† $1.20 *La Plata* (liner), 1901 .... 45 55
463† $1.20 *Lady Hawkins* (packet steamer),
       1929 .... 45 55
464† $1.20 *Avon* (paddle-steamer), 1843 .... 45 55

482 40c *Lady Nelson* (packet steamer), 1928
483 55c *Chignecto* (packet steamer), 1913
484 $1 *Solent* (packet steamer), 1878
485 $2 *Dee* (packet paddle-steamer), 1841
Set of 4 1.60 1.60

1981

510† 90c Royal Yacht *Charlotte* 25 25
512† $3 Royal Yacht *Portsmouth* 75 75
514† $4 Royal Yacht *Britannia* 1.00 1.00

519† 50c H.M.S. *Dorsetshire* (cruiser), 1931 .. 30 30

1983

Nos. 512 and 514 surcharged
582† 70c on $3 Royal Yacht *Portsmouth* 60 70
584† $1.15 on $4 Royal Yacht *Britannia* 1.00 1.10

1984

615 55c *Tagus* (packet steamer), 1907
616 90c *Cobequid* (packet steamer), 1913
617 $1.15 *Lady Drake* (packet steamer), 1914
618 $2 *Factor* (packet steamer), 1948
Set of 4 2.75 3.00

1985

No. 514 surcharged **CARIBBEAN ROYAL VISIT 1985 $1.60**
655† $1.60 on $4 Royal Yacht *Britannia* 3.50 3.50

1986

696 90c *Antelope* (sailing packet), 1793
697 $1.15 *Montagu* (sailing packet), 1810
698 $1.50 *Little Catherine* (sailing packet),
       1813
699 $2.30 *Hinchingbrook* (sailing packet),
       1813
Set of 4 3.25 3.25

710† 70c Sailing dinghy and sailboards 40 40

OFFICIAL STAMPS

1983

Nos. 510, 512 and 514 surcharged **O.H.M.S.** *and value*
O53† 45c on 90c Royal Yacht *Charlotte* 25 30
O55† 75c on $3 Royal Yacht *Portsmouth* 35 35
O57† $1 on $4 Royal Yacht *Britannia* 50 50

MOROCCO

North-west Africa
1960 100 centimes = 1 franc
1962 100 francs = 1 dirham

1960

90† 45f Olympic yacht 75 35

1966

191 40f *Maroc* (liner) 40 15

MOROCCO AGENCIES

North-west Africa
12 pence = 1 shilling
20 shillings = 1 pound

1951

Nos. 509/10 *of Great Britain overprinted* **MOROCCO AGENCIES**

99 2s6d H.M.S. *Victory* (Nelson) 8.00 12.00
100 5s Yacht and Thames sailing barge, Dover 11.00 16.00

1951

Nos. 509/10 *of Great Britain overprinted* **TANGIER**

286† 2s6d H.M.S. *Victory* (Nelson) 2.00 2.00
287† 5s Yacht and Thames sailing barge, Dover 6.50 8.50

MOZAMBIQUE

South-east Africa
1960 100 centavos = 1 escudo
1980 100 centavos = 1 metical

1913

Nos. 1/2, 5 *and* 7 *of Portuguese Colonies surcharged* **REPUBLICA MOCAMBIQUE** *and value*

173† ¼c on 2½r Departure of Vasco da Gama's fleet 45 30
174† ½c on 5r Vasco da Gama's fleet at Calicut 40 30
177† 5c on 50r *Sao Gabriel* (flagship) 40 30
179† 10c on 100r *Sao Gabriel* 50 45

Nos. 104/5, 108 *and* 110 *of Macao surcharged* **REPUBLICA MOCAMBIQUE** *and value*

181† ¼c on ½a Departure of Vasco da Gama's fleet 60 50
182† ½c on 1a Vasco da Gama's fleet at Calicut 60 50
185† 5c on 8a *Sao Gabriel* (flagship) 1.50 1.25
187† 10c on 16a *Sao Gabriel* 60 50

Nos. 58/9, 62 *and* 64 *of Timor surcharged* **REPUBLICA MOCAMBIQUE** *and value*

189† ¼c on ½a Departure of Vasco da Gama's fleet 60 50
190† ½c on 1a Vasco da Gama's fleet at Calicut 60 50
193† 5c on 8a *Sao Gabriel* (flagship) 90 70
195† 10c on 16a *Sao Gabriel* 50 40

1952

468 1e50 Liner 50 20

1953

492 1e Liner (on stamp No. 468)
493 3e Liner (on stamp No. 468)
Set of 2 2.40 60

1960

513 5e 15th-century caravel 40 15

1962

537† 15e Speedboat 90 45

1963

549 10c Nef, 1430
550 20c Caravel, 1436
551 30c Caravel, 1460
552 50c *Sao Gabriel* (Da Gama), 1497
553 1e Don Manuel's nau, 1498
554 1e50 Galleon, 1530
555 2e *Flor de la Mar* (nau), 1511
556 2e50 *Redonda* (caravel), 1519
557 3e50 Nau, 1520
558 4e Portuguese Indies galley, 1521
559 4e50 *Sao Tereza* (galleon), 1639
560 5e *N. Senhora da Conceicao* (nau), 1716
561 6e *N. Senhora da Boun Sucesso* (warship), 1764
562 7e50 Bomb launch, 1788
563 8e *Lebre* (naval brigantine), 1793
564 10e *Andorinha* (corvette), 1799
565 12e50 *Maria Teresa* (naval schooner), 1820
566 15e *Vasco da Gama* (warship), 1841
567 20e *Don Fernando II e Gloria* (sail frigate), 1843
568 30e *Sagres* (cadet ship), 1924
Set of 20 18.00 4.00

1964

571† 15c State barge of Joao V, 1728 .... 5 5
572† 35c State barge of Jose I, 1753 .... 5 5
573† 1e Alfandega barge, 1768 .... 20 5
575† 2e50 *Pinto da Fonsesca* (state barge), 1780 .... 12 8
576† 5e State barge of Carlota Joaquina, 1790 .... 25 12
577† 9e State barge of Don Miguel, 1831 .... 45 30

1967

592 3e *Tete* (paddle-gunboat)
593 10e *Granada* (paddle-gunboat)
Set of 2 80 30

1969

600† 50c Nau, 1553 .... 10 5
601† 1e50 14th-century caravels 20 5

1972

617† 4e 16th-century Portuguese galley and dhow 1.25 30

619† 1e Rowing boats 5 5

1973

620 1e Racing yachts
621 1e50 Racing yachts
622 3e Racing yachts
Set of 3 50 25

1975

Nos. 537 *and* 620/2 *overprinted* **INDEPENDENCIA 25 JUN 75**

634† 1e Racing yachts 30 25
635† 1e50 Racing yachts 60 50
639† 3e Racing yachts 45 40
644† 15e Speedboat 25 20

1981

915 50c *Matchedge* (tanker)
916 1m50 *Macubi* (tug)
917 3m *Vega 7* (trawler)
918 5m *Linde* (freighter)
919 7m50 *Pemba* (freighter)
920 12m50 *Rovuma* (dredger)
Set of 6 1.40 1.00

1982

969 1m Caique (sailing boat)
970 2m Machua (sailing boat)
971 4m Calaua (piroque)
972 8m Chitatarro (raft)
973 12m Cangaia (outrigger canoe)
974 16m Chata (punt)
Set of 6 2.75 2.50

1983

996† 20m Olympic yachts 75 65

1011† 4m Red Cross inflatable dinghy 20 12

1017† 50c Fishing canoe 10 5

1026† 8m Mail canoe 40 25

MOZAMBIQUE COMPANY

South-east Africa
100 centavos = 1 escudo

1918

204†	2¼c Dhow, River Buzi	10	8
254†	1e40 Liner, Beira	60	30

1920

No. 204 surcharged in words

219†	1½c on 2¼c Dhow, River Buzi	50	50
221†	2c on 2¼c Dhow, River Buzi	50	50

1937

288†	10c Dhow	5	5
298†	85c *Sao Gabriel* (Vasco da Gama)	8	8
299†	1e Dugout canoe	8	8

1939

Nos. 298/9 overprinted **28–VII–1939 Visita Presidencial**

309†	85c *Sao Gabriel*	35	30
310†	1e Dugout canoe	65	30

MUSCAT AND OMAN

Arabia
64 baizas = 1 rupee

1969

106†	20b Tankers, Mina el Fahal	45	25

NABHA

Indian subcontinent
12 pies = 1 anna
16 annas -1 rupee

1938

No. 256 of India overprinted **NABHA STATE**

86†	6a *Strathnaver* (liner)	1.40	4.25

NAURU

Pacific
1924 12 pence = 1 shilling
20 shillings = 1 pound
1966 100 cents = 1 dollar

1924

26	½d *Century* (freighter)	
27	1d *Century* (freighter)	
28	1½d *Century* (freighter)	
29	2d *Century* (freighter)	
30b	2½d *Century* (freighter)	
31a	3d *Century* (freighter)	
32	4d *Century* (freighter)	
33	5d *Century* (freighter)	
34	6d *Century* (freighter)	
35	9d *Century* (freighter)	
36	1s *Century* (freighter)	
37	2s6d *Century* (freighter)	
38	5s *Century* (freighter)	
39	10s *Century* (freighter)	
	Set of 14 £160 £190	

1935

Nos. 28/30b and 36 overprinted **HIS MAJESTY'S JUBILEE.**
1910 – 1935

40	1½d *Century*	
41	2d *Century*	
42	2½d *Century*	
43	1s *Century*	
	Set of 4 8.00 11.50	

1954

50†	3½d *Trienza* (freighter) loading phosphate	1.50	20
52†	6d Outrigger canoe	70	20

1966

As No. 50, but face value in decimal currency and colour changed

68†	3c *Trienza*	30	12

1968

No. 68 overprinted **REPUBLIC OF NAURU**

82†	3c *Trienza*	12	10

1974

116†	7c *Eigamoiya* (bulk carrier)	1.50	1.25
120†	35c H.M.S. *Hunter* (frigate), 1798	7.00	4.50
121†	50c H.M.S. *Hunter*	4.00	2.00

1975

131†	15c Freighter and barges	65	65

133	20c Micronesian outrigger canoe	
134	20c Polynesian double hulled canoe	
135	20c Melanesian outrigger canoe	
136	20c Polynesian outrigger canoe	
	Set of 4 2.50 2.50	

1976

151†	10c *Enna G* (cargo liner)	30	20

1977

161†	7c *Anglia* (cable ship)	20	20
163†	20c *Anglia*	30	30

1979

204†	5c *Hohenzollern* (German Imperial yacht) (on Marshall Islands stamp No. G17)	15	15

1981

239†	20c Outrigger canoe	30	30
240†	32c Outboard motor boat	45	45
241†	40c Trawler	50	50

253†	20c *Enna G* (cargo liner)	35	35

1982

267†	5c *Fido* (freighter)	15	12
270†	60c *Eigamoiya* (bulk carrier)	75	70
MS271†	$1 *Eigamoiya, Rosie-D* and *Kolle-D* (bulk carriers)	1.00	1.25

1983

288†	15c *Trienza* (freighter), 1946	20	25

NAURU (continued)

1984

LLOYD'S LIST

NAURU 20c

295	20c *Ocean Queen* (cargo liner)		
296	25c *Enna-G* (cargo liner)		
297	30c *Baron Minto* (bulk carrier)		
298	40c Sinking of *Triadic* (cargo liner), 1940		
	Set of 4	1.40	1.40

NAURU 5c

305†	5c Modern trawler	5	8

1985

326†	50c Outrigger canoe	65	65

1988

358†	25c Bulk carrier loading phosphate	20	25

362†	30c *Hohenzollern* (German Imperial yacht) (on Marshall Islands stamp No. G23)	25	30

NEGRI SEMBILAN

South-east Asia
100 cents = 1 dollar

1949

As No. 115 *of Antigua*

64†	15c Paddle-steamer	55	70

1957

75†	20c Malay fishing prau	20	5

COLLECT BIRDS ON STAMPS

Second revised edition of this Stanley Gibbons thematic catalogue – now available at £8.50 (p. + p. £2) from: Stanley Gibbons Publications Ltd, 5 Parkside, Christchurch Road, Ringwood, Hants BH24 3SH.

NEPAL

Central Asia
100 paisa = 1 rupee

1970

251†	25p Canoe, Lake Phewa Tal	30	30

NETHERLANDS

North-west Europe
100 cents = 1 gulden

1907

211	½c 17th-century naval battle		
212	1c 17th-century naval battle		
213	2½c 17th-century naval battle		
	Set of 3	8.00	3.50

1928

366†	5c + 1c Olympic yacht	1.40	60

1931

395b†	80c Liner and shipyard	75.00	2.50

1933

414†	5c + 3c *Hope* (hospital ship)	10.00	1.75
415†	6c + 4c Lifeboat	14.00	1.50

1934

441†	12½c Dutch warship, 1634	20.00	2.50

1944

596†	2½c *Nieuw Amsterdam* (liner)	8	8
598†	5c *De Ruyter* (cruiser)	8	8

1950

717†	10c + 5c Tugs towing bridge sections	3.50	15
718†	20c + 5c *Overijssel* (canal freighter)	12.00	10.00

1953

794†	10c + 5c Dutch tjalk	5	5

1956

831†	2c + 3c Olympic yacht	25	25

1957

843	4c + 3c *Gaasterland* (freighter)		
844	6c + 4c Coaster		
845	7c + 5c *Willem Barendsz* (freighter)		
846	10c + 8c *Curacao* (trawler)		
847	30c + 8c *Nieuw Amsterdam* (liner)		
	Set of 5	8.50	6.50

849†	30c *De Zeven Provincien* (De Ruyter)	3.75	1.75

851†	6c + 4c *J. Henry Dunant* (hospital ship)	65	45

1959

877†	4c + 4c Tugs	85	85
878†	6c + 4c Dredger	75	75

1962

924†	12c + 8c Figurehead	1.25	25

938†   10c Dredger   8   5

1973

1167   25c + 15c *De Zeven Provincien* (De Ruyter)
1168   30c + 10c *W.A. Scholten* (early steamship)
1169   35c + 15c *Veendam* (liner)
1170   50c + 20c Fishing boat

Set of 4   5.00   2.75

1974

1195†   40c Lifeboat   20   8

1975

1214   35c *Stad Middleburg* (schooner)   20   5

1976

1252†   40c Dutch tjalk   25   8

1977

1271†   55c + 20c Remains of Zammerdam Roman ship   30   20

1979

1316†   75c Liner   40   30

1980

1343   80c Motorised canal barge   40   10

NETHERLANDS ANTILLES

West Indies
100 cents = 1 gulden

1949

306†   6c Spanish galleon, 1499 ....   3.50   1.75
308†   15c Spanish galleon, 1499 ....   3.75   2.00

1952

339†   15c + 10c Tanker 7.00   3.50
340†   25c + 15c Liner 7.00   2.50

1961

428   20c *Andrew Doria* (American naval brig), 1776   70   60

1965

462†   20c *Asperalla* (tanker)   25   15

1967

486   6c *Gelderland* (cruiser)
487   10c *Pioneer* (schooner)
488   20c *Oscilla* (tanker)
489   25c *Santa Rosa* (liner)

Set of 4   55   50

1976

626†   40c *Andrew Doria* (American naval brig), 1776   60   35

1978

661†   20c + 10c Yacht   15   15

1983

769   70c Pilot gig, 1882
770   85c Pilot boat and modern liner
771   1g Pilot boat

Set of 3   2.10   2.10

803†   85c + 40c Sailboard 1.25   1.25

805†   45c Motor boat   70   50

807   1g Liner 1.10   95

809†   45c *Curacao* (paddle-steamer)   70   60

1984

862   1g Liner 1.40   1.10

1987

933†   85c Liner   65   65

NETHERLANDS INDIES

South-east Asia
100 cents = 1 gulden

1931

325†   5c + 2½c Fishing prau 3.00   2.50

NETHERLANDS NEW GUINEA

South-east Asia
100 cents = 1 gulden

1957

51†	5c + 5c Outrigger canoe	90	85
53†	25c + 10c Outrigger canoe	90	85

NEVIS

West Indies
100 cents = 1 dollar

1980

No. 399 of St. Kitts-Nevis with "St. Christopher" and "Anguilla" obliterated

42†	30c Europa (liner)	20	12

51	5c Nevis lighter		
52	30c Local fishing boat		
53	55c Caona (catamaran)		
54	$3 Polynesia (cruise schooner)		
	Set of 4	1.10	70

1981

58†	5c Fishing boat and coaster, Charlestown	5	5

72†	55c Royal Yacht Royal Caroline	20	20
74†	$2 Royal Yacht Royal Sovereign	50	50
76†	$5 Royal Yacht Britannia	1.00	1.00

1983

103	55c H.M.S. Boreas (frigate) (Nelson)		
104	$2 H.M.S. Boreas		
	Set of 2	85	85

No. 58 overprinted **INDEPENDENCE 1983**

109B†	5c Fishing boat and coaster, Charlestown	5	5

1985

No. 76 surcharged **CARIBBEAN ROYAL VISIT 1985 $1.50**

345†	$1.50 on $5 Royal Yacht Britannia	2.25	2.25

1986

381†	$2.50 Santa Maria and Pinta (Columbus)	1.25	1.40
382†	$2.50 Nina (Columbus)	1.25	1.40

405†	$3 Fishing boat on beach	1.50	1.60

444†	25c Schooner and Statue of Liberty	12	15
447†	75c Brigantine and Statue of Liberty	35	40
448†	$1 Libertad (cadet full-rigged ship)	15	50

458†	10c Sailing dinghies	5	5

1987

MS470	$5 Replica float of Hamilton (frigate), 1788	2.25	2.40

No. 54 overprinted **America's Cup 1987 Winners 'Stars & Stripes'**

471	$3 Polynesia (cruise schooner)	1.40	1.50

474†	$1 H.M.S. Boreas (frigate) (Nelson), 1787	45	50

OFFICIAL STAMPS

1980

No. 42 overprinted **OFFICIAL**

O3†	30c Europa	10	12

1983

Nos. 72, 74 and 76 surcharged or overprinted **OFFICIAL**

O23†	45c on $2 Royal Sovereign	20	25
O25†	55c Royal Caroline	20	25
O27†	$1.10 on $5 Britannia	45	50

NEW BRUNSWICK

North America
100 cents = 1 dollar

1860

18	12½c Washington (paddle-steamer)	50.00	40.00

NEW CALEDONIA

South Pacific
100 centimes = 1 franc

1905

99†	1f President Felix Faure (barque) (blue on green)	35	10
123†	1f President Felix Faure (blue)	50	30
100†	2f President Felix Faure (blue)	85	55
101†	5f President Felix Faure (black on orange)	3.00	2.25

1912

Nos. 99, 100/1 and 123, some with colours changed, surcharged in figures

126†	25c on 2f President Felix Faure	20	20
127†	25c on 5f President Felix Faure (black on orange)	25	25
132†	1f25 on 1f President Felix Faure (blue)	20	20
133†	1f50 on 1f President Felix Faure (blue on blue)	40	40
134†	3f on 5f President Felix Faure (mauve)	40	40
135†	10f on 5f President Felix Faure (green)	2.50	2.50
136†	20f on 5f President Felix Faure (red on yellow)	5.00	5.00

1928

137†	1c Fishing boat, Pointe des Paletuviers	5	5
138†	2c Fishing boat, Pointe des Paletuviers	5	5
139†	3c Fishing boat, Pointe des Paletuviers	5	5
140†	4c Fishing boat, Pointe des Paletuviers	5	5
141†	5c Fishing boat, Pointe des Paletuviers	5	5
142†	10c Fishing boat, Pointe des Paletuviers	5	5
143†	15c Fishing boat, Pointe des Paletuviers	10	10
144†	20c Fishing boat, Pointe des Paletuviers	10	10
145†	25c Fishing boat, Pointe des Paletuviers	10	10

161	1f L'Astrolabe (La Perouse) (red and brown)	2.00	1.10
162	1f L'Astrolabe (red)	50	50
163	1f L'Astrolabe (green and red)	15	10
164	1f10 L'Astrolabe	5.00	4.75
165	1f25 L'Astrolabe (green and brown)	35	25
166	1f25 L'Astrolabe (red)	25	25
167	1f40 L'Astrolabe	25	25
168	1f50 L'Astrolabe	10	5
169	1f60 L'Astrolabe	45	45
170	1f75 L'Astrolabe (orange and blue)	30	25
171	1f75 L'Astrolabe (blue)	25	20
172	2f L'Astrolabe	20	10
173	2f25 L'Astrolabe	35	35
174	2f50 L'Astrolabe	50	50
175	3f L'Astrolabe	30	20
176	5f L'Astrolabe	30	25
177	10f L'Astrolabe	50	40
178	20f L'Astrolabe	85	65

1931

As No. 109 of Cameroun

182†	1f50 Liner	1.25	1.50

1933

Nos. 137/8, 140/5, 161, 165, 168, 170, 172 and 175/8 overprinted with small aeroplane and **PARIS-NOUMEA Premiere liaison aerienne 5 Avil 1932**

185†	1c Fishing boat, Pointe des Paletuviers	2.75	2.75
186†	2c Fishing boat, Pointe des Paletuviers	2.75	2.75
187†	4c Fishing boat, Pointe des Paletuviers	2.75	2.75
188†	5c Fishing boat, Pointe des Paletuviers	2.75	2.75
189†	10c Fishing boat, Pointe des Paletuviers	2.75	2.75
190†	15c Fishing boat, Pointe des Paletuviers	2.75	2.75
191†	20c Fishing boat, Pointe des Paletuviers	2.75	2.75
192†	25c Fishing boat, Pointe des Paletuviers	2.75	2.75
202†	1f L'Astrolabe (La Perouse)	2.75	2.75
203†	1f25 L'Astrolabe	2.75	2.75
204†	1f50 L'Astrolabe	2.75	2.75
205†	1f75 L'Astrolabe	3.50	3.50
206†	2f L'Astrolabe	3.50	3.50
207†	3f L'Astrolabe	3.50	3.50
208†	5f L'Astrolabe	3.50	3.50
209†	10f L'Astrolabe	3.50	3.50
210†	20f L'Astrolabe	3.50	3.50

1937

As Nos. 110/11 of Cameroun

211†	20c Passenger liner	40	50
212†	30c Sailing ships	40	50

1941

Nos. 137/8, 140/5, 162, 165, 167/70 and 172/8 overprinted
France Libre

232†	1c Fishing boat, Pointe des Paletuviers	7.00	7.00
233†	2c Fishing boat, Pointe des Paletuviers	7.00	7.00
234†	3c Fishing boat, Pointe des Paletuviers	7.00	7.00
235†	4c Fishing boat, Pointe des Paletuviers	7.00	7.00
236†	5c Fishing boat, Pointe des Paletuviers	7.00	7.00
237†	10c Fishing boat, Pointe des Paletuviers	7.00	7.00
238†	15c Fishing boat, Pointe des Paletuviers	7.00	7.00
239†	20c Fishing boat, Pointe des Paletuviers	7.00	7.00
240†	25c Fishing boat, Pointe des Paletuviers	7.00	7.00
254†	1f *L'Astrolabe* (La Perouse)	7.00	7.00
255†	1f25 *L'Astrolabe*	7.00	7.00
256†	1f40 *L'Astrolabe*	7.00	7.00
257†	1f50 *L'Astrolabe*	7.00	7.00
258†	1f60 *L'Astrolabe*	7.00	7.00
259†	1f75 *L'Astrolabe*	7.00	7.00
260†	2f *L'Astrolabe*	7.00	7.00
261†	2f25 *L'Astrolabe*	7.00	7.00
262†	2f50 *L'Astrolabe*	8.00	8.00
263†	3f *L'Astrolabe*	8.00	8.00
264†	5f *L'Astrolabe*	8.00	8.00
265†	10f *L'Astrolabe*	10.00	10.00
266†	20f *L'Astrolabe*	10.00	10.00

1948

312†	1f Outrigger canoe, Porcupine Island	10	10
313†	1f20 Outrigger canoe, Porcupine Island	15	15
314†	1f40 Outrigger canoe, Porcupine Island	15	10
315†	2f Freighter	20	15
316†	2f40 Freighter	20	20
317†	3f Freighter	2.75	50
318†	4f Freighter	50	25

1953

331†	1f50 D'Entrecasteaux's ships, 1792	3.50	2.50

1954

As No. 264 of Cameroun

335	3f Landing craft, Normandy, 1944	2.75	1.75

1959

345†	2f Outrigger canoes racing	50	30
348†	5f Yachts	1.00	45
357†	200f Pirogue (air)	20.00	9.00

1966

402	30f Shipping, Noumea Harbour, 1866	2.00	2.00

1967

425	25f Ocean racing yachts	2.25	1.75

1968

442	9f Ferry, River Tontouta, *c.* 1900	85	70

1969

475	50f Outrigger canoe	3.00	2.25

1970

479	9f *Natal* (packet steamer), 1883	1.00	60

1971

483	20f Racing yachts	1.60	90
485	16f Ocean racing yachts	2.75	1.50
492	200f Yacht marina, Noumea	11.00	6.00

1973

516	60f *El Kantara* (liner)	4.25	2.50

1974

539†	20f H.M.S. *Endeavour* (Cook)	1.50	45
540†	25f *L'Astrolabe* (La Perouse)	1.00	60
542†	30f D'Entrecasteaux's ship, 1792	1.60	70
543†	36f *L'Astrolabe* (Dumont d'Urville)	1.75	1.25

1979

610†	11f Outrigger canoe, Ouvea Island	30	25
613†	49f 19th-century barque and modern container ship	1.00	55
618†	75f Shipping, Noumea Harbour, 1854	1.90	1.25
621	16f Catamarans	55	30

1980

630	45f Outrigger canoe	1.00	75
638	27f Sailing canoe	50	35

1981

655	29f Troopship, 1940	75	55
659	10f *Constantine* (sail corvette), 1854		
660	25f *Le Phoque* (paddle-gunboat), 1853		
	Set of 2	70	35

1982

680   44f *Le Cher* (naval transport barque)
681   59f *Kersaint* (sloop), 1902
           Set of 2   1.75   1.00

1984

725   18f *St Joseph* (freighter)
726   31f *St Antoine* (freighter)
           Set of 2   90   60

1985

763   17f Trawler   25   15

1987

802   30f *Challenge France* (yacht)
803   70f *French Kiss* (yacht)
           Set of 2   1.50   90

807   72f Canoe, Isle of Pines
808   90f Canoe, Ouvea
           Set of 2   2.25   1.60

1988

823   36f *L'Astrolabe* and *La Boussole* (La Perouse)   35   25

STANLEY GIBBONS
STAMP COLLECTING SERIES

Introductory booklets on *How to Start, How to Identify Stamps* and *Collecting by Theme*. A series of well illustrated guides at a low price.
Write for details.

POSTAGE DUE STAMPS

1906

D102   5c Outrigger canoe
D103   10c Outrigger canoe
D104   15c Outrigger canoe
D105   20c Outrigger canoe
D106   30c Outrigger canoe
D107   50c Outrigger canoe
D108   60c Outrigger canoe
D109   1f Outrigger canoe
           Set of 8   2.75   3.25

1926

As No. D109, but colour changed, surcharged
D137   2f on 1f Outrigger canoe 1.25   1.25
D138   3f on 1f Outrigger canoe 1.25   1.25

PARCEL POST STAMPS

1926

Nos. 100, 123 *and as No.* 101, *but colour changed, overprinted*
Colis Postaux *or surcharged also*
P137   50c on 5f *President Felix Faure* (green on mauve)
P138   1f *President Felix Faure*
P139   2f *President Felix Faure*
           Set of 3   1.75   1.75

NEWFOUNDLAND

North Atlantic
100 cents = 1 dollar

1865

29†   13c Schooner 60.00   48.00

1887

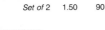

54†   10c Brigantine 45.00   35.00

1897

72†   8c Fishing boats 12.00   6.00
73†   10c *Matthew* (Cabot) 16.00   2.75
76†   24c Salmon-fishing boat 16.00   11.00

1910

98†   4c *Endeavour* (immigrant ship), 1610 ....   8.00   11.00

1928

180†   2c *Caribou* (cargo liner) 1.10   10

1931

193†   50c Sailing packet 15.00   18.00

1932

228†   24c *Willemplein* (freighter) loading ore ..   1.00   2.00
219†   25c Sealing fleet 1.75   1.75
220†   30c Fishing fleet 15.00   20.00

1933

231†   10c Canoe 5.00   14.00
232†   30c *Beothic* (sealer) 18.00   30.00
233†   60c Fishing schooners 32.00   50.00

242†   8c Sir Humphrey Gilbert's fleet, 1583 ....   5.50   7.50

1937

265†   24c *Willemplein* (freighter) loading ore ..   3.50   3.00
266†   25c Sealing fleet 4.00   3.00
267†   48c Fishing fleet 6.50   4.00

1941

275   5c *Maravel* (missionary ship)   15   15

NEW GUINEA

Australasia
1901 100 pfennig = 1 mark
1914 12 pence = 1 shilling
20 shillings = 1 pound

1901

As Nos. K7/19 of Cameroun, but inscribed
"DEUTSCH-NEU-GUINEA"
G7   3pf *Hohenzollern* (German Imperial yacht)
G8   5pf *Hohenzollern*
G9   10pf *Hohenzollern*
G10   20pf *Hohenzollern*
G11   25pf *Hohenzollern*
G12   30pf *Hohenzollern*
G13   40pf *Hohenzollern*
G14   50pf *Hohenzollern*
G15   80pf *Hohenzollern*
G16   1m *Hohenzollern*
G17   2m *Hohenzollern*
G18   3m *Hohenzollern*
G19   5m *Hohenzollern*
           Set of 13   £130   £550

1914

Nos. G7/19 surcharged **G.R.I.** and value in English currency

16	1d on 3pf *Hohenzollern*	30.00	30.00
17	1d on 5pf *Hohenzollern*	10.00	10.00
3	2d on 10pf *Hohenzollern*	30.00	30.00
4	2d on 20pf *Hohenzollern*	25.00	25.00
5	2½d on 10pf *Hohenzollern*	55.00	50.00
6	2½d on 20pf *Hohenzollern*	60.00	60.00
22	3d on 25pf *Hohenzollern*	75.00	70.00
23	3d on 30pf *Hohenzollern*	70.00	80.00
24	4d on 40pf *Hohenzollern*	75.00	75.00
25	5d on 50pf *Hohenzollern*	£120	£120
26	8d on 80pf *Hohenzollern*	£450	£400
12	1s on 1m *Hohenzollern*	£1300	£1100
13	2s on 2m *Hohenzollern*	£1500	£1400
14	3s on 3m *Hohenzollern*	£2250	£1800
15	5s on 5m *Hohenzollern*	£4750	£4000

Nos. 3/4 surcharged **1**

31	1 on 2d on 10pf *Hohenzollern*	£8000	£8000
32	1 on 2d on 20pf *Hohenzollern*	£8000	£5000

Nos. G11/23 of Marshall Islands surcharged **G.R.I.** and value in English currency

50	1d on 3pf *Hohenzollern*	35.00	35.00
51	1d on 5pf *Hohenzollern*	40.00	42.00
52	2d on 10pf *Hohenzollern*	12.00	14.00
53	2d on 20pf *Hohenzollern*	13.00	16.00
54	3d on 25pf *Hohenzollern*	£275	£275
55	3d on 30pf *Hohenzollern*	£275	£275
56	4d on 40pf *Hohenzollern*	80.00	90.00
57	5d on 50pf *Hohenzollern*	£100	£120
58	8d on 80pf *Hohenzollern*	£450	£500
59	1s on 1m *Hohenzollern*	£1300	£1100
60	2s on 2m *Hohenzollern*	£900	£800
61	3s on 3m *Hohenzollern*	£1900	£2000
62	5s on 5m *Hohenzollern*	£4500	£4250

1915

Nos. 52/3 surcharged **1**

63	1 on 2d on 10pf *Hohenzollern*	£140	£160
64	1 on 2d on 20pf *Hohenzollern*	£2250	£1400

OFFICIAL STAMPS

1914

Nos. 16/17 overprinted **O.S.**

O48	1d on 3pf *Hohenzollern*	25.00	35.00
O49	1d on 5pf *Hohenzollern*	75.00	£100

NEW HEBRIDES

South Pacific
100 centimes = 1 franc

BRITISH ADMINISTRATION

52	5c Outrigger canoe, Lopevi Islands	
53	10c Outrigger canoe, Lopevi Islands	
54	15c Outrigger canoe, Lopevi Islands	
55	20c Outrigger canoe, Lopevi Islands	
56	25c Outrigger canoe, Lopevi Islands	
57	30c Outrigger canoe, Lopevi Islands	
58	40c Outrigger canoe, Lopevi Islands	
59	50c Outrigger canoe, Lopevi Islands	
60	1f Outrigger canoe, Lopevi Islands	
61	2f Outrigger canoe, Lopevi Islands	
62	5f Outrigger canoe, Lopevi Islands	
63	10f Outrigger canoe, Lopevi Islands	
	Set of 12	£180 £130

1953

68†	5c Outrigger sailing canoes	25	5
69†	10c Outrigger sailing canoes	25	5
70†	15c Outrigger sailing canoes	25	5
71†	20c Outrigger sailing canoes	25	10

1956

80†	5c Portuguese galleon, 1606	12	5
81†	10c Portuguese galleon, 1606	12	5

1963

98†	5c Freighter loading manganese	20	25
101†	20c Trawlers	45	10

1967

127†	60c H.M.A.S. *Canberra* (cruiser)	20	15

1968

131†	25c *La Boudeuse* and *L'Etoile* (French warships), 1768	20	10
132†	60c Ship's figurehead	20	10

1970

No. 101 surcharged **35**

144	35c on 20c Trawlers	30	30

1973

178	25c Freighters at wharf, Vila		
179	70c Freighters at wharf, Vila		
	Set of 2	1.25	85

183†	70c Outrigger canoe	15	15

1974

192†	35c H.M.S. *Resolution* (Cook)	1.75	1.25
193†	35c Ship's boat	1.75	1.25
195†	1f15 H.M.S. *Resolution* (Cook)	4.00	4.00

1975

203†	5f Outrigger canoe	6.00	4.75

1977

250†	50f Outrigger canoe, Shepherd Island	70	60

1979

271†	10f Outrigger canoe, Lopevi Island, (on stamp No. 52)	20	20

POSTAGE DUE STAMPS

1938

Nos. 52/3, 55, 58 and 60 overprinted **POSTAGE DUE**

D6	5c Outrigger canoe, Lopevi Islands		
D7	10c Outrigger canoe, Lopevi Islands		
D8	20c Outrigger canoe, Lopevi Islands		
D9	40c Outrigger canoe, Lopevi Islands		
D10	1f Outrigger canoe, Lopevi Islands		
	Set of 5	85.00	85.00

1953

Nos. 68/9 and 71 overprinted **POSTAGE DUE**

D11†	5c Outrigger sailing canoes	1.50	3.00
D12†	10c Outrigger sailing canoes	1.00	2.75
D13†	20c Outrigger sailing canoes	2.25	4.75

FRENCH ADMINISTRATION

1908

No. 99 of New Caledonia overprinted **NOUVELLES HEBRIDES**

F5†	1f *President Felix Faure* (barque)	5.50	6.50

1910

No. 99 of New Caledonia overprinted **NOUVELLES HEBRIDES CONDOMINIUM**

F10†	1f *President Felix Faure* (barque)	6.50	8.50

The following are as issues of the British Administration, but are inscribed "NOUVELLES HEBRIDES"

1938

As Nos. 52/63

F53	5c Outrigger canoe, Lopevi Islands	
F54	10c Outrigger canoe, Lopevi Islands	
F55	15c Outrigger canoe, Lopevi Islands	
F56	20c Outrigger canoe, Lopevi Islands	
F57	25c Outrigger canoe, Lopevi Islands	
F58	30c Outrigger canoe, Lopevi Islands	
F59	40c Outrigger canoe, Lopevi Islands	
F60	50c Outrigger canoe, Lopevi Islands	
F61	1f Outrigger canoe, Lopevi Islands	
F62	2f Outrigger canoe, Lopevi Islands	
F63	5f Outrigger canoe, Lopevi Islands	
F64	10f Outrigger canoe, Lopevi Islands	
	Set of 12	75.00 75.00

1938

As Nos. 52/63

F53 5c Outrigger canoe, Lopevi Islands
F54 10c Outrigger canoe, Lopevi Islands
F55 15c Outrigger canoe, Lopevi Islands
F56 20c Outrigger canoe, Lopevi Islands
F57 25c Outrigger canoe, Lopevi Islands
F58 30c Outrigger canoe, Lopevi Islands
F59 40c Outrigger canoe, Lopevi Islands
F60 50c Outrigger canoe, Lopevi Islands
F61 1f Outrigger canoe, Lopevi Islands
F62 2f Outrigger canoe, Lopevi Islands
F63 5f Outrigger canoe, Lopevi Islands
F64 10f Outrigger canoe, Lopevi Islands
                        Set of 12 75.00 75.00

1941

Nos. F53/64 overprinted **France Libre**

F65 5c Outrigger canoe, Lopevi Islands
F66 10c Outrigger canoe, Lopevi Islands
F67 15c Outrigger canoe, Lopevi Islands
F68 20c Outrigger canoe, Lopevi Islands
F69 25c Outrigger canoe, Lopevi Islands
F70 30c Outrigger canoe, Lopevi Islands
F71 40c Outrigger canoe, Lopevi Islands
F72 50c Outrigger canoe, Lopevi Islands
F73 1f Outrigger canoe, Lopevi Islands
F74 2f Outrigger canoe, Lopevi Islands
F75 5f Outrigger canoe, Lopevi Islands
F76 10f Outrigger canoe, Lopevi Islands
                        Set of 12 65.00 70.00

1953

As Nos. 68/71

F81† 5c Outrigger sailing canoes 5 5
F82† 10c Outrigger sailing canoes 12 12
F83† 15c Outrigger sailing canoes 15 15
F84† 20c Outrigger sailing canoes 30 30

1956

As Nos. 80/1

F92† 5c Portuguese galleon, 1606 .... 35 25
F93† 10c Portuguese galleon, 1606 .... 35 25

1963

As No. 98 and 101

F110† 5c Freighter loading manganese 40 30
F114† 20c Trawlers ("RF" at left) 2.25 2.25
F115† 20c Trawlers ("RF" at right) 60 25

1967

As No. 127

F143† 60c H.M.A.S. *Canberra* (cruiser) 95 85

1968

As Nos. 131/2

F146† 25c *La Boudeuse* and *L'Etoile* (French
         warships), 1768 .... 40 40
F147† 60c Ship's figurehead 90 90

1970

No. F115 surcharged **35**

F159 35c on 20c Trawlers 60 50

1973

As Nos. 178/9

F193 25c Freighters at wharf, Vila
F194 70c Freighters at wharf, Vila
                        Set of 2 2.25 1.60

As No. 183

F198† 70c Outrigger canoe 65 50

1974

As Nos. 192/3 and 195

F207† 35c H.M.S. *Resolution* (Cook) 2.25 1.75
F208† 35c Ship's boat 2.25 1.75
F210† 1f15 H.M.S. *Resolution* (Cook) 5.50 6.00

1975

As No. 203

F217† 5f Outrigger canoe 10.00 7.50

1977

As No. 250

F264† 50f Outrigger canoe, Shepherd Island 1.25 75

1979

As No. 271

F285† 10f Outrigger canoe, Lopevi Islands,
         (on stamp No. F53) 35 35

POSTAGE DUE STAMPS

1938

Nos. F53/4, F56, F59 and F61 overprinted **CHIFFRE TAX**

FD65 5c Outrigger canoe, Lopevi Islands
FD66 10c Outrigger canoe, Lopevi Islands
FD67 20c Outrigger canoe, Lopevi Islands
FD68 40c Outrigger canoe, Lopevi Islands
FD69 1f Outrigger canoe, Lopevi Islands
                        Set of 5 60.00 75.00

1941

Nos. FD65/9 overprinted **France Libre**

FD77 5c Outrigger canoe, Lopevi Islands
FD78 10c Outrigger canoe, Lopevi Islands
FD79 20c Outrigger canoe, Lopevi Islands
FD80 40c Outrigger canoe, Lopevi Islands
FD81 1f Outrigger canoe, Lopevi Islands
                        Set of 5 27.00 32.00

1953

Nos. F81/2 and F84 overprinted **TIMBRE-TAXE**

FD92† 5c Outrigger sailing canoes 1.25 2.00
FD93† 10c Outrigger sailing canoes 1.25 2.00
FD94† 20c Outrigger sailing canoes 2.75 4.50

NEW ZEALAND

Australasia
1898 12 pence = 1 shilling
20 shillings = 1 pound
1967 100 cents = 1 dollar

1898

325† 8d Maori war canoe 25.00 6.00

1906

370† ½d *Te Arawa* (Maori canoe) 20.00 23.00
372† 3d H.M.S. *Endeavour* (Cook) 45.00 48.00
373† 6d H.M.S. *Britomart* (sloop), 1840 ...... £130 £200

1936

597† 6d *Tamaroa* (freighter) 1.00 3.25

1940

614† 1d H.M.S. *Endeavour* (Cook) 1.25 5
616† 2d *Heemskerk* (Tasman) 1.25 5
618† 3d *Aurora, Helena* and *Cuba* (emigrant
         ships), 1840 .... 2.00 40
619† 4d *Awatea* (liner) 5.00 80
620† 5d H.M.S. *Britomart* (sloop), 1840 ...... 3.25 3.25
621† 6d *Dunedin* (refrigerated full-rigged
         sailing ship), 1882 .... 5.00 45
624† 9d Gold dredger, 1940 .... 6.00 1.50

1946

673† 5d H.M.N.Z.S. *Achilles* (cruiser) and
         Dominion Monarch (liner) 20 15

1948

692† 1d John Wickliffe and Philip Lang
         (emigrant ships), 1848 .... 8 10

1951

708 1½d + ½d Health (yacht)
709 2d + 1d Health (yacht)
                        Set of 2 20 20

1956

752† 2d 19th-century whaleboat and whaling
         ship, Foveaux Strait 15 10

1957

759† 8d *Dunedin* (refrigerated full-rigged
         sailing ship), 1882 and *Port Brisbane*
         (refrigerated freighter),1957 .... 75 1.25

1959

772† 2d H.M.S. *Endeavour* (Cook) careened 20 10
773† 3d Wool lighter, Wairau, 1857 .... 20 5

1967

870† 7c *Kaiti* (trawler) 75 75

1968

886† 28c H.M.N.Z.S. *Achilles* (cruiser) at the
         River Plate, 1939, and H.M.N.Z.S.
         Waikato (modern frigate) 1.00 2.25

1969

907† 6c H.M.S. *Endeavour* (Cook) 1.75 3.00

1970

930a† 25c Yachts, Hauraki Gulf 70 40

1971

950† 5c *Rainbow II* (yacht) 15 20

1972

981† 8c French frigate, 1772 .... 1.50 2.50

996† 23c Speed boat, Lake Rotomahana 1.50 2.50

1975

1069	4c *Lake Erie* (scow)		
1070	5c *Herald* (schooner)		
1071	8c *New Zealander* (brigantine)		
1072	10c *Jessie Kelly* (schooner)		
1073	18c *Tory* (barque)		
1074	23c *Rangitiki* (full-rigged clipper)		
		Set of 6	3.50 3.50

1976

1112† 8c *William Bryan* (emigrant ship), 1876 15 10

1978

1174† 12c Gas drilling rig 20 15
1175† 15c Stern trawler 30 25

1982

1259† 30c *Dunedin* (refrigerated full-rigged
sailing ship), 1882, and modern
container ship 35 40

1276† 45c Surf lifeboat 50 50

1983

1312† 24c Fishing boats 50 50

1984

1332 24c *Mountaineer* (paddle-ferry), Lake
Wakatipu
1333 40c *Waikana* (ferry), Otago
1334 58c *Britannia* (paddle-ferry), Wakatipu
1335 70c *Wakatere* (paddle-ferry), Firth of
Thames
Set of 4 1.60 1.60

1985

1379 25c H.M.N.Z.S. *Philomel* (cruiser), 1914
1380 45c H.M.N.Z.S. *Achilles* (cruiser), 1936
1381 60c H.M.N.Z.S. *Rotoiti* (frigate), 1949
1382 75c H.M.N.Z.S. *Canterbury* (frigate),
1971
Set of 4 2.00 2.10

1986

1388† 25c Police patrol boat 25 30

COLLECT MAMMALS ON STAMPS

A Stanley Gibbons thematic catalogue on this popular
subject. Copies available at £7.50 (p. + p. £2) from:
Stanley Gibbons Publications Ltd, 5 Parkside, Christchurch Road, Ringwood, Hants BH24 3SH.

1987

NEW ZEALAND

1411† 60c Jet boat 40 45
1414† 85c Sailboard 60 65
1416† $1.30 Inflatable dinghy 90 95

1417 40c Yacht (Southern Cross Cup)
1418 80c Yacht (Admiral's Cup)
1419 $1.50 Yacht (Kenwood Cup)
1420 $1.30 Yacht (America's Cup)
Set of 4 2.25 2.50

LIFE INSURANCE DEPARTMENT

1947

L43† 1d *Pamir* (full-rigged sailing ship) 60 30

1967

No. L43 *surcharged* **1c**
L50† 1c on 1d *Pamir* 2.00 3.50

OFFICIAL STAMPS

Nos. 614, 616, 618/19, 621 *and* 624 *overprinted* **Official**
O142† 1d H.M.S. *Endeavour* (Cook) 1.25 5
O144† 2d *Heemskerk* (Tasman) 1.75 10
O146† 3d *Aurora, Helena* and *Cuba* (emigrant
ships), 1840 .... 4.50 80
O147† 4d *Awatea* (liner) 23.00 1.75
O148† 6d *Dunedin* (refrigerated full-rigged
sailing ship), 1882 .... 14.00 2.00
O150† 9d Gold dredger, 1940 .... 6.00 8.00

NICARAGUA

Central America
100 centavos = 1 cordoba

1937

997† 3c Yacht 15 12
998† 5c Packet steamer 15 12

1939

1013† 2c Fishing boats, Lake Managua 8 8
1014† 3c Fishing boats, Lake Managua 8 8
1015† 8c Fishing boats, Lake Managua 8 8
1016† 16c Fishing boats, Lake Managua 15 12
1017† 24c Fishing boats, Lake Managua 15 12
1018† 32c Fishing boats, Lake Managua 20 15
1019† 50c Fishing boats, Lake Managua 25 15

1945

1068†	20c Fleet of Columbus, 1492	15	10
1069†	35c Fleet of Columbus, 1492	30	15
1070†	75c Fleet of Columbus, 1492	40	25
1071†	90c Fleet of Columbus, 1492	60	40
1072†	1cor Fleet of Columbus, 1492	80	30
1073†	2cor50 Fleet of Columbus, 1492	2.00	1.75

1949

1129†	40c Yachts	1.10	25
1137†	5c Yachts (air)	25	8

1952

1160†	96c Fleet of Columbus	40	30
1161†	98c *Santa Maria* (Columbus)	40	30
1166†	3cor *Santa Maria* (air)	1.40	1.10
1167†	3cor30 Fleet of Columbus	1.40	1.25

1957

1300†	4c *Honduras* (freighter)	5	5
1301†	5c *Guatemala* (freighter)	5	5
1302†	6c *Guatemala* (freighter)	5	5
1303†	10c *Salvador* (freighter)	10	5
1304†	15c Freighter	15	8
1306†	25c *Managua* (freighter)	10	10
1309†	60c *Costa Rica* (freighter)	25	20
1310†	1cor *Nicarao* (freighter)	35	30
1311†	2cor50 Freighter	90	80

1960

No. 1166 *overprinted* **X Aniversario Club Filatelico S. J.—C. R.**

1385	3cor *Santa Maria* (Columbus)	95	90

1973

1849†	10c Elizabethan galleon	10	5

1974

1911†	10c Landing craft, Normandy, 1944	5	5

1936†	3c Packet steamer (on stamp No. 998)	5	5

1975

2013†	2cor American Presidential barge, 1789	45	30

2017†	2c Scout canoe	5	5

1976

2068†	2cor75 Battle of Flamborough Head, 1779	80	55
2069†	2cor75 Nuclear submarine	80	55

1981

2279†	3cor Container ship	60	25

MS2303	10cor 17th-century frigate	2.00	1.25

1982

2356†	1cor20 *Victoria* (packet steamer)	25	10

2407†	50c *Santa Maria* (Columbus)	15	5
2408†	1cor *Nina* (Columbus)	20	8

2409†	1cor50 *Pinta* (Columbus)	30	12
2410†	2cor Fleet of Columbus	40	20
2411†	2cor50 Fleet of Columbus (air)	45	20
MS2414†	10cor *Santa Maria*	1.75	90

1983

MS2440†	15cor Olympic yacht	2.25	1.25

2496†	1cor Container ship	25	8

2534†	1cor Sinking liner and ship's lifeboat	25	8

1984

2607	15cor Container ship	3.00	2.10

MS2628	15cor H.M.S. *Discovery* (Cook)	3.00	2.40

1985

2699†	3cor Lifeboat	5	5

1986

2791†	1cor *Pinta* (Columbus)	10	5
2792†	1cor *Santa Maria* and *Nina* (Columbus) ...	10	5

NIGER

West Africa
100 centimes = 1 franc

1926

37†	20c Canoe, River Niger	. . . .	10	10
38†	25c Canoe, River Niger	. . . .	10	10
39†	30c Canoe, River Niger (green)	. . . .	20	20
40†	30c Canoe, River Niger (mauve and yellow)	. . . .	10	10
41†	35c Canoe, River Niger (blue and red on blue)	. . . .	10	10
42†	35c Canoe, River Niger (turquoise)	. . . . . .	20	20
43†	40c Canoe, River Niger	. . . .	10	10
44†	45c Canoe, River Niger (mauve and yellow)	. . . .	30	30
45†	45c Canoe, River Niger (green)	. . . .	10	10
46†	50c Canoe, River Niger	. . . .	10	5
47†	55c Canoe, River Niger	. . . .	30	30
48†	60c Canoe, River Niger	. . . .	10	10
49†	65c Canoe, River Niger	. . . .	10	10
50†	70c Canoe, River Niger	. . . .	35	35
51†	75c Canoe, River Niger	. . . .	35	35
52†	80c Canoe, River Niger	. . . .	40	40
53†	90c Canoe, River Niger (orange and red)	. . .	30	30
54†	90c Canoe, River Niger (green and red)	. . .	35	35

1931

As No. 109 of Cameroun

76†	1f50 Liner	. . . .	1.25	1.50

1937

As Nos. 110/11 of Cameroun

77†	20c Liner	. . . .	30	30
78†	30c Sailing ships	. . . .	30	30
MS82†	3f Liner	. . . .	75	75

1941

Nos. 46 and 52 surcharged **SECOURS NATIONAL** *and value*

98a†	1f on 50c Canoe, River Niger	. . . .	25	30
98b†	2f on 80c Canoe, River Niger	. . . .	1.50	2.00

1963

140†	100f Canoe building	. . . .	1.00	50

1966

215	50f *France I* (weather ship)	. . . .	70	40

1967

257	50f Weather ship	. . . .	70	45

1968

281†	45f Pirogue	. . . .	55	35

1972

429†	40f 16th-century galleon	. . . .	60	25

1973

515	50f Barges on River Niger			
516	75f Tug and barge			
		Set of 2	85	55

1974

534	50f *Elettra* (Marconi's steam yacht)	. . . . . .	40	30

545†	150f Liner	. . . .	1.50	80

1975

593†	40f River Niger trading canoe	. . . .	25	20

1976

624†	40f Yachts, Lake Constance	. . . .	25	15

630†	100f Freighter	. . . .	80	50

1979

765†	100f Mail canoes	. . . .	45	25

1982

897	65f Scout pirogue			
898	85f Scout inflatable dinghy			
899	130f Scout canoe			
900	200f Scout raft			
		Set of 4	2.75	2.25

903†	65f Fishing pirogue	. . . .	30	30

1984

989	80f *Paris* (early steamer)			
990	120f *Jacques Coeur* (full-rigged sailing ship)			
991	150f *Bosphorus* (full-rigged sailing ship)			
992	300f *Comet* (full-rigged sailing ship)			
		Set of 4	3.00	2.25

997	300f *Rickmer Rickmers* (full-rigged sailing ship)	. . . .	1.50	1.25

999† 120f Canoes, Ayerou Market 60 40

1985

1053 110f Power boats
1054 150f Power boat
1055 250f Power boat
Set of 3 2.50 2.00

NIGERIA

West Africa
1936 12 pence = 1 shilling
20 shillings = 1 pound
1973 100 kobo = 1 naira

1936

34† ½d Freighter at wharf, Apapa 35 40
36† 1½d Tin dredger 30 20
38† 3d Fishing canoes 50 90
45† £1 Canoe 70.00 £110

1949

As No. 115 of Antigua
65† 3d Paddle-steamer 50 45

1953

69† ½d 19th-century brigantine and canoes .. 12 5
80† £1 Shipping at Lagos in 19th and 20th
centuries 9.00 3.75

1961

105† 2s6d Liner 30 40

1962

125† 2s6d *British Petroleum* (tanker) 15 25

COLLECT RAILWAYS ON STAMPS
A Stanley Gibbons thematic catalogue on this popular subject. Copies available at £7.50 (p. + p. £2) from: Stanley Gibbons Publications Ltd, 5 Parkside, Christchurch Road, Ringwood, Hants BH24 3SH.

1963

132† 1s3d *Kingsport* (satellite communications
vessel) 15 15

1970

248† 2d Oil rig 10 5

1973

294† 7d Freighter at timber wharf 30 10
349† 25k Freighter at wharf 85 30

1974

324† 30k Freighter and canoe 1.90 2.75

326† 18k *Mercury* (cable ship) 1.00 1.00

1980

418† 25k Bulk carrier 20 30

1986

517† 15k Freighter at wharf 5 5

NIUAFO'OU

South Pacific
100 sentiti = 1 pa'anga

1983

26† 1p50 Sailing canoe 1.50 1.75

1985

53† 47s Tongan canoes 45 50
54† 1p50 *Eendracht* (Le Maire), 1616 .... 1.50 1.60
MS55† 1p50 *Eendracht* 1.50 1.75

56 9s *Ysabel* (barquentine), 1902
57 13s *Tofua I* (cargo liner), 1908
58 47s *Mariposa* (cargo liner), 1934
59 1p50 *Matua* (cargo liner), 1936
Set of 4 1.90 2.00

61† 42s Freighter off Niuafo'ou 35 40
63† 1p50 Freighter off Niuafo'ou 1.25 1.40

1986

86† 57s Outrigger canoe 45 50
87† 1p Freighter 80 85
88† 2p50 Outrigger canoe 2.10 2.25

NIUE

South Pacific
1920 12 pence = 1 shilling
20 shillings = 1 pound
1967 100 cents = 1 dollar

1920

As Nos. 82 and 84 of Cook Islands, but inscribed "NIUE"
38† 1d Schooner 2.00 3.25
47† 4d Local sailing canoe 2.00 7.00

1932

*As Nos. 106, 108/9 and 111 of Cook Islands, but additionally
inscribed "NIUE"*
62† ½d Captain Cook and ship 50 75
64† 2d Double Maori canoe 40 70
65† 2½d Schooner 50 1.75
94† 6d *Monowai* (liner) 80 1.75

1935

Nos. 65 and 94 overprinted **SILVER JUBILEE OF KING
GEORGE V. 1910 – 1935.**
70† 2½d Schooner 3.00 3.00
71† 6d *Monowai* (liner) 3.50 7.00

1938

As No. 145 of Cook Islands, but additionally inscribed "NIUE"
77† 3s Canoe 8.50 8.00

1950

114† 1d H.M.S. *Resolution* (Cook) 1.25 20
115† 2d Canoes, Alofi 10 10
118† 6d *Maui Pomare* (freighter), Alofi 20 15

1967

Nos. 114/15 and 118 surcharged

126†	1c on 1d H.M.S. *Resolution* (Cook)	80	20
127†	2c on 2d Canoes, Alofi	5	5
130†	5c on 6d *Maui Pomare* (freighter), Alofi	10	10

1970

155†	3c Outrigger canoe	10	10
156†	5c Cargo liner	15	10

1974

183†	3c H.M.S. *Resolution* (Cook)	30	25

1976

205†	50c Outrigger canoe	50	60

1978

236†	16c H.M.S. *Resolution* and canoes, Hawaii, 1778	65	45
238†	30c Hawaiian canoes, 1778	90	60
239†	35c Hawaiian canoe, 1778	1.00	65

Design as No. 205 but with silver frame

256†	$1.10 Outrigger canoe	1.10	1.10

1979

As No. 256, but with gold frame and inscribed "AIRMAIL"

267†	50c Outrigger canoe	70	30

288†	35c First trans-Atlantic mail paddle-steamer and U.S.A. stamp	35	35
289†	35c First trans-Atlantic mail paddle-steamer and Rowland Hill	35	35

296†	30c Ship's boat	50	40
297†	35c H.M.S. *Resolution* and H.M.S. *Discovery* (Cook), Queen Charlotte's Sound	55	45

302†	60c American aircraft carrier	1.10	90

1980

Nos. 288/9, 297 and 302 surcharged **HURRICANE RELIEF Plus 2c** *(over pair for Nos. 314/15)*

314†	35c + 2c First trans-Atlantic mail paddle-steamer and U.S.A. Stamp	35	40
315†	35c + 2c First trans-Atlantic mail paddle-steamer and Rowland Hill	35	40
322†	35c + 2c H.M.S. *Resolution* and H.M.S. *Discovery* (Cook), Queen Charlotte's Sound	35	40
326†	60c + 2c American aircraft carrier	60	65

Nos. 288/9 overprinted **ZEAPEX'80 AUCKLAND** *(No. 357) or* **NEW ZEALAND STAMP EXHIBITION** *and emblem (No. 358)*

357†	35c First trans-Atlantic mail paddle-steamer and U.S.A. Stamp	35	30
358†	35c First trans-Atlantic mail paddle-steamer and Rowland Hill	35	30

370†	30c "Soling" class yachts (yacht with green sail at left)	25	25
371†	30c "Soling" class yachts (yacht with red sail at left)	25	25

1983

476†	70c H.M.S. *Resolution* and H.M.S. *Adventure* (Cook), 1774	65	70

1987

MS648 Two sheets. 75c Cadet full-rigged ship and Brooklyn Bridge; 75c *Esmeralda* (Chilean cadet full-rigged ship); 75c Cadet barque at dusk (sheets also contain seven other designs)

Set of 2 sheets	4.25	4.50

NORFOLK ISLAND

Australasia
100 cents = 1 dollar

1967

77	1c H.M.S. *Resolution* (Cook), 1774		
78	2c *La Boussole* and *L'Astrolabe* (La Perouse), 1788		
79	3c H.M.S. *Supply* (brig), 1788		
80	4c H.M.S. *Sirius* (frigate), 1790		
81	5c *Norfolk* (cutter), 1798		
82	7c H.M.S. *Mermaid* (survey cutter), 1825		
83	9c *Lady Franklin* (full-rigged sailing ship), 1853		
84	10c *Morayshire* (emigrant ship), 1856		
85	15c *Southern Cross* (missionary ship), 1866		
86	20c *Pitcairn* (missionary schooner), 1891		
87	25c Norfolk Island whaleboat, 1895		
88	30c *Iris* (cable ship), 1907		
89	50c *Resolution* (schooner), 1926		
90	$1 *Morinda* (freighter), 1931		
	Set of 14	15.00	8.00

1969

100	5c 19th-century cutter	
101	30c 19th-century cutter	
	Set of 2	25	15

1970

119†	10c H.M.S. *Endeavour* (Cook)	15	10

1973

129	35c H.M.S. *Resolution* (Cook) in the Antarctic	3.00	2.25

1974

153†	10c H.M.S. *Resolution* (Cook)	2.25	1.75

1975

163†	10c H.M.S. *Mermaid* (survey cutter), 1825	30	30

170	25c *Resolution* (schooner), 1926		
171	45c *Resolution* (schooner), 1926		
	Set of 2	85	70

1976

172†	18c *Charles W. Morgan* (whaling ship)	30	25

1978

214† 90c H.M.S. *Resolution* and H.M.S. *Discovery* (Cook) in Antarctic 1.25 1.25

1979

220† 20c H.M.S. *Resolution* (Cook) 50 40
223† 40c H.M.S. *Resolution* and H.M.S. *Discovery* (Cook), Hawaii 70 60

1981

258† 5c *Morayshire* (emigrant ship), 1856 .... 15 15

1982

287 24c Shipwreck of H.M.S. *Sirius*, 1790
288 27c Shipwreck of *Diocet* (brigantine), 1873
289 35c Shipwreck of *Friendship* (brigantine), 1835
290 40c Shipwreck of *Mary Hamilton* (barque), 1873
291 55c Shipwreck of *Fairlie* (full-rigged sailing ship), 1840
292 65c Shipwreck of *Warrigal* (brigantine), 1918
Set of 6 2.75 2.75

1983

314† 30c *Chantik* (inshore cable ship) 35 40
315† 45c *Chantik* 50 55
316† 75c *Mercury* (cable ship) 90 95

1984

343† 30c H.M.S. *Resolution* (on stamp No. 153) 30 35

349† 30c Full-rigged sailing ship, 1884 ...... 40 45

1985

356 5c *Fanny Fisher* (19th-century whaling ship)
357 33c *Costa Rica Packet* (19th-century whaling ship)
358 50c *Splendid* (19th-century whaling ship)
359 90c *Onward* (19th-century whaling ship)
Set of 4 1.75 2.25

360 15c *Waterwitch* (whaling ship)
361 20c *Canton* (whaling ship)
362 60c *Aladdin* (whaling ship)
363 80c *California* (whaling ship)
Set of 4 2.25 1.75

1986

385† 33c 19th-century whaling ship 40 35

403† 36c Outrigger canoe 45 35

1987

421† 5c Loading First Fleet supply ship, 1787 5 5
422† 55c First Fleet leaving Spithead, 1787 .. 50 55
423† 55c H.M.S. *Sirius* (frigate), 1787 .... 50 55

434† 90c *L'Astrolabe* and *La Boussole* (La Perouse) off Norfolk Island, 1788 ...... 80 85
435† $1 *L'Astrolabe* wrecked in Solomon Islands, 1788 .... 90 95

STAMP MONTHLY

— finest and most informative magazine for all collectors. Obtainable from your newsagent or by postal subscription — details on request.

1988

436 37c Ship's cutter, 1788
437 $1 First Fleet at Sydney Cove, 1788
Set of 2 1.10 1.25

439† 37c H.M.S. *Supply* (brig), 1788 .... 30 35
441† 70c H.M.S. *Supply*, 1788 .... 60 65
442† 90c H.M.S. *Supply*, 1788 .... 80 85

444† 37c Container ship 30 35

NORTH BORNEO

South-east Asia
100 cents = 1 dollar

1894

74† 8c Malay prau 2.50 7.00

1897

102b† 8c Malay prau 10.00
3.75

1899

No. 102b *surcharged* **4 CENTS**
114† 4c on 8c Malay prau 11.00 10.00

1901

No. 102b *overprinted* **BRITISH PROTECTORATE.**
133† 8c Malay prau 2.75 3.50

1904

No. 102b *surcharged* **4 cents**
148† 4c on 8c Malay prau 11.00 23.00

1939

313† 25c Malay prau 5.50 3.50

1945
No. 313 overprinted **BMA**

330† 25c Malay prau 1.50 75

1947
No. 313 overprinted **GR** *and cypher with bars obliterating* "THE STATE OF" *and* "BRITISH PROTECTORATE"

345† 25c Malay prau 35 35

1949
As No. 115 of Antigua

353† 10c Paddle-steamer 70 30

1950

363† 15c Malay prau, Sandakan 25 20
365† 30c Suluk river canoe 45 15

1954
As Nos. 363 and 365, but with portrait of Queen Elizabeth II

379† 15c Malay prau, Sandakan 25 5
381† 30c Suluk river canoe 35 5

1961

388† 15c Malay prau 25 15

NORTHERN RHODESIA
Central Africa
12 pence = 1 shilling
20 shillings = 1 pound

1949
As No. 115 of Antigua

51† 3d Paddle-steamer 90 1.25

NORWAY
Northern Europe
100 ore = 1 krone

1930

Size 35½ × 21½ mm
223 15ore + 25ore *Bergensfjord* (liner)
224 20ore + 25ore *Bergensfjord*
225 30ore + 25ore *Bergensfjord*
Set of 3 70.00 70.00

1938
As Nos. 224/5, but reduced to 27½ × 21 mm
349 15ore + 25ore *Bergensfjord* (liner)
350 20ore + 25ore *Bergensfjord*
351 30ore + 25ore *Bergensfjord*
Set of 3 2.75 3.25

1941

296 15ore + 10ore *Femboring* (fishing boat) 60 2.25

---

297 10ore + 10ore *Colin Archer* (lifeboat)
298 15ore + 10ore *Colin Archer*
299 20ore + 10ore *Osloskoyta* (lifeboat)
300 30ore + 10ore *Osloskoyta*
Set of 4 5.00 6.00

327† 30ore Viking fleet 1.25 1.25

1942

333† 15ore Viking fleet 1.25 1.25

1943

341† 5ore *Sleipner* (destroyer) 10 10
342† 7ore Convoy of merchant ships 20 20
343† 10ore *Sleipner* (destroyer) 8 10
346† 30ore Convoy of merchant ships 40 60

357† 10ore + 10ore Trawlers 70 2.25

1944

360 10ore+ 10ore Sinking of *Baroy* (freighter)
361 15ore + 10ore Sinking of *Sanct Svithun* (cargo liner)
362 20ore + 10ore Sinking of *Irma* (freighter)
Set of 3 1.10 6.00

1947

386† 15ore *Lowendahls* (18th-century warship) 45 5
388† 30ore *Restaurationen* (emigrant ship), 1825 . . . . 75 15
389† 40ore *Constitutionen* (paddle-steamer), 1827 . . . . 80 10
391† 50ore *Spes and Fides* (whale catcher) . . 1.25 15
392† 55ore *Fram* (polar ship) 4.00 20

1953
Design as Nos. 223/5, but reduced to 27½ × 21 mm
442 20ore + 10ore *Bergensfjord*
464 25ore + 10ore *Bergensfjord*
443 30ore + 15ore *Bergensfjord*
465 35ore + 15ore *Bergensfjord*
444 55ore + 25ore *Bergensfjord*
466 65ore + 25ore *Bergensfjord*
Set of 6 32.00 32.00

1960

501 20ore Viking longship
502 25ore Hanse kogge
503 45ore *Skomvaer* (barque)
504 55ore *Dalfon* (tanker)
505 90ore *Oslofjord* (liner)
Set of 5 4.25 4.00

1961

511† 90ore Yacht 70 80

518† 45ore *Fram* (polar ship), 1911 . . . . 50 15

1963

551 50ore River mail boat
552 90ore Northern femboring (sailing vessel)
Set of 2 1.75 1.40

1969

625† 50ore *Princesse Ragnild* (liner) 40 30

1970

649† 100ore Second World War convoy of merchant ships 80 80

1972

682† 80ore Figurehead of Oseberg viking ship 60 10

690 60ore *Maud* (polar ship)
691 80ore *Fram* (polar ship)
692 1k20 *Gjoa* (polar ship)
Set of 3 2.25 1.40

1974

716† 1k Fishing boat, Hardanger Fjord 40   10

1975

734† 1k Trawlers, Nusfjord 50   20

1977

800 1k *Constitutionen* (paddle-steamer)
801 1k25 *Westeraalen* (freighter)
802 1k30 *Kong Haakon* and *Dronningen*
     (ferries)
803 1k80 *Nordstjernen* and *Harald Jarl*
     (ferries)
                         Set of 4   2.25 1.50

804† 1k25 Trawler 20   10

1979

844† 1k50 Rowing boat, Skjernoysund 20   10

850† 10k Statfjord "A" (drilling platform) 1.25   35

1980

MS862 1k25 *Bergen* (paddle-steamer) (sheet
       contains three other designs) 7.00 7.00

1981

879† 2k20 *Christian Radich* (cadet ship) 50   40

880 1k10 *Skibladner* (lake paddle-steamer)
881 1k30 *Victoria* (lake ferry)
882 1k50 *Faemund II* (lake ferry)
883 2k30 *Storegut* (train ferry)
                         Set of 4   90   65

1983

913† 3k50 Cruise liner 35   25

922 2k Northern femboring (sailing vessel)
923 3k Northern jekt (sailing vessel)
                         Set of 2   55   30

1984

931† 3k50 Rowing boat 40   20

1985

MS960 2k + 1k *Neptuno Nordraug* (oil rig);
       2k + 1k Statfjord "C" (oil platform); 2k + 1k
       Treasure Scout (drilling platform) and *Odin
       Viking* (supply ship) (sheet contains one other
       design) 1.75 2.00

965† 2k50 *Berghavn* (dredger) 35   10

1986

983 2k50 Cabin cruisers, Moss
984 4k Fishing boats, Alesund
                         Set of 2   80   30

STAMP MONTHLY

— finest and most informative magazine for all
collectors. Obtainable from your newsagent or by
postal subscription — details on request.

1988

1039† 4k60 Pontoons 75   35

1045 2k90 *Prinds Gustav* (paddle-steamer)
1046 3k80 Trawler
                         Set of 2   1.00   35

NYASALAND

Central Africa
12 pence = 1 shilling
20 shillings = 1 pound

1945

144† ½d Canoe, Lake Nyasa 10   5
151† 9d Canoe, Lake Nyasa 45   2.00

1949

As No. 115 *of Antigua*
164† 3d Paddle-steamer 1.25   75

1953

As Nos. 144 *and* 151, *but with portrait of Queen Elizabeth II*
173a† ½d Canoe, Lake Nyasa 10   15
181† 9d Canoe, Lake Nyasa 70   2.00

1964

203† 4d Fishing pirogue 20   20

NYASSA COMPANY

South-east Africa
1911 1000 reis = 1 milreis
1912 100 centavos = 1 escudo

1911

Overprinted **REPUBLICA**
62† 300r *Sao Gabriel* (Vasco da Gama) 1.25   90
63† 400r *Sao Gabriel* 1.40 1.00
64† 500r *Sao Gabriel* 1.75 1.40

1921

Nos. 62/4 *surcharged in figures and words*
87† 1½c on 300r *Sao Gabriel* 80   80
90† 3c on 400r *Sao Gabriel* 80   80
94† 12c on 500r *Sao Gabriel* 80   80

103† 5c *Sao Gabriel* 55   40
104† 6c *Sao Gabriel* 55   40

105†	7½c *Sao Gabriel*	55	40
106†	8c *Sao Gabriel*	55	40
107†	10c *Sao Gabriel*	55	40
108†	15c *Sao Gabriel*	55	40
109†	20c *Sao Gabriel*	65	50
114†	2e Dhow	2.00	1.25
115†	5e Dhow	1.60	1.10

POSTAGE DUE STAMPS

1924

D136†	5c *Sao Gabriel*	1.75	1.25
D137†	6c *Sao Gabriel*	1.75	1.25
D138†	10c *Sao Gabriel*	1.75	1.25

OCEANIC SETTLEMENTS

East Pacific Ocean
100 centimes = 1 franc

1931

As No. 109 of Cameroun

82†	1f50 Liner	2.00	2.25

1934

83†	1c Fishing canoe	5	10
84†	2c Fishing canoe	5	10
85†	3c Fishing canoe	10	10
86†	4c Fishing canoe	20	20
87†	5c Fishing canoe	30	30
88†	10c Fishing canoe	10	10
89†	15c Fishing canoe	20	20
90†	20c Fishing canoe	10	10

1937

As Nos. 110/11 of Cameroun

121†	20c Liner	70	70
122†	30c Sailing ships	70	70

1942

147†	5c Polynesian travelling canoe	5	10
148†	10c Polynesian travelling canoe	5	10
149†	25c Polynesian travelling canoe	10	10
150†	30c Polynesian travelling canoe	10	10
151†	40c Polynesian travelling canoe	10	10
152†	80c Polynesian travelling canoe	10	15
153†	1f Polynesian travelling canoe	10	10
154†	1f50 Polynesian travelling canoe	20	15
155†	2f Polynesian travelling canoe	20	20
156†	2f50 Polynesian travelling canoe	70	70
157†	4f Polynesian travelling canoe	30	30
158†	5f Polynesian travelling canoe	40	40
159†	10f Polynesian travelling canoe	40	40
160†	20f Polynesian travelling canoe	65	65

1945

Nos. 147, 149 and 156 surcharged

169	50c on 5c Polynesian travelling canoe	
170	60c on 5c Polynesian travelling canoe	
171	70c on 5c Polynesian travelling canoe	
172	1f20 on 5c Polynesian travelling canoe	
173	2f40 on 25c Polynesian travelling canoe	
174	3f on 25c Polynesian travelling canoe	
175	4f50 on 25c Polynesian travelling canoe	
176	15f on 2f50 Polynesian travelling canoe	
	Set of 8	2.75 2.75

1948

186†	10c Outrigger canoe, Moorea	10	10
187†	30c Outrigger canoe, Moorea	10	10
188†	40c Outrigger canoe, Moorea	10	10
192†	1f Outrigger canoe, Faa	15	10
193†	1f20 Outrigger canoe, Faa	20	15
194†	1f50 Outrigger canoe, Faa	20	20
199†	5f Outrigger canoe, Bora-Bora	50	40
200†	6f Outrigger canoe, Bora-Bora	60	40
202†	10f Outrigger canoe, Bora-Bora	95	35

1954

As No. 264 of Cameroun

214	3f Landing craft, Normandy, 1944	1.50	1.50

1956

215	3f Schooner in dry dock, Papeete	1.10	1.10

OMAN

Arabia
1000 baizas = 1 rial saidi

1972

146	5b Dhow and British warship, Matrah, 1809		
147	10b Dhow and British warship, Matrah, 1809		
160	20b Dhow and British warship Matrah, 1809		
192	25b Dhow and British warship, Matrah, 1809		
193	30b British warship, Shinas, 1809		
194	40b British warship, Shinas, 1809		
195	50b British warship, Shinas, 1809		
196	75b British warship, Shinas, 1809		
197	100b British warship, Muscat, 1809		
155	½r British warship, Muscat, 1809		
156	¾r British warship, Muscat, 1809		
157	1r British warship, Muscat, 1809		
	Set of 12	17.00	11.00

1973

172†	15b Dhow building	30	15
174†	65b Dhow and tanker	1.25	85

1979

226†	75b Dhow and modern trawler	1.00	75

227†	40b Landing craft	80	30

1980

235†	150b Naval patrol boat	1.25	1.00

1981

No. 235 surcharged **POSTAGE 20 BAISA**

241†	20b on 150b Naval patrol boat	30	30

250	50b *Sohar* (replica of medieval dhow), Muscat	50	50
251	100b *Sohar*	1.00	1.00
252	130b *Sohar*	1.25	1.25
253	200b *Sohar*, and 17th-century Portuguese galleons	1.75	1.75
	Set of 4	4.00	4.00

256†	400b Missile-armed corvettes	3.25	3.25

1982

257	50b Police launch	60	40

1984

298	100b *Al Munassir* (landing craft)	90	70

1985

299	100b Helicopter rescue from tanker	1.00	75

314 100b Missile-armed corvettes 60 40

1986

323 50b *Sultana* (full-rigged sailing ship),
       1840
324 100b *Shabab Oman* (cadet barquentine)
                               Set of 2 70 50

PAHANG

South-east Asia
100 cents = 1 dollar

1949
As No. 115 of Antigua
50† 15c Paddle-steamer 40 70

1957

82† 20c Malay fishing prau 25 5

PAKISTAN

Indian Sub-continent
100 paisa = 1 rupee

1954

71† 2r Fishing boats, East Pakistan 1.50 5

1960

120 14a Freighter 15 10

1965

227† 15p *Tughril* (destroyer) 15 5

1968

268† 50p *Tughril* (destroyer) and *Ghazi*
        (submarine) 35 15

1975

383 2r25 African canoe 1.00 1.25

1980

532 1r Dhow 30 35

1983

619 60p "Enterprise" class yacht
620 60p "O.K." class dinghy
                               Set of 2 30 10

1987

707† 5r Landing ship 30 35

OFFICIAL STAMPS

1954
No. 71 overprinted **SERVICE**
O59† 2r Fishing boats, East Pakistan 2.00 5

PALAU

North Pacific
100 cents = 1 dollar

1983

34 20c *Antelope* (sail merchantman), 1783
35 20c *Antelope* and Palau canoe

36 20c *Antelope*
37 20c *Antelope*
38 20c *Antelope*
39 20c *Antelope* and Palau canoe at sea
40 20c *Antelope* and building *Oroolong*
        (schooner)
41 20c *Antelope*
                               Set of 8 2.50 1.25

1984

56 40c *Oroolong* (schooner), 1783
57 40c *Duff* (full-rigged missionary ship), 1797
58 40c *Peiho* (expedition steamer), 1908
59 40c *Albatross* (German gunboat), 1885
                               Set of 4 2.00 1.25

61† 20c Fishing pirogue 25 15

1985

73 22c Borotong (cargo canoe)
74 22c Kabeki (war canoe)
75 22c Olechutel (bamboo raft)
76 22c Kaeb (sailing canoe)
                               Set of 4 1.40 80

81 44c German warship, 1885
82 44c Outrigger canoe
83 44c *Hohenzollern* (German Imperial yacht)
        (on Caroline Islands stamp No. 25)
84 44c *Cormoran* (German cruiser), 1914, and
        Hohenzollern (German Imperial yacht)
        (on Caroline Islands stamp No. 19)
                               Set of 4 2.40 1.50

94 44c Kaeb (sailing canoe)
95 44c U.S.S. *Vincennes*, 1835
96 44c *Scharnhorst* (German cruiser), 1910
97 44c Tourist cabin cruiser
                               Set of 4 2.50 1.50

1986

103† 14c Olechutel (raft) 20 10
104† 14c Kaebs (sailing canoes) 20 10
106† 14c Inter-island ferry 20 10

44c AIR MAIL
REPUBLIC OF PALAU
In Memoriam –Haruo I. Remeliik
First President: 1981-1985

"Just now, racing through the waters beneath the Koror- Babeldaob Bridge, our war canoes quickened all our hearts. We are to enter the high seas to sail with all of the other nations."
Haruo I. Remeliik, First Inaugural Address

143† 44c Kabeki (war canoe) 55 30

153† 22c Abandoned landing craft, Airai 30 15

1987

213 22c Three outrigger canoes
214 22c Kaeb and bird
215 22c Holy Family in kaeb
216 22c Kaeb
217 22c Two outrigger canoes
Set of 5 1.00 65

1988

MS236† 25c Kaeb; 25c Spanish "Vizcaya" class cruiser; 25c *Cormoran* (German cruiser); 25c U.S. Trust Territory freighter at Malakal (sheet also contains two other designs) 2.00 1.00

PANAMA

Central America
100 centesimos = 1 balboa

1918

178† 12c *Panama* (cargo liner) at Culebra Cut 14.00 5.50
179† 15c *Panama* at Culebra Cut 9.00 2.75
180† 24c *Cristobal* (cargo liner) in Gatun Lock 18.00 5.50
181† 50c Freighters in Balboa docks 22.00 14.00
182† 1b *Nereus* (U.S. Navy collier) in Pedro Miguel Lock 30.00 18.00

1929

No. 182 overprinted **CORREO AEREO** *and aeroplane*
239† 1b *Nereus* (U.S. navy collier) in Pedro Miguel Lock 18.00 14.00

1936

281† 50c *Resolute* (liner) in Gaillard Cut 6.00 2.75

1937

No. 281 overprinted **UPU**
297† 50c *Resolute* (liner) in Gaillard Cut 7.00 4.25

No. 182 surcharged **CORREO AEREO 5c**
322† 5c on 1b *Nereus* (U.S. Navy collier) in Pedro Miguel Lock 2.50 1.25

1939

358† 1c *Santa Elena* (liner) in Pedro Miguel Lock 1.50 1.00
360† 5c *Rangitata* (liner) in Culebra Cut 1.25 20
361† 10c Panama Canal ferry 1.50 50

1955

574† 1b *Ancon* (liner), 1914 .... 2.75 1.75

1964

878† 10c Yachts 1.50 60
879† 21c Speedboats 2.75 1.50

1970

984† 13c Tanker 45 20

1979

1144 3c Liner in Panama Canal lock
1145 23c Liner
Set of 2 45 25

1984

1377 19c Liner in Panama Canal lock 55 25

1985

1399 19c Tanker in Panama Canal lock 45 20

APPENDIX
The following stamps have either been issued in excess of postal needs, or have not been available to the public in reasonable quantities, at face value. Miniature sheets, imperforate stamps etc., are excluded from this section.

1965
Peaceful Uses of Atomic Energy. Postage ½c US Navy atomic submarine, 1c *Savannah* (nuclear powered freighter); Air 6c *Lenin* (atomic ice-breaker)

1968
Sailing Ship Paintings. Postage 1, 3, 4c; Air 5, 13c

PAPUA

Australasia
12 pence = 1 shilling
20 shillings = 1 pound

1901

9 ½d Lakatoi (trading canoe)
10 1d Lakatoi
11 2d Lakatoi
12 2½d Lakatoi
5 4d Lakatoi
6 6d Lakatoi
14a 1s Lakatoi
8 2s6d Lakatoi
Set of 8 £700 £650

1906
Nos. 9, etc, overprinted **Papua.**
40 ½d Lakatoi
41 1d Lakatoi
42 2d Lakatoi
38 2½d Lakatoi
43 4d Lakatoi
44 6d Lakatoi
25 1s Lakatoi
46 2s6d Lakatoi
Set of 8 £110 £160

1907
As Nos. 9, etc, but inscribed "PAPUA"
66 ½d Lakatoi (black & green)
100 1d Lakatoi (black & red)
68 2d Lakatoi (black & purple)
51a 2½d Lakatoi (black & blue)
52 4d Lakatoi (black & brown)
80 6d lakatoi (black & green)
54 1s Lakatoi (black & orange)
83 2s6d Lakatoi (black & brown)
Set of 8 70.00 95.00

1911
As Nos. 66, etc, but colours changed
84a ½d Lakatoi (green)
85 1d Lakatoi (red)
86 2d Lakatoi (mauve)
87 2½d Lakatoi (blue)
88 4d Lakatoi (olive)
89 6d Lakatoi (brown)
90 1s Lakatoi (yellow)
91 2s6d Lakatoi (red)
Set of 8 48.00 70.00

1917
Nos. 84a, 86/9 and 91 surcharged **ONE PENNY**
93 1d on ½d Lakatoi
94 1d on 2d Lakatoi
95 1d on 2½d Lakatoi
96 1d on 4d Lakatoi
97 1d on 6d Lakatoi
98 1d on 2s6d Lakatoi
Set of 6 24.00 38.00

1919
As Nos. 66, etc, but colours changed and additional values
99 ½d Lakatoi (green & olive)
101 1½d Lakatoi
102 2d Lakatoi (brown & purple)
102a 2d Lakatoi (brown & red)
103 2½d Lakatoi (green & blue)
104 3d Lakatoi
105 4d Lakatoi (brown & orange)
106 5d Lakatoi
107 6d Lakatoi (purple & red)
127 9d Lakatoi
108 1s Lakatoi (brown & green)
128 1s3d Lakatoi
109a 2s6d Lakatoi (red & pink)
110 5s Lakatoi
111 10s Lakatoi
Set of 15 £200 £300

1929

No. 104 overprinted **AIR MAIL**

114	3d Lakatoi	....	1.10	6.00

1930

Nos. 104 and 107/8 overprinted **AIR MAIL** *on aeroplane*

118	3d Lakatoi		
119	6d Lakatoi		
120	1s Lakatoi		
		Set of 3 10.50	23.00

1931

Nos. 101 and 108/10 surcharged in words or figures

122	2d on 1½d Lakatoi	
125	5d on 1s Lakatoi	
126	9d on 2s6d Lakatoi	
123	1s3d on 5d Lakatoi	
		Set of 4 9.50 20.00

1932

140†	1s3d Lakatoi (trading canoe)	....	12.00	20.00

1938

158	2d Freighter, Port Moresby	
159	3d Freighter, Port Moresby	
160	5d Freighter, Port Moresby	
161	8d Freighter, Port Moresby	
162	1s Freighter, Port Moresby	
		Set of 5 35.00 22.00

1939

163	2d Outrigger canoes	
164	3d Outrigger canoes	
165	5d Outrigger canoes	
166	8d Outrigger canoes	
167	1s Outrigger canoes	
168	1s6d Outrigger canoes	
		Set of 6 55.00 40.00

OFFICIAL STAMPS

1931

Nos. 99/102 and 104/9a overprinted **O S**

O1	½d Lakatoi	
O2a	1d Lakatoi	
O3	1½d Lakatoi	
O4	2d Lakatoi	
O5	3d Lakatoi	
O6	4d Lakatoi	
O7	5d Lakatoi	
O8	6d Lakatoi	
O9	9d Lakatoi	
O10	1s Lakatoi	
O11	1s3d Lakatoi	
O12a	2s6d Lakatoi	
		Set of 12 95.00 £180

PAPUA NEW GUINEA

Australasia

1952 12 pence = 1 shilling
20 shillings = 1 pound
1966 100 cents = 1 dollar
1975 100 toea = 1 kina

1952

10†	1s Lakatoi (trading canoe)	....	2.75	5

1957

No. 10 surcharged **7d**

17†	7d on 1s Lakatoi (trading canoe)	....	20	5

1961

47†	8d *Dedele* (freighter)	....	30	15

1965

72	4d Canoe figurehead	
73	1s3d Canoe figurehead	
74	1s6d Canoe figurehead	
75	4s Canoe figurehead	
		Set of 4 4.50 1.40

1967

120†	50c U.S.S. *Lexington* (aircraft carrier), 1942	....	50	30

1969

156†	5c "Fireball" class yacht	....	10	5

1970

170†	10c Masawa canoe	....	30	15
172†	30c H.M.S. *Basilisk* (paddle-sloop), 1873		80	25

1971

204†	7c Outrigger canoe	....	15	5

1972

220†	7c *Eureka* (schooner), 1922	....	50	5
222†	20c Gold dredger	....	1.50	1.50

1973

245†	7c Lakatoi (trading canoe)	....	20	5
249†	14c Outrigger canoe	....	45	30
251†	20c Racing canoes, Manus		85	40
255†	30c Outrigger canoe	....	1.00	75
256†	40c Fishing canoes, Madang	....	1.50	80

261†	6c *Hohenzollern* (German Imperial yacht) (on New Guinea stamp No. G17)	......	20	35
263†	9c Lakatoi (trading canoe) (on Papua stamp No. 14a)	....	30	45

1974

277	7c Lakatoi (trading canoe), Motu	
278	10c Morobe (canoe), Tami	
279	25c Racing canoe, Aramia	
280	30c Buka Island canoe	
		Set of 4 2.75 2.75

1976

297	7t *Bulolo* (liner)	
298	15t *Macdhui* (liner)	
299	25t *Malaita* (liner)	
300	60t *Montoro* (cargo liner)	
		Set of 4 3.50 3.75

311†	15t Scout outrigger canoe	....	65	75

1979

363	14t East New Britain canoe figurehead	
364	21t Sepik war canoe figurehead	
365	25t Tobriand Island canoe figurehead	
366	40t Milne Bay canoe	
		Set of 4 1.10 1.50

1981

410†	40t *Aitape* (patrol boat)	....	70	65

418†	15t Fishing canoe	30	30
420†	60t Fishing canoe	95	85

1982

457†	10t French sail warship, 1882	15	10

1983

467†	50t Freighter at wharf	70	75

1984

487	10t H.M.S. *Nelson* (armoured frigate), 1884		
488	10t Yacht, 1984		
489	45t Coaster and yacht, 1984		
490	45t *Elizabeth* (German warship), 1884		
	Set of 4	2.00	2.00

1987

543	5t *Roebuck* (Dampier), 1700		
544	15t H.M.S. *Fly* (sail sloop) (Blackwood), 1845		
545	17t H.M.S. *Fly*		
546	20t H.M.S. *Rattlesnake* (survey ship) (Owen Stanley), 1849		
548	35t *San Pedrico* and zabra (Torres), 1606		
549	40t *L'Astrolabe* (D'Urville), 1827		
550	45t *Neva* (steam launch) (D'Albertis), 1876		
551	60t Spanish galleon (Jorge de Meneses), 1526		
552	70t *Eendracht* (Schouten and Le Maire), 1616		
553	1k H.M.S. *Blanche* (screw sloop) (Simpson), 1872		
555	2k *Merrie England* (screw steamer), 1889		
	Set of 11	6.00	6.50

1988

575	35t Lakatoi (trading canoe)	45	50

PARAGUAY

South America
1931 10 centavos = 1 peso
1944 100 centimos = 1 guarani

1931

397	1p *Paraguay* (gunboat) (red)		
398	1p *Paraguay* (blue)		
399	2p *Paraguay* (orange)		
400	2p *Paraguay* (brown)		
401	3p *Paraguay* (green)		
402	3p *Paraguay* (blue)		
403	3p *Paraguay* (red)		
404	6p *Paraguay* (green)		
405	6p *Paraguay* (mauve)		
406	6p *Paraguay* (blue)		
407	10p *Paraguay* (red)		
408	10p *Paraguay* (green)		
409	10p *Paraguay* (brown)		
410	10p *Paraguay* (blue)		
411	10p *Paraguay* (pink)		
	Set of 15	9.00	8.50

412	1p50 *Humaita* (gunboat) (violet)		
413	1p50 *Humaita* (blue)		
	Set of 2	55	40

1933

456	10c Fleet of Columbus		
457	20c Fleet of Columbus		
458	50c Fleet of Columbus		
459	1p Fleet of Columbus		
460	1p50 Fleet of Columbus		
461	2p Fleet of Columbus		
462	5p Fleet of Columbus		
463	10p Fleet of Columbus		
	Set of 8	2.75	2.75

1944

591†	10c *Tacuary* (paddle-steamer)	40	25
595†	1c Freighter, Port Asuncion (air)	8	5
597†	3c *Tacuary*	15	12

1946
As Nos. 591 and 595

640†	1c *Tacuary*	5	5
648†	20c Freighter, Port Asuncion (air)	10	10

1948

678	2c *Paraghari* (freighter)		
679	5c *Paraghari*		
680	10c *Paraghari*		
681	15c *Paraghari*		
682	50c *Paraghari*		
683	1g *Paraghari*		
	Set of 6	1.25	60

1961

901†	90c Motorised timber barge	5	5
903†	2g Motorised timber barge	10	5
906†	18g15 Motorised timber barge (air)	45	35

1962

1030†	30c Freighter	5	5
1031†	90c Freighter	5	5
1032†	1g50 Freighter	10	5
1033†	2g Freighter	10	8
1034†	4g20 Freighter	15	10

1973

1162	50g *President Stroessner* (liner)	55	35

APPENDIX

The following stamps have either been issued in excess of postal needs, or have not been available to the public in reasonable quantities, at face value. Miniature sheets, imperforate stamps, etc. are excluded from this section.

1965

Pres J. Kennedy Commem. 15c American motor torpedo-boat

1968

Mexico Olympic Games. 36g Olympic yacht

1971

Munich Olympic Games. 75c Olympic yachts
150th Death Anniv. of Napoleon. 12g45 Battle of Trafalgar, 1805

1972

Famous Sailing Ships. Postage 10, 15, 20, 25, 30, 50, 75c; Air 12g45, 18g25, 50g
Visit of President of Paraguay to Japan. 10c Paddle-steamer and launch, 1871

1973

"Apollo" Moon Missions and Future Space Projects. 20c American aircraft carrier

1974

Sailing Ships (diamond-shaped designs). 5, 10, 15, 20, 25, 35, 40, 50c
Centenary of U.P.U. Air 20g Full-rigged sailing ship and modern liner

1975

"Expo '75", Okinawa, Japan. 10g Japanese junk
Bicentenary of American Revolution. Ship Paintings. 5, 10, 15, 20, 25, 35, 40, 50c
Bicentenary of American Revolution (2nd issue). 40g Battle of Flamborough Head, 1779

1976

Ship Paintings (sailing ships and first oil tanker). Postage 1, 2, 3, 4, 5g; Air 10, 15, 20g
German Ship Paintings. (1st series). Postage 1, 2, 3, 4, 5g; Air 10, 15, 20g
Bicentenary of American Revolution (4th series). 4g *Savannah* (paddle-steamer)

1977

German Ship Paintings (2nd series). Postage 1, 2, 3, 4, 5g; Air 10, 15, 20g

1978

Paintings and Stamp Exhibition Emblems. 3g Schooner

1979

Famous Sailing Ships (1st series). Postage 3, 4, 5, 6, 7, 8, 20g; Air 10, 25g

1980
Famous Sailings Ships (2nd series). Postage 3, 4, 5, 6, 7, 8, 20g; Air 10, 25g

1981
Wedding of Prince of Wales. Historic British Ships. Postage 25, 50c, 1, 2, 3, 4, 5g; Air 5, 10, 30g

1983
Aircraft carriers. 25, 50c, 1, 2, 3, 4, 5g
25th Anniv. of International Maritime Organization (sailing ships). 5, 10, 30g

---

PATIALA
Indian Sub-continent
12 pies = 1 anna
16 annas = 1 rupee

1937
No. 256 of India overprinted **PATIALA STATE**
89† 6a *Strathnaver* (liner) 4.00 6.00

PENANG
South-east Asia
100 cents = 1 dollar

1949
As No. 115 of Antigua
24† 15c Paddle-steamer 45 40

1957

50† 20c Malay fishing prau 20 20

1960
As No. 50, but with crest in place of Queen Elizabeth II
61† 20c Malay fishing prau 20 5

PENRHYN ISLAND
South Pacific
1920 12 pence = 1 shilling
20 shillings = 1 pound
1973 100 cents = 1 dollar

1920
As No. 82 of Cook Islands, but inscribed "PENRHYN"
39† 1d Schooner 2.00 4.75

1981

166	1c *Amatasi* (canoe)		
167	1c *Ndrua* (canoe)		
168	1c *Waka* (canoe)		
169	1c *Tongiaki* (canoe)		
170	3c *Va'a Teu'ua* (canoe		
171	3c *Victoria* (Del Cano)		
172	3c *Golden Hind* (Drake)		
173	3c *Boudeuse* (Bougainville)		
174	4c *H.M.S. Bounty* (Bligh)		
175	4c *L'Astrolabe* (Dumont D'Urville)		
176	4c *Star of India* (sailing clipper), 1861		
177	4c *Great Republic* (sailing clipper), 1853		
178	6c *Balcutha* (sailing clipper), 1886		
179	6c *Coonatto* (sailing clipper), 1863		
180	6c *Antiope* (sailing clipper), 1866		
181	6c *Taeping* (sailing clipper), 1863		
182	10c *Preussen* (full-rigged sailing ship), 1902		
183	10c *Pamir* (barque), 1921		
184	10c *Cap Hornier* (full-rigged sailing ship), 1910		
185	10c *Patriarch* (sailing clipper), 1869		
186	15c *Amatasi*		
187	15c *Ndrua*		
188	15c *Waka*		
189	15c *Tongiaki*		
190	20c *Va'a Teu'ua*		
191	20c *Victoria*		
192	20c *Golden Hind*		

193	20c *Boudeuse*		
194	30c *H.M.S. Bounty*		
195	30c *L'Astrolabe*		
196	30c *Star of India*		
197	30c *Great Republic*		
198	50c *Balcutha*		
199	50c *Coonatto*		
200	50c *Antiope*		
201	50c *Taeping*		
202	$1 *Preussen*		
203	$1 *Pamir*		
204	$1 *Cap Hornier*		
205	$1 *Patriarch*		
206	$2 *Cutty Sark* (sailing clipper), 1869		
207	$4 *Mermerus* (sailing clipper), 1872		
208	$6 *H.M.S. Resolution* and *H.M.S. Discovery* (Cook)		

Set of 43 21.00 21.00

1983

290†	8c 19th-century whaling ship	15	10
292†	35c 19th-century whaleboat	60	45
293†	60c 19th-century whaling ship	95	75

295†	36c *Mercury* (cable ship)	40	35
297†	60c *Mercury*	70	60
MS298	36c + 3c *Mercury*, 60c + 3c *Mercury* (sheet contains one other design)	1.50	1.60

Nos. 182/5, 190/7 and 206 surcharged

299†	18c on 10c *Preussen*	15	20
300†	18c on 10c *Pamir*	15	20
301†	18c on 10c *Cap Hornier*	15	20
302†	18c on 10c *Patriarch*	15	20
303†	36c on 20c *Va'a Teu'ua*	30	35
304†	36c on 20c *Victoria*	30	35
305†	36c on 20c *Boudeuse*	30	35
307†	36c on 30c *H.M.S. Bounty*	30	35
308†	36c on 30c *L'Astrolabe*	30	35
309†	36c on 30c *Star of India*	30	35
310†	36c on 30c *Great Republic*	30	35
311†	$1.20 on $2 *Cutty Sark*	1.25	1.40

No. 208 surcharged **$5.60**

319†	$5.60 on $6 *H.M.S. Resolution* and *H.M.S. Discovery*	3.75	3.75

1984

337	2c *Waka*		
338	4c *Amatasi*		
339	5c *Ndrua*		
340	8c *Tongiaki*		
341	10c *Victoria*		
342	18c *Golden Hind*		
343	20c *Boudeuse*		
344	30c *H.M.S. Bounty*		
345	36c *L'Astrolabe*		
346	48c *Great Republic*		
347	50c *Star of India*		
348	50c *Coonatto*		
349	72c *Antiope*		
350	80c *Balcutha*		
351	96c *Cap Hornier*		
352	$1.20 *Pamir*		
353	$3 *Mermerus*		
354	$5 *Cutty Sark*		
355	$9.60 *H.M.S. Resolution* and *H.M.S. Discovery*		

Set of 19 15.00 16.00

1985
Nos. 206/8, 337/47 and 349/55 overprinted **O.H.M.S.** *or surcharged also*

O18†	2c *Waka*	5	5
O19†	4c *Amatasi*	5	5
O20†	5c *Ndrua*	5	5
O21†	8c *Tongiaki*	5	5
O22†	10c *Victoria*	8	10
O23†	18c *Golden Hind*	12	15
O24†	20c *Boudeuse*	15	20
O25†	30c *H.M.S. Bounty*	20	25
O26†	40c on 36c *L'Astrolabe*	30	35
O27†	50c *Star of India*	35	40
O28†	55c on 48c *Great Republic*	40	45
O29†	75c on 72c *Antiope*	50	55
O30†	75c on 96c *Cap Hornier*	50	55
O31†	80c *Balcutha*	55	60
O32†	$1.20 *Pamir*	85	90
O33†	$2 *Cutty Sark*	1.40	1.50
O34†	$3 *Mermerus*	2.10	2.25
O35†	$4 *Mermerus*	2.75	3.00
O36†	$5 *Cutty Sark*	3.00	3.25
O37†	$6 *H.M.S. Resolution* and *H.M.S. Discovery*	3.75	4.00
O38†	$9.60 *H.M.S. Resolution* and *H.M.S. Discovery*	6.00	6.25

PERAK
South-east Asia
100 cents = 1 dollar

1949
As No. 115 of Antigua
125† 15c Paddle-steamer 60 45

1957

157† 20c Malay fishing prau 20 5

PERLIS
South-east Asia
100 cents = 1 dollar

1949
As No. 115 of Antigua
4† 15c Paddle-steamer 65 1.75

1957

36† 20c Malay fishing prau 20 35

PERU
South America
1936 100 centavos = 1 peso
1985 100 centimos = 1 inti

1936

567†	2c *San Cristobal* (caravel), 1527	70	20
571†	15c *Reina del Pacifico* (liner) in Callao docks	70	25
574†	1s *Sacramento* (gunboat), 1821	12.00	1.60

597†   15c *Inca* (mail steamer), Lake Titicaca
(blue)   50   10

1952

775†   5c Tuna fishing boat   5   5
784†   40c *Maranon* (river gunboat) (green) (air)   8   5

1953

793†   1s25 *Santa Maria, Pinta* and *Nina*
(Columbus)   40   15
795†   2s20 *Santa Maria, Pinta* and *Nina*
(Columbus) 1.00   30

1957

800†   1s25 *La Victorieuse* (French 19th-century
steam frigate)   35   20

803†   10c *Peru* (paddle-steamer) (on Pacific
Steam Navigation local stamp of 1857)   5   5
804†   15c *Peru* (paddle-steamer) (on Pacific
Steam Navigation local stamp of 1857)   5   5

1961

847   50c *Amazonas* (cadet sailing ship)
848   80c *Amazonas* (cadet sailing ship)
849   1s *Amazonas* (cadet sailing ship)
Set of 3   60   20

1963

*As No. 784 but colour changed. Inscribed "THOMAS DE LA RUE
CO, LTD" at foot*
869†   40c *Maranon* (river gunboat) (orange) ..   20   5

1966

As No. 869, but inscribed "INA" at foot
923†   40c *Maranon* (river gunboat) (orange) ..   5   5

1969

987   2s50 *Kon Tiki* (replica raft)
988   3s *Kon Tiki* (air)
989   4s *Kon Tiki*
990   5s50 *Kon Tiki*
991   6s50 *Kon Tiki*
Set of 5   90   60

1005   50s *Huascar* (ironclad warship), 1879 ..   3.00   1.75

1971

1100†   7s50 *Sacramento* (naval schooner),
1821   50   25

1973

1198†   50s Reed boats 2.75   1.00

1216†   1s50 *Ilo* (freighter)   15   5
1217†   2s50 Trawler   20   5

1977

1341   14s Tanker 1.00   25

1979

1440†   14s Battle of Iquique, 1879   10   5
1442†   25s *Union* (steam corvette), 1879   30   12
1443†   25s Battle of Angamos, 1879   30   12
1446†   100s *Huascar* (ironclad warship), 1877   85   45

1980

No. 1440 surcharged 25
1473†   25s on 14s Battle of Iquique, 1879   20   12

1983

1558   150s *Almirante Grau* (cruiser), 1907
1559   350s *Ferre* (submarine), 1913
Set of 2   1.25   55

1984

1577   250s Container ship at wharf
1578   300s Container ship
Set of 2   60   30

1593†   600s Battle of Angamos, 1879   35   20
1595†   600s Battle of Iquique, 1879   35   20

1597   250s *Almirante Guise* (destroyer), 1934
1598   400s *America* (river gunboat), 1905
Set of 2   45   25

1986

1636   3i50 Reed canoe   35   20

1641   1i50 *Casma (R-1)* (submarine), 1926
1642   2e50 *Abtao* (submarine), 1954
Set of 2   40   25

1652   1i *Gamarra* (brigantine)
1653   1i *Manco Capac* (ironclad warship)
Set of 2   30   20

1987

1668   1i *Peru* (paddle-steamer) (on Pacific
Steam Navigation local stamps of
1857) 10   5

1988

1688   7i *Humboldt* (Antarctic supply vessel) .. 30   20

POSTAGE DUE STAMPS

1874

D32†   5c *Adriatic* (paddle-steamer) 12   12
D33†   10c *Adriatic* 15   15
D34†   20c *Adriatic* 30   30
D35†   50c *Adriatic* 8.75   3.50

1881

Nos. D32/5 *overprinted* **UNION POSTAL UNIVERSAL LIMA
PLATA** *in oval*

D48†   5c *Adriatic* 6.75   6.00
D49†   10c *Adriatic* 6.75   6.00
D50†   20c *Adriatic* 25.00   20.00
D51†   50c *Adriatic* 60.00   50.00

Nos. D32/5 *overprinted* **LIMA CORREOS** *in double-lined circle*

D53†   5c *Adriatic* 6.75   6.00
D54†   10c *Adriatic* 8.00   6.75
D55†   20c *Adriatic* 25.00   20.00
D56†   50c *Adriatic* 80.00   70.00

1883

Nos. D48/51 *additionally overprinted* **PERU** *within triangle*

D250†   5c *Adriatic* 6.75   6.00
D253†   10c *Adriatic* 6.75   6.00
D256†   20c *Adriatic* £475   £475
D257†   50c *Adriatic* 55.00   48.00

1884

Nos. D32/5 *overprinted* **PERU** *in triangle*

D262†   5c *Adriatic* 20   20
D267†   10c *Adriatic* 25   25
D269†   20c *Adriatic* 35   35
D271†   50c *Adriatic* 2.75   1.10

1896

Nos. D32/4 *overprinted* **DEFICIT**

D349†   5c *Adriatic* 12   12
D350†   10c *Adriatic* 20   12
D351†   20c *Adriatic* 25   20

1902

No. D34 *surcharged* **DEFICIT** *and value in words*

D363   1c on 20c *Adriatic*
D364   5c on 20c *Adriatic*
Set of 2   1.50   1.40

STAMP MONTHLY

— finest and most informative magazine for all
collectors. Obtainable from your newsagent or by
postal subscription — details on request.

PHILIPPINES

South-east Asia
1932 100 centavos = 1 peso
1962 100 sentimes = 1 piso

1932

426†   12c Freighters at pier, Manila 50   50

1935

470   2p U.S.S. *Olympia* (cruiser) and *Reina
Christian* (Spanish warship), Manila
Bay, 1898 .... 3.50   1.25

1941

566   8c Filipino vinta
567   20c Filipino vinta
568   60c Filipino vinta
569   1p Filipino vinta
Set of 4   1.50   2.25

1954

774   5c Filipino vinta
775   18c Filipino vinta
776   50c Filipino vinta (air)
Set of 3   3.50   1.75

1960

848   6c Filipino vinta, Manila Bay
849   25c Filipino vinta, Manila Bay
Set of 2   50   35

1963

946†   20s Outrigger canoe 35   30

950   6s 16th-century Spanish galleon
951   30s 16th-century Spanish galleon
Set of 2   55   25

1965

1003†   70s 16th-century Spanish galleon 90   40

1967

1051   4s River launches
1052   20s River launches
1053   50s River launches
Set of 3   75   45

1054   70s Outrigger canoes   70   50

1969

No. 1051 *overprinted* **PHILATELIC WEEK NOV. 24-30. 1968**
1099   4s River launches 15   5

No. 946 *surcharged* **1969 PHILATELIC WEEK 10s KOREO**
1135†   10s on 20s Outrigger canoe 25   8

1970

1167†   10s Outrigger tourist canoe 5   5

1971

1193†   20s Outrigger canoe, Mindanao 15   10

1196†   10s Filipino vinta, Fort Del Pilar 5   5

1208   10s 16th-century Spanish galleon
1209   75s 16th-century Spanish galleon
Set of 2   70   40

1972

No. 950 *surcharged* **1972 PHILATELIC WEEK TEN 10s**
1275†   10s on 6s 16th-century Spanish galleon   10   10

1975

1352 15s Malayan prau 10 5

1382 1p50 Full-rigged sailing ship and junks, Manila, 1875 .... 1.00 35

1977

1437 1p30 *Mercury* (cable ship) 45 25

1978

1461† 5p Filipino vinta 2.75 2.00
MS1462† 7p50 Filipino vinta, 7p50 Schooner (sheet contains two other designs) ... 35.00 35.00

1472 1p40 *Mercury* (cable ship) 55 25

1979

1502 30s Oil rig
1503 45s Oil rig
                      Set of 2 25 15

1532 30s Fast patrol boat
1533 45s Fast patrol boat
                      Set of 2 25 15

1980

1606 30s Filipino vinta
1607 2p30 Filipino vinta
                      Set of 2 1.40 80

1984

MS1822† 7p50 16th-century Spanish galleon (sheet contains three other designs) 4.00 4.00

Stamp from No. MS1822 *surcharged* **420TH PHIL-MEXICAN FRIEND-SHIP 8.3.84 20**
1832 7p20 on 7p50 16th-century Spanish galleon 85 40

1836† 7p20 Sailboards 75 35
MS1839† 6p Sailboards (sheet contains three other designs) 3.00 3.00

1850 60s Caracao (canoes)
1851 1p20 Junk
1852 6p Spanish galleon
1853 7p20 Casco (Filipino cargo prau)
1854 8p40 Early paddle-steamer
1855 20p Modern liner
                      Set of 6 5.25 2.50

1985

1908 1p20 Spanish galleon, 1565
1909 3p60 Spanish galleon, 1565
                      Set of 2 50 15

1987

2046† 1p Shipwrecked 16th-century Spanish galleon 5 5

PITCAIRN ISLANDS

South Pacific
1940 12 pence = 1 shilling
20 shillings = 1 pound
1968 100 cents = 1 dollar

1940

4† 2d H.M.S. *Bounty* (Bligh) 1.60 1.00
6† 6d H.M.S. *Bounty* 2.50 2.00

1949

As No. 115 *of Antigua*
14† 3d Paddle-steamer 8.50 4.50

1957

26† 1s Model of H.M.S. *Bounty* 70 50
28† 2s6d Pitcairn whaleboat 15.00 6.50

1961

31† 1s *Mary Ann* (brigantine), 1859 .... 75 35

1964

36† ½d Pitcairn longboat 5 12
37† 1d H.M.S. *Bounty* 30 15
38† 2d Pitcairn longboat 40 20

1967

64 ½d Mangarevan canoe, *c.* 1325
65 1d *San Pedro y Pablo* (Quiros), 1606
66 8d *San Pedro y Pablo* and *Los Tres Reyes* (Quiros), 1606
67 1s H.M.S. *Swallow* (Carteret), 1767
68 1s 6d *Hercules* (East Indiaman), 1819
                      Set of 5 45 35

Nos. 36/8 *surcharged with Bounty anchor and value*
69† ½c on ½d Pitcairn longboat 5 5
70† 1c on 1d H.M.S. *Bounty* 30 15
71† 2c on 2d Pitcairn longboat 35 15

82† 1c Launch from H.M.S. *Bounty* 10 5
83† 8c Launch from H.M.S. *Bounty* 20 10

1969

97† 4c H.M.S. *Bounty* (plans) 25 15
100† 8c Pitcairn longboat 35 15

1972

124 4c Pitcairn longboat
125 20c Pitcairn longboat
                      Set of 2 1.25 1.75

1974

154†   35c Pitcairn longboat and mail steamer   65   70

1975

157   4c H.M.S. *Seringapatam*, 1830
158   10c *Pitcairn* (mission schooner), 1890
159   18c *Atheni* (liner), 1901
160   50c *Gothic* (liner), 1948
           Set of 4   6.00   5.00

1976

168†   10c H.M.S. *Bounty*   60   65
170†   50c *Mayflower* (Pilgrim Fathers), 1620 . .   1.25   1.40

1977

175†   2c Building a longboat   5   5
176†   5c Pitcairn longboats   5   5
183† $1 Royal Yacht *Britannia*   85   95

1978

191†   20c R.F.A. *Sir Geraint* (landing ship) and
       landing craft   40   50

1980

MS205   35c Pitcairn longboats (sheet contains
     three other designs) 1.00   1.50

1981

216†   9c *Morayshire* (full-rigged sailing ship),
       1856   15   20
218†   70c *Morayshire*   45   65

1983

234†   6c Freighter   5   8
236†   70c Fishing punt   60   65

238†   6c *Topaz* (American sealer), 1808   20   15
239†   20c *Topaz* and canoe   30   30

1984

MS263   50c Aluminium longboat, 50c Wooden
     longboat 1.75   2.25

1985

273   50c *ACT 6* (container ship)
274   50c *Columbus Louisiana* (container ship)
275   50c *Essi Gina* (tanker)
276   50c *Stolt Spirit* (tanker)
           Set of 4   2.25   2.25

1986

293†   20c *Pitcairn* (mission schooner), 1890 . .   25   25
295† $2 Pitcairn longboat 1.75   1.75

1987

296   50c *Samoan Reefer* (freighter)
297   50c *Brussel* (container ship)
298   50c *Australian Exporter* (container ship)
299   50c *Taupo* (cargo liner)
           Set of 4   2.25   2.25

COLLECT MAMMALS ON STAMPS

A Stanley Gibbons thematic catalogue on this popular subject. Copies available at £7.50 (p. + p. £2) from: Stanley Gibbons Publications Ltd, 5 Parkside, Christchurch Road, Ringwood, Hants BH24 3SH.

1988

MS314 $3 H.M.S. *Bounty* (full-size replica) 2.25   2.40

315   5c H.M.S. *Swallow* (survey ship), 1767
316   10c H.M.S. *Pandora* (frigate), 1791
317   15c H.M.S. *Briton* and H.M.S. *Tagus*
       (frigates), 1814
318   20c H.M.S. *Blossom* (survey ship), 1825
319   30c *Lucy Anne* (barque), 1831
320   35c *Charles Doggett* (whaling ship), 1831
321   40c H.M.S. *Fly* (sloop), 1838
322   60c *Camden* (missionary brig), 1840
323   90c H.M.S. *Virago* (paddle-sloop), 1853
324   $1.20 *Rakaia* (screw-steamer), 1867
325   $1.80 H.M.S. *Sappho* (screw-sloop), 1882
326   $5 H.M.S. *Champion* (corvette), 1893
           Set of 12   7.25   8.00

POLAND

Eastern Europe
100 groszy = 1 zloty

1925

247†   20g Galleon 2.00   8
251†   45g Galleon 7.50   35

1935

318†   10g *Batory* (liner)   60   10
315†   15g *Pilsudski* (liner) 2.40   5

1941

485†   1z50 *Orzel* (submarine) 6.00   5.00

1943

486†   5g U-boat under attack   85   85

1944

No. 485 *surcharged* **MONTE CASSINO 18.V.1944 Zt1 Gr20**
497†   1z20 on 1z50 *Orzel* 10.00   13.00

1945

526†	50g + 2z H.M.S. *Dragon* (cruiser) (loaned to Polish Navy, 1943–44)	7.00	5.50
527†	1z + 3z *Dar Pomorza* (cadet ship)	3.50	5.50

1948

619	6z Shipbuilding yard		
620	15z Freighter at wharf		
621	35z *General M. Zaruski* (cadet ketch)		
	Set of 3	5.75	6.00

1949

653	30z Liner	1.50	1.60

1952

738†	55g Tug and freighters	25	25

762	30g + 15g Yachts		
763	45g + 15g *Dar Pomorza* (cadet ship)		
764	90g Freighter under construction		
	Set of 3	3.00	95

783	5g Shipbuilding yard, Gdansk		
784	15g Shipbuilding yard, Gdansk		
	Set of 2	30	10

1953

814	80c *Dalmor* (trawler)		
815	1z35 *Czech* (freighter) at wharf		
	Set of 2	2.50	3.00

1954

883†	1z55 *Soldek* (freighter) at wharf	3.00	55

1956

962	5g *Kilinski* (freighter)		
963	10g Tug and barges		
964	20g *Pokoj* (freighter)		
965	45gf *Marceii Nowatka* (freighter) in shipyard		
966	60g *Fryderyk Chopin* (freighter) and *Radunia* (trawler)		
	Set of 5	1.50	55

1957

1040c†	50z *Batory* (liner)	6.00	1.60

1043	60g *Torrens* (full-rigged sailing ship), 1884		
1044	2z50 *Torrens*		
	Set of 2	75	15

1958

1067†	3z40 Kogge	25	10

1959

1080†	40g Yacht	35	12

1100†	6z40 Barges and fishing boats	2.75	1.00

1960

1190†	95g *Czarny Orzel* (17th-century warship)	15	5
1192†	1z15 Galleon	10	5
1194†	1z50 Hanseatic kogge	15	5
1195†	1z55 17th-century sailing barge	15	5

1961

1231	60g *Leskov* (trawler support ship)		
1232	1z55 *Severodvinsk* (depot ship)		
1233	2z50 *Rambutan* (coaster)		
1234	3z40 *Krynica* (freighter)		
1235	4z *B54* (freighter)		
1236	5z60 *Bavsk* (tanker)		
	Set of 6	7.00	2.75

1245†	2z50 Tug and floating crane	30	12

1962

1311†	1z55 Shipyard, Gdansk	15	5

1343	60g *Aurora* (Russian cruiser)	25	5

1963

Coloured backgrounds

1370	5g 15th-century B.C. Egyptian galley		
1371	10g 15th-century B.C. Phoenician merchantman		
1372	20g 5th-century B.C. Greek trireme		
1373	30g 3rd-century B.C. Roman merchantman		
1374	40g 9th-century Viking longship		
1375	60g 14th-century Hanse kogge		
1376	1z 16th-century hulk		
1377	1z15 15th-century carrack		
	Set of 8	1.40	35

1412†	40g *Blyskawica* (destroyer)	15	5
1417†	2z50 Amphibious troop carrier	40	5

1964

As No. 1370/7, but without coloured backgrounds, and some new designs

1451	5g 15th-century B.C. Egyptian galley		
1452	10g 15th-century B.C. Phoenician merchantman		
1453	20g 5th-century B.C. Greek trireme		
1454	30g 3rd-century Roman merchantman		
1455	40g 9th-century Viking longship		
1456	60g 14th-century Hanse kogge		
1457	1z 16th-century hulk		
1458	1z15 15th-century carrack		
1459	1z35 *Santa Maria* (Columbus)		
1460	1z50 *Ark Royal* (British galleon), 1587		
1461	1z55 17th-century Polish warship		
1462	2z 17th-century Dutch fleute		
1463	2z10 18th-century ship of the line		
1464	2z50 19th-century sail frigate		
1465	3z *Flying Cloud* (sailing clipper)		
1466	3z40 *Dar Pomorza* (cadet ship)		
	Set of 18	4.00	80

1501† 60g Shipbuilding yard, Gdansk 10 5

1526† 60g Pontoon 12 5

1965

1566 30g "Dragon" class yachts
1567 40g "5.5m" class yachts
1568 50g "Finn" class yachts
1569 60g "V" class yachts
1570 1z35 "Cadet" class yachts
1571 4z "Star" class yachts
1572 5z60 "Flying Dutchman" class yachts
1573 6z50 "Amethyst" class yachts
　　　　　　　　　　 Set of 8 4.25 1.50
MS1573a 15z "Finn" class yachts 2.00 1.10

1966

1633† 60g Freighter 15 5

1686† 40g Yacht 5 5
1687† 40g Yacht, Warsaw 5 5
1692† 2z Batory (liner) 35 5

1967

1774† 60g Aurora (Russian cruiser) 12 5

1968

1860† 60g Blyskawica (destroyer) 15 5

1969

1898† 1z35 Cruising yacht 20 5
1899† 1z50 Trawler 20 5

1904 60g Opty (yacht) 20 5

1970

2010 40g Piorun (destroyer)
2011 60g Orzel (submarine)
2012 2z50 H.M.S. Garland (destroyer) (loaned
　　　 to Polish Navy 1940–46)
　　　　　　　　　　 Set of 3 75 25

1971

2030 40g Dar Pomorza (cadet ship)
2031 60g Stefan Batory (liner)
2032 1z15 Perkun (ice-breaker)
2033 1z35 R-I (lifeboat)
2034 1z50 Ziemia Szczecinska (bulk carrier)
2035 2z50 Beskidy (tanker)
2036 5z Hel (fast freighter)
2037 8z50 Gryf (ferry)
　　　　　　　　　　 Set of 8 3.50 1.00

2110† 60g Manifest Lipcowy (container ship)
　　　 and ship under construction 5 5

1973

2263† 1z50 Missile boat 30 12

2268† 1z50 Lucy Margaret (schooner) 20 5
2271† 2z70 Drzewiecki's submarine, 1877 .... 35 15

STANLEY GIBBONS
STAMP COLLECTING SERIES

Introductory booklets on *How to Start, How to Identify Stamps* and *Collecting by Theme.* A series of well illustrated guides at a low price.
Write for details.

1974

2304 1z 16th-century galleon
2305 1z50 Dal (sloop), 1934
2306 2z70 Opty (yacht), 1969
2307 4z Dar Pomorza (cadet ship), 1972
2308 4z90 Polenez (yacht), 1973
　　　　　　　　　　 Set of 5 1.75 70

1975

2388 1z Mary and Margaret (emigrant ship),
　　　 1608 .... 10 5

2463 1z Zawrat (tanker)
2464 1z Gryf (ferry)
2465 1z50 Container ship
2466 1z50 Stefan Batory (liner)
2467 2z Ziema Szczecinska (bulk carrier)
2468 4z20 Bulk carrier
2469 6z90 Hydrofoil and river boat
2470 8z40 Bulk carrier and tanker
　　　　　　　　　　 Set of 9 3.00 75

1979

2619 1z Ksiaze Ksawery (river paddle-
　　　 steamer), 1830
2620 1z50 General Swierczewski (river
　　　 paddle-steamer), 1914
2621 4z50 Zubr (river tug), 1960
2622 6z Syrena (passenger launch), 1959
　　　　　　　　　　 Set of 4 1.40 30

1980

2685 2z Lwow (cadet ship)
2686 2z50 Antoni Garnuszewski (cadet ship)
2687 6z Zenit (cadet ship)
2688 6z50 Jan Turleski (cadet ship)
2689 6z90 Horyzont (cadet ship)
2690 8z40 Dar Pomorza (cadet ship)
　　　　　　　　　　 Set of 6 3.00 65

1981

2765† 2z Model of Atlas 2 (tug) 20 5

1982

2846†	12z Log rafts, River Vistula	10	5
2848†	25z 16th-century merchant ships, Danzig	20	8

1983

2890	6z Medieval ships	20	10

1984

2938†	6z Vistula river craft	20	8
2939†	25z Punts	1.00	25

1985

3000	5z *Iskra* (cadet ship)	20	5

1986

3042	10z *Wilanow* (ferry)
3043	10z *Wawel* (ferry)
3044	15z *Pomerania* (ferry)
3045	25z *Rogalin* (ferry)

	Set of 4	1.25	15

3047	5z *Kopernik* (Antarctic research vessel)
3048	40z *Professor Siedlecki* (Antarctic research vessel)

	Set of 2	1.50	35

3055†	10z Sailboards	30	5

1987

3089	5z *Antoni Garnuszewski* (supply ship)
3090	5z *Zulawy* (supply ship)
3091	10z *Pogoria* (cadet ship)
3092	10z *Gedania* (yacht)
3093	30z *Dziunia* (research vessel)
3094	40z *Kapitan Ledochowski* (research vessel)

	Set of 6	40	25

POLISH POST IN DANZIG

Eastern Europe
100 groszy = 1 zloty

1936

No. 315 of Poland overprinted **PORT GDANSK**

R30	15g *Pilsudski* (liner)	2.50	3.75

PORTUGAL

South-west Europe
1898 100 reis = 1 milreis
1912 100 centavos = 1 escudo

1898

378†	2½r Departure of Vasco da Gama's fleet	60	25
379†	5r Vasco da Gama's fleet at Calicut	60	25
382†	50r *Sao Gabriel* (flagship)	2.25	1.25
384†	100r *Sao Gabriel*	6.75	2.75

1911

Nos. 378/9, 382 and 384 overprinted **REPUBLICA** *or surcharged also*

441†	2½r Departure of Vasco da Gama's fleet	20	15
444†	15r on 5r Vasco da Gama's fleet at Calicut	35	20
447†	50r *Sao Gabriel* (flagship)	90	60
450†	100r *Sao Gabriel*	1.60	1.00

Nos. 134/5, 138 and 140 of Madeira overprinted **REPUBLICA** *or surcharged also*

455†	2½r Departure of Vasco da Gama's fleet	70	70
456†	15r on 5r Vasco da Gama's fleet at Calicut	70	50
458†	50r *Sao Gabriel* (flagship)	2.25	2.00
461†	100r *Sao Gabriel*	5.25	1.75

1923

578	1c Portuguese galleon, 1500
579	2c Portuguese galleon, 1500
580	3c Portuguese galleon, 1500
581	4c Portuguese galleon, 1500
582	5c Portuguese galleon, 1500
583	10c Portuguese galleon, 1500
584	15c Portuguese galleon, 1500
585	20c Portuguese galleon, 1500
586	25c Portuguese galleon, 1500
587	30c Portuguese galleon, 1500
588	40c Portuguese galleon, 1500
589	50c Portuguese galleon, 1500
590	75c Portuguese galleon, 1500
591	1e Portuguese galleon, 1500
592	1e50 Portuguese galleon, 1500
593	2e Portuguese galleon, 1500

	Set of 16	3.00	2.25

1941

937†	40c Fishing boat, Aveiro	8	5

1943

942	5c Caravel
943	10c Caravel
944	15c Caravel
945	20c Caravel
946	30c Caravel
947	35c Caravel
948	50c Caravel
948a	80c Caravel
949	1e Caravel (red)
949a	1e Caravel (lilac)
949b	1e20 Caravel
949c	1e50 Caravel
950	1e75 Caravel
950a	1e80 Caravel
951	2e Caravel (red)
951a	2e Caravel (blue)
952	2e50 Caravel
953	3e50 Caravel
953a	4e Caravel
954	5e Caravel
954a	6e Caravel
954b	7e50 Caravel
955	10e Caravel
956	15e Caravel
957	20e Caravel
958	50e Caravel

	Set of 26	£120	4.00

1958

1156	1e Liner
1157	4e50 Liner

	Set of 2	1.50	50

1960

1179†	2e50 15th-century caravel	45	25
1182†	8e 15th-century barketta	25	50

1961

1191	1e Barkettas
1192	4e30 Barkettas

	Set of 2	2.25	2.00

1966

1294†	1e *Normandie* (liner)	30	5
1295†	2e50 *Normandie*	85	30

1967

1322†	1e Lisnave shipyard, Lisbon	10	5
1324†	3e50 Lisnave shipyard, Lisbon	45	20

1969

1355†	6e50 Cabral's fleet, 1500	80	60

1377†	4e Vasco da Gama's fleet, 1497	55	25

1970

1399†	1e Great Eastern (cable ship)	10	5
1400†	2e50 Great Eastern	75	75

1405	3e50 Wine barge, Oporto	60	10

1972

1480†	4e50 Olympic yachts	50	20

1974

1538†	3e30 Sailing packet and modern liner	30	10

1977

1673	2e Poviero (fishing boat)
1674	3e Rowing boat, Mar
1675	4e Rowing boat, Nazare
1676	7e Caicque, Algarve
1677	10e Tunny fishing boat, Xavega
1678	15e Buarcos fishing boat

	Set of 6	2.40	80

1978

1689†	5e Trawler and tunny fishing boats, Xavega	12	8
1703†	100e Tanker and shipyard	90	55

1725	5e Trawler
1726	9e Trawler
1727	12e50 Trawler
1728	15e Trawler

	Set of 4	1.10	40

1980

1794†	60e Vasco da Gama's ships, 1499	70	30

1804†	10e 16th-century sea battle	25	10

1809†	19e50 Fishing boats, River Aveiro	40	15

1811	6e50 Caravel
1812	8e Nau
1813	16e Galleon
1814	19e50 Early paddle-steamer

	Set of 4	1.25	45

1981

1824	8e Fragata, River Tejo
1825	8e50 Rabelo, River Douro
1826	10e Moliceiro, River Aveiro
1827	16e Barco, River Lima
1828	19e50 Carocho, River Minho
1829	20e Varino, River Tejo

	Set of 6	1.75	70

1982

1849†	8e50 15th-century caravel	20	10

1870†	19e Shipyard	40	12

1873†	27e Sagres (cadet ship)	50	20
1875†	50e "470" class yachts	85	40

1983

1906	10e Tug and container ship	20	10

1908	12e50 Vasco da Gama (frigate), 1782
1909	25e Estefania (steam corvette), 1845
1910	30e Adamastor (cruiser), 1900
1911	37e50 Joao Belo (frigate), 1983

	Set of 4	1.75	75

1918†	25e 16th-century caravel	45	20

1987

2068†	57e Fishing boats, Espinho	55	45

2083	25e Dias's fleet leaving Lisbon, 1487
2084	25e Dias's fleet off Africa

	Set of 2	40	25

1988

2099†	27e Dias's ships in storm, 1488	20	12

PORTUGUESE COLONIES IN AFRICA

100 reis = 1 milreis

1898

As Nos. 378/9, 382 *and* 384 *of Portugal, but inscribed* "AFRICA"

1†	2½r Departure of Vasco da Gama's fleet	40	30
2†	5r Vasco da Gama's fleet at Calicut	40	30
5†	50r *Sao Gabriel* (flagship)	40	40
7†	100r *Sao Gabriel*	1.40	1.00

PORTUGUESE CONGO

South-west Africa
100 centavos = 1 escudo

1913

Surcharged **REPUBLICA CONGO** *and value*

(a) On Nos. 1/2, 5 *and* 7 *of Portuguese Colonies in Africa*

95†	¼c on 2½r Departure of Vasco da Gama's fleet	50	45
96†	½c on 5r Vasco da Gama's fleet at Calicut	50	45
99†	5c on 50r *Sao Gabriel* (flagship)	50	45
101†	10c on 100r *Sao Gabriel*	50	45

(b) On Nos. 104/5, 108 *and* 110 *of Macao*

103†	¼c on ½a Departure of Vasco da Gama's fleet	60	50
104†	½c on 1a Vasco da Gama's fleet at Calicut	60	50
107†	5c on 8a *Sao Gabriel* (flagship)	60	50
109†	10c on 16a *Sao Gabriel*	85	65

(c) On Nos. 58/9, 62 *and* 64 *of Timor*

111†	¼c on ½a Departure of Vasco da Gama's fleet	70	60
112†	½c on 1a Vasco da Gama's fleet at Calicut	70	60
115†	5c on 8a *Sao Gabriel* (flagship)	70	60
117†	10c on 16a *Sao Gabriel*	90	60

PORTUGUESE GUINEA

West Africa
100 centavos = 1 escudo

1913

Surcharged **REPUBLICA GUINE** *and value*

(a) On Nos. 1/2, 5 *and* 7 *of Portuguese Colonies in Africa*

138†	¼c on 2½r Departure of Vasco da Gama's fleet	70	70
139†	½c on 5r Vasco da Gama's fleet at Calicut	70	70
142†	5c on 50r *Sao Gabriel* (flagship)	70	70
144†	10c on 100r *Sao Gabriel*	70	50

(b) On Nos. 104/5, 108 *and* 110 *of Macao*

146†	¼c on ½a Departure of Vasco da Gama's fleet	80	70
147†	½c on 1a Vasco da Gama's fleet at Calicut	80	70
150†	5c on 8a *Sao Gabriel* (flagship)	80	70
152†	10c on 16a *Sao Gabriel*	1.25	1.10

(c) On Nos. 58/9, 62 *and* 64 *of Timor*

154†	¼c on ½a Departure of Vasco da Gama's fleet	80	70
155†	½c on 1a Vasco da Gama's fleet at Calicut	80	70
158†	5c on 8a *Sao Gabriel* (flagship)	80	70
160†	10c on 16a *Sao Gabriel*	1.25	1.00

1967

376	50c *Republica* (cruiser)		
377	1e *Guadiana* (destroyer)		
	Set of 2	40	25

STAMP MONTHLY

— finest and most informative magazine for all collectors. Obtainable from your newsagent or by postal subscription — details on request.

PORTUGUESE INDIA

Indian Sub-continent
12 reis = 1 tanga
16 tangas = 1 rupia

1898

As Nos. 378/9, 383 *and* 384 *of Portugal, but inscribed* "INDIA"

275†	1½r Departure of Vasco da Gama's fleet	35	25
276†	4½r Vasco da Gama's fleet at Calicut	35	25
279†	1t *Sao Gabriel* (flagship)	75	55
281†	4t *Sao Gabriel*	1.00	75

1913

Nos. 275/6, 279 *and* 281 *overprinted* **REPUBLICA**

389†	1½r Departure of Vasco da Gama's fleet	25	15
390†	4½r Vasco da Gama's fleet at Calicut	25	25
393†	1t *Sao Gabriel* (flagship)	25	20
395†	4t *Sao Gabriel*	50	20

1925

493	6r *Sao Gabriel* (Vasco da Gama)		
494	1t *Sao Gabriel*		
	Set of 2	4.00	2.50

1933

504	1r Portuguese galeasse		
505	2r Portuguese galeasse		
506	4r Portuguese galeasse		
507	6r Portuguese galeasse		
508	8r Portuguese galeasse		
509	1t Portuguese galeasse		
510	1½t Portuguese galeasse		
511	2t Portuguese galeasse		
512	2½t Portuguese galeasse		
513	3t Portuguese galeasse		
514	5t Portuguese galeasse		
515	1rp Portuguese galeasse		
516	2rp Portuguese galeasse		
517	3rp Portuguese galeasse		
518	5rp Portuguese galeasse		
	Set of 15	25.00	15.00

1942

Nos. 508 *and* 510/18 *surcharged*

549	1r on 8r Portuguese galeasse		
546	1r on 5t Portuguese galeasse		
550	2r on 8r Portuguese galeasse		
547	3r on 1½t Portuguese galeasse		
551	3r on 2t Portuguese galeasse		
552	3r on 3rp Portuguese galeasse		
553	6r on 2½t Portuguese galeasse		
554	6r on 3t Portuguese galeasse		
542	1t on 1½t Portuguese galeasse		
548	1t on 2t Portuguese galeasse		
543	1t on 1rp Portuguese galeasse		
544	1t on 2rp Portuguese galeasse		
545	1t on 5rp Portuguese galeasse		
	Set of 13	8.00	6.00

POSTAGE DUE STAMPS

1943

Nos. 512/14 *surcharged* **Porteado** *and new value*

D549	3r on 2½t Portuguese galeasse
D550	6r on 3t Portuguese galeasse
D551	1t on 5t Portuguese galeasse

PUERTO RICO

West Indies
100 centavos = 1 peso

1893

110	3c Ship's boat, 1493	90.00	22.00

QATAR

Arabia
1961 100 naye paise = 1 rupee
1966 100 dirhams = 1 riyal

1961

33†	75np Dhow	60	20

1964

No. 33 *overprinted* **1964,** *Olympic Rings and Arabic inscription*

39†	75np Dhow	1.75	1.75

No. 33 *overprinted* **John F. Kennedy 1917 – 1963** *in English and Arabic*

44†	75np Dhow	1.75	1.75

1966

No. 33 *surcharged* **Dirham**

147†	75d on 75np Dhow	60	35

1967

222	1d Norman ship, 1066		
223	2d *Santa Maria* (Columbus)		
224	3d *Sao Gabriel* (Vasco da Gama)		
225	75d *Victoria* (Magellan)		
226	1r *Golden Hind* (Drake)		
227	2r *Gipsy Moth IV* (Sir Francis Chichester)		
	Set of 6	5.50	3.25

1968

231†	60d Rowing boat	60	40

244†	35d Dhow	35	15
246†	60d Tanker	60	25

1969

276†	1d *Ross Rayyan* (trawler)	5	5

288†	1d *Sivella* (tanker)	5	5
290†	3d Oil rig	5	5
293†	3r Tankers from 1890 to 1968	2.25	1.60

294† 1d Dhow building 5 5

306† 2r Inflatable dinghy 1.75 1.00

1970

308† 2d *Oriental Empress* (liner) 5 5

333† 3d Japanese fishing boat 5 5

1971

345† 3d Felucca 5 5

356† 2d *Ariel* (cable ship) 5 5

1972

426† 5d *Sea Shell* (oil rig) 5 5
429† 3r *Sea Shell* 4.00 3.00

1973

471† 2d Weather ship 5 5

1974

503† 10d Paddle-steamer and modern liner .. 20 10

532† 35d Yachts 25 15
533† 55d Fishing boat 40 20

1975

539† 55d Pipe-laying barge 40 20

1976

592 10d Dhow at anchor
593 35d Dhows at anchor
594 80d Dhows at anchor
595 1r25 Dhow at anchor
596 1r50 Dhow under construction
597 2r Dhow under construction
                                Set of 6 4.00 2.50

599† 10d Olympic yacht 5 5

618† 1r25 Oil rig 80 50

1982

745 20d Container ship
746 2r35 Container ship
                                Set of 2 2.25 1.75

COLLECT BIRDS ON STAMPS
Second revised edition of this Stanley Gibbons thematic catalogue – now available at £8.50 (p. + p. £2) from: Stanley Gibbons Publications Ltd, 5 Parkside, Christchurch Road, Ringwood, Hants BH24 3SH.

1984

765† 15d Dhow 8 5
766† 40d Dhow 25 15
767† 50d Dhow 25 15

1986

798 1r50 *Qatari ibn al-Fuja'a* (container ship)
799 4r *Al-Wajda* (container ship)
                                Set of 2 2.50 1.25

QUELIMANE
East Africa
100 centavos = 1 escudo

1913
Surcharged **REPUBLICA QUELIMANE** *and value*

(a) On Nos. 1/2, 5 and 7 of Portuguese Colonies in Africa
1† ½c on 2½r Departure of Vasco da Gama's
        fleet 70 50
2† ½c on 5r Vasco da Gama's fleet at Calicut 70 50
5† 5c on 50r *Sao Gabriel* (flagship) 70 50
7† 10c on 100r *Sao Gabriel* 60 40

(b) On Nos. 104/5, 108 and 110 of Macao
9† ½c on ½a Departure of Vasco da Gama's
        fleet 70 50
10† ½c on 1a Vasco da Gama's fleet at Calicut 70 50
13† 5c on 8a *Sao Gabriel* (flagship) 70 50
15† 10c on 16a *Sao Gabriel* 60 40

(c) On Nos. 58/9, 62 and 64 of Timor
17† ½c on ½a Departure of Vasco da Gama's
        fleet 70 50
18† ½c on 1a Vasco da Gama's fleet at Calicut 70 50
21† 5c on 8a *Sao Gabriel* (flagship) 70 50
23† 10c on 16a *Sao Gabriel* 60 40

RAS AL KHAIMA
Arabia
100 dirhams = 1 riyal

1964

6† 1r Dhow 80 45
7† 2r Dhow 1.60 1.25
8† 5r Dhow 4.50 3.00

1965
Nos. 6/8 overprinted **OLYMPIC TOKYO 1964** *in English and Arabic with Olympic rings*
15 1r Dhow
16 2r Dhow
17 5r Dhow
                                Set of 3 3.50 3.00

Nos. 6/8 overprinted **ABRAHAM LINCOLN 1809-1865** *in English and Arabic*
18 1r Dhow
19 2r Dhow
20 5r Dhow
                                Set of 3 3.50 3.00

Nos. 6/8 overprinted **FRANKLIN D. ROOSEVELT 1882-1945** *in English and Arabic*
21 1r Dhow
22 2r Dhow
23 5r Dhow
                                Set of 3 3.50 3.00

1966

Nos. 6/8 surcharged in dirhams or riyals

64a†	5d on 5r Dhow		10	5
65†	1r on 1r Dhow		50	30
66†	2r on 2r Dhow		1.25	1.00
67†	5r on 5r Dhow		2.25	2.00

Appendix

The following stamps have either been issued in excess of postal needs, or have not been made available to the public in reasonable quantities at face value. Miniature sheets, imperforate stamps etc., are excluded from this section.

1967

European Paintings. 2r Fishing boats, Les Saines-Maries
Summer Olympics Preparation, Mexico 1968. 40d Mexican fishing boats.

1969

Famous Men. 20d Dhow

1971

13th World Jamboree, Japan. 60d Scout rowing boat

REDONDA

West Indies
100 cents = 1 dollar

Appendix

The following stamps were issued in anticipation of commercial and tourist development, philatelic mail being handled by a bureau in Antigua. Since the island is at present uninhabited we do not list these items in full. It is understood that such stamps are valid for the payment of postage in Antigua. Miniature sheets, imperforate stamps etc, are excluded from this section.

1980

Olympic Medal Winners, Lake Placid and Moscow. 25c Olympic yacht

1982

Boy Scout Anniversaries. 8c Scout sailing dinghy

REUNION

Indian Ocean
100 centimes = 1 franc

1907

73†	1f Brigantine, St. Pierre (blue & brown)	25	15
110†	1f Brigantine, St. Pierre (blue)	20	20
111†	1f Brigantine, St. Pierre (lilac & brown) ..	25	15
112†	1f10 Brigantine, St. Pierre	30	30
113†	1f50 Brigantine, St. Pierre	4.00	2.50
74†	2f Brigantine, St. Pierre	2.00	1.25
114†	3f Brigantine, St. Pierre	5.00	3.50
75†	5f Brigantine, St. Pierre (brown & pink)	3.75	2.25

1917

Nos. 75 (some with colours changed) and 110 surcharged

124†	25c on 5f Brigantine, St. Pierre	20	20
125†	1f25 on 1f Brigantine, St. Pierre	15	15
126†	1f50 on 1f Brigantine, St. Pierre	20	20
127†	3f on 5f Brigantine, St. Pierre (blue & red)	60	60
128†	10f on 5f Brigantine, St. Pierre (red & green)	5.50	4.50
129†	20f on 5f Brigantine, St. Pierre (pink & brown)	8.00	6.00

1931

As No. 109 of Cameroun

133†	1f50 Liner	1.10	1.10

1937

As Nos. 110/11 of Cameroun

175†	20c Liner	45	55
176†	30c Sailing ships	45	55
MS180a†	3f Liner	1.25	1.25

1943

No. 75 overprinted **France Libre**

197†	5f Brigantine, St. Pierre	17.00	17.00

1947

300†	15f *Ville de Strasbourg* (liner)	1.50	90
301†	20f *Ville de Strasbourg*	2.00	1.40
302†	25f *Ville de Strasbourg*	2.50	1.50

1949

No. 1263 of France surcharged **3F CFA**

370†	3f on 8f Fishing boats, Marseille	40	30

1965

As No. 1692 of France but additionally inscribed "CFA"

439	15f *La Taureau* (warship), 1665	30	20

1971

No. 1920 of France surcharged **40F CFA**

467	40f on 80c *Antoinette* (barque)	65	35

1972

479	45f Antarctic exploration ship, 1772	1.75	85

1973

No. 2011 of France surcharged **45F CFA**

488	45f on 90c *France II* (barque)	60	50

1974

No. 2040 of France surcharged **45 FCFA**

500	45f on 90c Shipwreck and modern lifeboat	60	45

RHODESIA

Central Africa
100 cents = 1 dollar

1970

443b†	6c *Seaflight* (hydrofoil)	3.50	1.50
445†	10c Yachts, Lake McIlwaine	60	5

RHODESIA AND NYASALAND

Central Africa
12 pence = 1 shilling
20 shillings = 1 pound

1959

23†	4d Pirogue, Lake Bangweulu	40	5
26†	1s3d *Ilala II* (Lake Nyassa steamer)	1.75	5

ROSS DEPENDENCY

Antarctica
1957 12 pence = 1 shilling
20 shillings = 1 pound
1968 100 cents = 1 dollar

1957

1†	3d H.M.S. *Erebus* (Ross), 1839	3.25	75

1968

As No. 1, but with face value in decimal currency

5†	2c H.M.S. *Erebus*	7.00	4.75

1972

12a†	8c H.M.N.Z.S. *Endeavour* (supply ship), 1962	45	60

RUANDA-URUNDI

Central Africa
100 centimes = 1 franc

1916

No. 74 of Belgian Congo overprinted **RUANDA.** (*No. 5*) or **URUNDI.** (*No. 12*)

5†	40c Native canoe	10.00	
12†	40c Native canoe	10.00	

No. 74 of Belgian Congo overprinted **EST AFRICAIN ALLEMAND OCCUPATION BELGE. DUITSCH OOST AFRIKA BELGISCHE BEZETTING.**

19†	40c Native canoe	4.25	3.50

1918

Nos. 82 and 86 of Belgian Congo overprinted **A. O.**

27†	40c + 40c Native canoe	25	25
31†	10f + 10f *Deliverance* (stern wheel paddle-steamer)	45.00	45.00

1922

No.19 surcharged **.25c.**

34†	25c on 40c Native canoe	2.00	90

1925

No. 141 of Belgian Congo overprinted **RUANDA-URUNDI**

61†	25c + 25c Native canoe	20	20

RUMANIA

South-east Europe
100 bani = 1 leu

1913

629†	10b Gunboat, River Danube	45	8

1931

1205	6le *Mircea* (cadet ship), 1882	
1206	10le *Lascar Catargiu and Mihail Kogalniceaunu* (monitors)	
1207	16le *Ardeal* (monitor)	
1208	20le *Regele Ferdinand* (destroyer)	
	Set of 4	32.00 12.00

1936

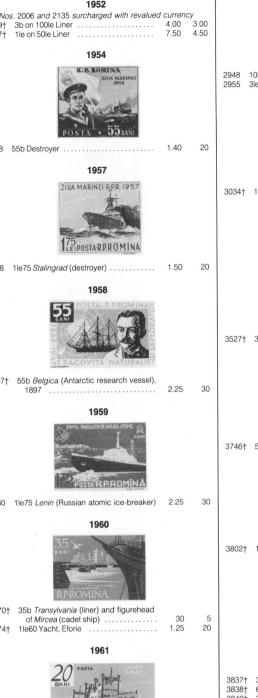

1343 1le + 1le *Delfinul* (submarine)
1344 3le + 2le *Mircea* (cadet ship), 1882
1345 6le + 3le *Transylvania* (liner)

Set of 3   13.00   9.00

1947

1899†   15le *Transylvania* (liner) 1.00   20
1901†   32le Liner, Constantza 4.00   3.75

1948

Nos. 1899 and 1901 overprinted **R·P·R·**

1940†   15le *Transylvania* (liner) 2.00   40
1942†   32le Liner, Constantza 8.50   3.75

1971†   8le + 8le Destroyer 1.50   1.50

1991   2le + 2le Yachts
1992   5le + 5le *Mircea* (cadet ship), 1882
1993   8le + 8le *Romana Mare* (Danube river steamer)
1994   10le + 10le *Transylvania* (liner)

Set of 4   6.25   6.25

2006†   100le Liner 4.00   3.25

2007†   1le + 1le Freighter at wharf   60   60

1951

2135†   50le Liner 4.50   3.50

COLLECT MAMMALS ON STAMPS

A Stanley Gibbons thematic catalogue on this popular subject. Copies available at £7.50 (p. + p. £2) from: Stanley Gibbons Publications Ltd, 5 Parkside, Christchurch Road, Ringwood, Hants BH24 3SH.

1952

Nos. 2006 and 2135 surcharged with revalued currency

2159†   3b on 100le Liner 4.00   3.00
2217†   1le on 50le Liner 7.50   4.50

1954

2338   55b Destroyer 1.40   20

1957

2528   1le75 *Stalingrad* (destroyer) 1.50   20

1958

2597†   55b *Belgica* (Antarctic research vessel), 1897 ....   2.25   30

1959

2680   1le75 *Lenin* (Russian atomic ice-breaker)   2.25   30

1960

2770†   35b *Transylvania* (liner) and figurehead of *Mircea* (cadet ship)   30   5
2774†   1le60 Yacht, Eforie 1.25   20

1961

2841   20b *Galati* (freighter)
2842   40b *Oltenita* (Danube passenger vessel)
2843   55b *Tomis* (hydrofoil)
2844   1le *Arad* (freighter)
2845   1le55 *N.Cristea* (tug)
2846   1le75 *Dobrogea* (freighter)

Set of 6   4.50   65

1962

2922†   1le Yachts (blue & red)   80   12
2923†   1le20 Power boats (blue & purple) 1.00   12
2924†   1le55 Yacht (blue & orange) 1.25   15

As Nos. 2922/4, but imperforate and colours changed

2930†   1le Yachts (blue & brown) 1.10   60
2931†   1le20 Power boats (blue & violet) 1.25   75
2932†   1le55 Yacht (blue & red) 1.40   85

2948   10b Fishing punts   5   5
2955   3le25 Fishing punts 1.60   20

1963

3034†   1le35 *Oltenita* (Danube passenger vessel) 1.25   30

1967

Size 23 × 29 mm

3527†   3le25 *Transylvania* (liner) 1.75   10

1970

3746†   55b Freighter   30   5

1971

3802†   1le Fishing punt and tourist launch   45   5

3837†   35b 17th-century Dutch jacht   15   5
3838†   60b Fishing boats   25   5
3840†   3le Fishing boats, Braila 1.40   40
MS3841†   5le Fishing boats, Venice 4.50   4.50

As No. 3527, but smaller, 17 × 23mm

3852†   3le25 *Transylvania* (liner) 1.10   5

3881†   40b Magellan and ships, 1521   20   5

1972

3910   1le35 Danube tug and barge
3911   1le75 Danube tourist launch
3912   2le75 Danube freighter

Set of 3   2.75   55

3952† 20b Gondolas, Venice 10 5

1974

4042 1le35 Tug and barges, River Danube
4043 1le45 *Dimbovita* (freighter)
4044 1le50 *Muntenia* (Danube passenger vessel)
4045 1le55 *Mircea* (cadet ship), 1938
4046 1le75 *Transylvania* (liner)
4047 2le20 *Oltul* (bulk carrier)
4048 3le65 *Mures* (trawler)
4049 4le70 *Arges* (tanker)
                Set of 8   3.00   50

4075† 20b Postal motor boat 5 5

1977

4346† 55b *Carpati* (Danube passenger vessel) 20 8
4347† 1le *Mircesti* (Danube passenger vessel) 30 8
4348† 1le50 *Oltenita* (Danube passenger vessel) 50 12
4349† 2le15 Hydrofoil 55 25
4350† 3le *Herculani* (Danube passenger vessel) 70 30
4351† 3le40 *Muntenia* (Danube passenger vessel) 85 35

1979

4476 55b *Galati* (freighter)
4477 1le *Bucuresti* (freighter)
4478 1le50 *Resita* (bulk carrier)
4479 2le15 *Tomis* (bulk carrier)
4480 3le40 *Dacia* (tanker)
4481 4le80 *Independenta* (tanker)
                Set of 6   1.50   80

1981

4620 55b *Stefan cel Mare* (Danube paddle-steamer)
4621 1le Danube Commission steam launch
4622 1le50 *Tudor Vladimirescu* (Danube paddle-steamer)
4623 2le15 *Sulina* (dredger)
4624 3le40 *Republica Populara Romana* (Danube paddle-steamer)
4625 4le80 Freighter
                Set of 6   2.50   1.00
MS4626 10le *Moldova* (tourist ship) 3.50 3.50

1982

4722† 5le Sailing dinghy, Neptun 1.00 40

1983

MS4792 Two sheets. 3le *Pizarro* (Humboldt), 1799 (sheets also contain seven other designs)
          Price for 2 sheets   9.50   9.50

1984

MS4846 Two sheets. 3le Danube barge, 3le Barges, Innsbruck, 3le Pleasure steamer, London (sheets also contain five other designs).
          Price for 2 sheets   9.75   9.75

1985

4932† 2le Danube barges 60 25
4933† 3le *Dacia* (motorised barge) 80 25
4934† 4le Tug and barges 1.10 35

5007† 1le50 *Calypso* (Cousteau) 40 12
5012† 5le Polar supply ship (Byrd) 1.50 45

1988

MS5179 Two sheets 31e *Santa Maria* (Columbus) (sheets also contain seven other designs)
          Price for 2 sheets   3.50   3.50

RUSSIA

Eastern Europe and Northern Asia
100 kopeks = 1 rouble

1922

286† (20r + 5r) Freighter 20 1.50

1928

530† 14k *Aurora* (cruiser), 1917 . . . . 2.25 50

1930

576† 3k *Potemkin* (battleship), 1905 . . . . 1.50 35

1931

584 30k *Malygin* (ice-breaker)
585 35k *Malygin*
586 1r *Malygin*
587 2r *Malygin*
                Set of 4   80.00   40.00

1932

588 50k *Sibiriakov* (ice-breaker)
589 1r *Sibiriakov*
                Set of 2   £110   38.00

1933

626† 20k Koryak kayak 6.00 1.40

1934

647† 80k *Ob* (ice-breaker) 11.00 3.25

1935

678† 1k *Chelyuskin* (ice-breaker) 3.75 1.00

1938

787† 10k *Murman* (ice-breaker) 3.50 50
788† 20k *Murman* 3.50 70

829† 80k *Marat* (battleship) 4.50 1.10

1940

898† 15k *Iosif Stalin* (ice-breaker) 2.00 25
899† 30k *Georgy Sedov* (ice-breaker) 2.75 35

1941

945a† 20k Passenger launches, Moscow–
Volga Canal 1.50 70

973† 30k Galley on the Volga 2.75 70
975† 1r Galley on the Volga 8.00 2.50

1943

1018 30k *Sv. Pyotr* (Bering), 1741
1019 60k *Sv. Pyotr* (Bering), 1741
1020 1r *Sv. Pyotr* (Bering), 1741
1021 2r *Sv. Pyotr* (Bering), 1741
                            Set of 4 12.00 1.60

1946

1220† 15k Liner 1.25 20

1947

1237† 20k *Senyavin* (sail corvette), 1862
(brown) 1.25 30
1238† 20k *Senyavin* (blue) 1.25 30

1273† 50k Tourist launch, Moscow 1.10 15

1295† 60k *Moskovich* (river launch) 1.75 55

1948

1346† 30k Battleship, 1918 .... 1.00 20

1396† 45k Power boat 2.25 35

1406† 1r *Vyacheslav Molotov* (liner) 5.00 2.50

1949

1465† 1r Dezhnev's ship exploring North-east
Passage, 1648 .... 13.00 4.75

1493 40k *Boksirni Typlokod* (tug)
1494 1r *Bolshaya Volga* (tanker)
                            Set of 2 13.50 11.00

1497† 20k Yachts 55 10

1543† 1r *Ukraina* (liner) 4.50 1.90

1950

1648† 1r *Mirnyi* and *Vostok* (Antarctic
exploration vessels), 1820 .... 28.00 10.00

1952

1763 40k *Orel* (battleship), 1905 .... 3.00 50

STAMP MONTHLY

— finest and most informative magazine for all
collectors. Obtainable from your newsagent or by
postal subscription — details on request.

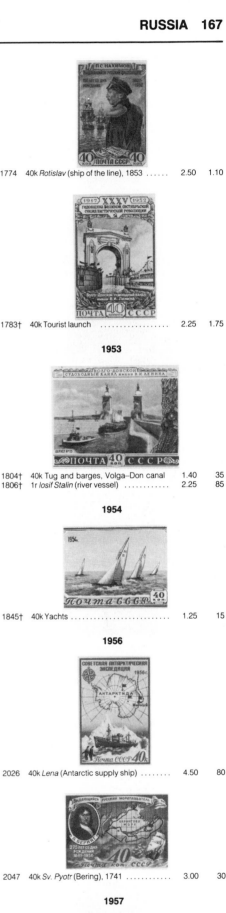

1774 40k *Rotislav* (ship of the line), 1853 ...... 2.50 1.10

1783† 40k Tourist launch 2.25 1.75

1953

1804† 40k Tug and barges, Volga–Don canal 1.40 35
1806† 1r *Iosif Stalin* (river vessel) 2.25 85

1954

1845† 40k Yachts 1.25 15

1956

2026 40k *Lena* (Antarctic supply ship) 4.50 80

2047 40k *Sv. Pyotr* (Bering), 1741 .... 3.00 30

1957

2095b† 40k *Zarya* (full-rigged research ship) 2.00 15

1958

2184   40k *Varyag* (cruiser), 1901 ....   1.60   45

2217   60k *Lenin* (atomic ice-breaker) 3.00   40

2239†   40k *Aurora* (cruiser)   40   15
2245†   1r *Rossiya* (liner) 1.40   40

2298†   40k *Lenin* (atomic ice-breaker) 1.75   55

1959

2314†   40k *Ermak* (ice-breaker), 1900   70   25

2326   10k *Sovetsky Soyuz* (liner)
2327   20k *Feliks Dzerzhinsky* (liner)
2328   40k *Rossiya* (liner)
2329   40k *Kooperatsiya* (liner)
2330   60k *Mikhail Kalinin* (liner)
2331   1r *Baltika* (liner)
                    Set of 6   3.25   95

2372†   25k *Vityaz* (oceanographic survey ship)   1.25   10

1960

2489   25k *Karl Marx* (river vessel)
2490   40k *Lenin* (river vessel)
2491   60k *Raketa* (hydrofoil)
                    Set of 3   1.75   40

1961

2570   6k *Lenin* (atomic ice-breaker)   90   30

2621†   10k *Lenin* (atomic ice-breaker) (on stamp No. 2298) 1.10   30

2658   6k *Fram* (Nansen) 1.25   15

1962

2665†   6k *K-3* (submarine), 1942 ....   1.00   20

2773†   4k Ice-breaker and hydrofoil   55   12

1963

2880†   6k Freighter   50   12

2894†   3k *Ob* (Antarctic supply ship) 1.50   20
2897†   12k *Sovetskaya Ukraina* (whale factory ship) and whale catcher 3.00   40

2913   4k *Aurora* (cruiser) (orange, black & red)
2914   4k *Aurora* (cruiser) (pink, black & red)
                    Set of 2   80   20

1964

3040   6k *Havel* (German freighter)   40   10

1965

3194†   2k Medieval kogge   20   5
3196†   4k Modern mail boat   55   5

3199†   4k *Taimir* and *Vaigach* (ice-breakers), 1915   70   15
3200†   4k *Lenin* (atomic ice-breaker)   70   15
3202†   10k *Vostok* and *Mirnyi* (Antarctic exploration vessels), 1820 ....   1.25   25

1966

3251†   10k *Ob* (Antarctic supply ship), 1956 ..   2.00   35

3272†   12k *Aleksandr Pushkin* (liner)   90   15

3319†   4k Cruise ships, River Volga   20   5

3334†   6k Trawler   25   8

3370†   1k *Sv. Pyotr* (Bering)   25   10
3372†   4k *Ilich* (liner) and freighter   50   10

1967

3390 6k *Cheryashevsky* (fish factory ship)
3391 6k Refrigerated trawler
3392 6k Crab-canning ship
3393 6k Trawler
3394 6k Seine-fishing boat, Black Sea
                  Set of 5 1.75   35

3506† 4k Liner 15 5

3509† 4k Brig, 1840 .... 25 8

1968

3577† 6k Yachts 20 5

3600 6k *Ivan Franko* (liner) 15 8

1969

3678† 4k Tourist launch 12 5

3773† 4k Speed boat 12 5

1970

3788† 4k *Vostok* and *Mirnyi* (Antarctic
        exploration vessels), 1820 .... 1.25 15

3843 3k *Aurora* (cruiser)
3844 4k *Groznyi* (missile cruiser)
3845 10k *Oktyabrskaya Revolyutsiya* (cruiser)
3846 12k *Varyag* (missile cruiser)
3847 20k *Leninsky Komsomol* (nuclear
        submarine)
                 Set of 5 3.25   60

1971

3965 16k Hydrofoil 40 20

3974 4k Tourist ship, Gorky 10 5

4016 1k Peter the Great's Imperial barge,
        1723
4017 4k *Orel* (galleon), 1668
4018 10k *Poltava* (ship of the line), 1712
4019 12k *Ingermanland* (ship of the line), 1715
4020 16k *Vladimir* (steam frigate), 1848
                 Set of 5 2.75   65

1972

4087† 6k Cruiser 20 8

4117 2k *Pyotr Veliky* (battleship), 1872
4118 3k *Varyag* (cruiser), 1899
4119 4k *Potemkin* (battleship), 1900
4120 6k *Ochakov* (cruiser), 1902
4121 10k *Amur* (minelayer), 1907
                 Set of 5 1.90   45

1973

4171 16k *Mikhail Lermontov* (liner) 40 20

4172 4k Ice-breaker 45 5

4209 3k *Kirov* (cruiser)
4210 4k *Oktyabrskaya Revolyutsiya*
        (battleship)
4211 6k *Krasnogvardeets* (submarine)
4212 10k *Soobrazitelnyi* (destroyer)
4213 16k *Krasnyi Kavkaz* (cruiser)
                 Set of 5 1.75   60

1974

4264† 4k Battle of Chesme, 1770 .... 15 5
4266† 10k Brig, 1868 .... 30 10

4303 3k Minesweeper
4304 4k Landing ship
4305 6k Helicopter carrier
4306 16k *Otvazhny* (destroyer)
                 Set of 4 1.40   35

4311† 6k Yachts 20 5
4313† 16k Fishing boats 65 20

4328 6k Viking longship 20 5

4341　4k *Aleksandr Pushkin* (liner), freighter and tanker .... 20　5

1976

4598　4k *Pailot* (ice-breaker)
4599　6k *Ermak* (ice-breaker)
4600　10k *Fedor Litke* (ice-breaker)
4601　16k *Vladimir Ilich* (ice-breaker)
4602　20k *Krasin* (ice-breaker)
　　　　　　　　Set of 5　3.50　70

1977

4611　4k *Sv. Foka* (polar vessel) .... 75　15

4654　4k *Aleksandr Sibiryakov* (ice-breaker)
4655　6k *Georgy Sedov* (ice-breaker)
4656　10k *Sadko* (ice-breaker)
4657　12k *Dezhnev* (ice-breaker)
4658　14k *Sibir* (ice-breaker)
4659　16k *Lena* (ice-breaker)
4660　20k *Amguema* (ice-breaker)
　　　　　　　　Set of 7　4.00　90

MS4683　50k *Arktika* (atomic ice-breaker) ....　9.00　5.00

4704†　4k *Aurora* (cruiser) .... 12　5

1978

4779†　32k *Vladimir Komorov* (research vessel)　75　25

4814　6k Russian warships, 1903 .... 15　5

MS4818　30k Hydrofoil .... 55　35

4820　4k + 2k "Star" class yacht
4821　6k + 3k "Soling" class yacht
4822　10k + 5k "470" class yacht
4823　16k + 6k "Finn" class yacht
4824　20k + 10k "Flying Dutchman" class yacht
　　　　　　　　Set of 5　2.25　75
MS4825　50k + 25k "Tornado" class catamaran ....　5.00　2.50

4827　6k Black Sea ferry .... 12　5

4843　4k *Vasily Pronchishchev* (ice-breaker)
4844　6k *Kapitan Belousov* (ice-breaker)
4845　10k *Moskva* (ice-breaker)
4846　12k *Admiral Makarov* (ice-breaker)
4847　16k *Lenin* (atomic ice-breaker)
4848　20k *Arktika* (atomic ice-breaker)
　　　　　　　　Set of 6　2.00　50

1979

4879　15k Satellite communication ship ......　30　15

STAMP MONTHLY
— finest and most informative magazine for all collectors. Obtainable from your newsagent or by postal subscription — details on request.

4948　1k *Vulkanolog* (research ship)
4949　2k *Professor Bogorov* (research ship)
4950　4k *Ernst Krenkel* (research ship)
4951　6k *Kosmonavt Vladislav Volkov* (research ship)
4952　10k *Kosmonavt Yury Gagarin* (research ship)
4953　15k *Akademik Kurchatov* (research ship)
　　　　　　　　Set of 6　1.75　60

1980

5053　2k *Ayu-dag* (research vessel)
5054　3k *Valerian Uryvaev* (research vessel)
5055　4k *Mikhail Somov* (research vessel)
5056　6k *Akademik Sergei Korolev* (research vessel)
5057　10k *Otto Schmidt* (research vessel)
5058　15k *Akademik Mstislav Keldysh* (research vessel)
　　　　　　　　Set of 6　1.25　50

5067†　2r Atomic ice-breaker ....　4.25　2.00

1981

5085†　15k Antarctic supply ship ....　1.40　40

5099　15k Freighter .... 40　15

5101　4k Liner .... 10　5

5143　4k *Lenin* (river vessel)
5144　6k *Kosmonavt Gagarin* (river tourist ship)
5145　15k *Valerian Kuibyshev* (river tourist ship)
5146　32k *Baltysky* (river tanker)
　　　　　　　　Set of 4　1.75　75

5147   15k *Malygin* (ice-breaker)   65   15

5151†   4k Tanker   15   5

5167   4k *Tovarishch* (four-masted cadet
        barque)
5168   6k *Vega* (cadet barquentine)
5169   10k *Kodor* (cadet schooner)
5170   15k *Tovarishch* (three-masted cadet
        barque)
5171   20k *Kruzenshtern* (four-masted cadet
        barque)
5172   32k *Sedov* (four-masted cadet barque)
                            Set of 6   2.50   95

1982

5270   4k *S-56* (submarine)
5271   6k *Gremyashchy* (minelayer)
5272   15k *Gafel* (minesweeper)
5273   20k *Krasnyi Krym* (cruiser)
5274   45k *Sevastopol* (battleship)
                            Set of 5   2.75   1.10

5296†   6k Full-rigged ship   30   10

1983

5323   4k Hydrofoil, River Don   10   5

5330   5k 15th-century warship and modern
        missile cruiser   12   8

STAMP MONTHLY
— finest and most informative magazine for all collectors. Obtainable from your newsagent or by postal subscription — details on request.

5341   4k Coastal trawlers
5342   6k Refrigerated trawler
5343   10k Deep-sea trawler
5344   15k Refrigerated freighter
5345   20k Factory ship
                            Set of 5   1.50   70

1984

5429†   6k *Chelyuskin* (Arctic exploration ship),
        1934   15   8
5430†   15k *Chelyuskin* sinking   40   15

5447   5k Freighter   12   5

5455   10k Liner   12   10

1985

5563   5k *Potemkin* (battleship), 1905   10   5

5600   5k *Aurora* (cruiser), 1917   10   5

1986

5673†   15k Oceanographic research vessel ...   35   15

5690   15k *Mukran* (train ferry)   40   15

5693   5k *Vladivostok* (ice-breaker)
5694   10k *Mikhail Somov* (ice-breaker)
                            Set of 2   35   15
MS5695 50k *Mikhail Somov* 1.50   1.60

15.III – 26.VII.1985
Дрейф во льдах Антарктики

                    No. 5055 *overprinted*
5696   4k *Mikhail Somov*   8   5

1987

5758   5k *Maksım Gorky* (river tourist ship)
5759   10k *Aleksandr Pushkin* (river tourist ship)
5760   30k *Sovetsky Soyuz* (river tourist ship)
                            Set of 3   80   40

5788†   10k 16th and 18th-century sailing
        packets   20   10

5824   4k *Trinity* (ship of the line) (Spiridov),
        1770
5825   5k *Sv. Pavel* (ship of the line) (Ushakov),
        1799
5826   10k Battle of Afon (Senyavin), 1807
5827   25k *Azov* (ship of the line) (Lazarev),
        1827
5828   30k *Imperatsia* (ship of the line)
        (Nakhimov), 1853
                            Set of 5   1.25   60

1988

5859   5k Yacht, Sochi   10   5

RUSSIAN POST OFFICES IN TURKEY

South-east Europe and Asia Minor
1865 100 kopeks = 1 rouble
1900 40 paras = 1 piastre

1865

4   2k Early steamship £600   £400
5   20k Early steamship £800   £450

6	2k Early steamship	18.00	25.00
7	20k Early steamship	35.00	40.00

1909

57	5pa on 1k Liner, 1907	
58	10pa on 2k Liner, 1907	
59	20pa on 4k Liner, 1907	
60	1pi on 10k Liner, 1907	
61	5pi on 50k Liner, 1907	
62	7pi on 70k Liner, 1907	
63	10pi on 1r Liner, 1907	
64	35pi on 3r50 Liner, 1907	
65	70pi on 7r Liner, 1907	

Set of 9 28.00 45.00

RWANDA

Central Africa
100 centimes = 1 franc

1969

187†	1f Nile felucca	5	5
191†	15f Nile felucca	60	50

331†	80c Shipbuilding, Ostend	5	5

1970

MS344	100f 16th-century naval battle, Bay of Naples	2.25	2.25

1972

495†	18f Olympic yachts	35	30

1973

No. **MS**344 *cut down and overprinted* **NAPLES 1973**
MS573 100f 16th-century naval battle, Bay of
Naples 2.00 1.90

1974

602†	20c *Elettra* (Marconi's steam yacht)	5	5
603†	30c *Carlo Alberto* (freighter)	5	5
MS608†	50f *Elettra*	1.25	1.25

1976

MS735†	100f Battle of Flamborough Head, 1779	2.25	2.25

743†	20c Olympic yachts	5	5

1977

816†	1f *Goliath* (cable paddle-steamer)	5	5
818†	18f *Kingsport* (satellite communications ship)	40	40
MS822†	Two sheets. 60f 17th-century Dutch warship (other sheet shows a non-maritime subject)		

Set of 2 sheets 2.00 2.00

1978

856†	18f Scouts in canoe	35	35

1979

948†	20c Native canoe (on Ruanda-Urundi stamp No. 5)	5	5
950†	50c *Deliverance* (stern wheel paddle-steamer) (on Ruanda-Urundi stamp No. 31)	5	5

1981

1062†	15f Tanker	25	25

1984

1187†	30c Liner	5	5

1201†	200f Freighter	3.00	2.75

1203†	30c Sailboards	5	5

1985

1225†	30c Pirogue	5	5

RYUKYU ISLANDS

Northern Pacific
1948 100 sen = 1 yen
1958 100 cents = 1 dollar

1948

4†	30s Junk	2.40	3.50
6†	50s Junk	2.40	3.50

1953

40†	6y American fleet, Naha, 1853	1.00	2.40

1961

106	3c Junk and liner	1.75	1.25

1969

221†	3c Canoe race	5	25

SAAR

Western Europe
1921 100 pfennige = 1 mark
1921 100 centimes = 1 franc

1921

56†	25pf Tug and barges	35	15

No. 56 surcharged

71†	5c on 25 pf Tug and barges	15	30

1922

As No. 56, but larger

92†	50c Tug and barges	75	5

1952

318†	3f Temporary bridge on barges, Gersweiler	15	5
327†	18f Temporary bridge on barges, Gersweiler	2.50	2.75

1955

No. 327 overprinted **VOLKSBEFRAGUNG 1955**

360†	18f Temporary bridge on barges, Gersweiler	15	30

OFFICIAL STAMPS

1922

No. 92 overprinted **DIENSTMARKE**

O106†	50c Tug and barges	70	12

ST. HELENA

South Atlantic
1922 12 pence = 1 shilling
20 shillings = 1 pound
1971 100 pence = 1 pound

1922

97	½d *London* (East Indiaman), 1659	
98	1d *London*	
99	1½d *London*	
100	2d *London*	
101	3d *London*	
92	4d *London*	
103	5d *London*	
104	6d *London*	
105	8d *London*	
106	1s *London*	
107	1s6d *London*	
108	2s *London*	
109	2s6d *London*	
110	5s *London*	
111	7s6d *London*	
112	10s *London*	
113	15s *London*	
96	£1 *London*	

	Set of 18	£1500	£2000

1934

123†	10s *London* (East Indiaman), 1659	£200	£250

1938

131	½d *London* (East Indiaman), 1659	
132	1d *London* (green)	
132a	1d *London* (orange)	
149	1d *London* (black & green)	
133	1½d *London* (red)	
150	1½d *London* (black & red)	
134	2d *London* (orange)	
151	2d *London* (black & red)	
135	3d *London* (blue)	
135a	3d *London* (grey)	
135b	4d *London*	
136	6d *London*	
136a	8d *London*	
137	1s *London*	
138	2s6d *London*	
139	5s *London*	
140	10s *London*	

	Set of 17	£120	70.00

1949

As No. 115 of Antigua

146†	4d Paddle-steamer	1.75	1.25

1953

153†	½d *London* (East Indiaman), 1659	25	20

1959

170†	6d *London* (East Indiaman), 1659	40	20

1967

212	1s *London* (East Indiaman), 1659	
213	2s6d *London*	

	Set of 2	35	25

215†	3d *Charles* (East Indiaman), 1667	15	10
216†	6d Ship's boat, 1667	15	10

1968

240†	£1 *John Dutton* (lifeboat)	13.00	16.00

1969

241	4d *Perseverance* (brig), 1819	
242	8d *Dane* (screw steamer), 1857	
243	1s9d *Llandovery Castle* (liner), 1925	
244	2s3d *Good Hope Castle* (cargo liner), 1969	

	Set of 4	1.60	65

1973

297	1½p *Westminster* and *Claudine* (East Indiamen), 1849	
298	4p *True Briton* (East Indiaman), 1790	
299	6p *General Goddard* (East Indiaman), 1795	
300	22½p *Kent* (East Indiaman) on fire, 1825	

	Set of 4	3.00	3.25

1974

301†	5p Freighters	30	30

1975

307†	5p H.M.S. *Resolution* (Cook)	75	50

1976

317† 8p *London* (East Indiaman) (on stamp
　　No. 98) 30 35
318† 25p *Good Hope Castle* (cargo liner) 45 50

330† £1 *British warships, 1815* 2.00 2.25
331† £2 *British warships, 1821* 4.50 5.00

1977

332† 8p *Local longboat, 1947* 25 35

1978

341† 3p *17th-century Dutch East Indiaman* 15 15
346† 20p *17th-century Dutch East Indiaman* 70 70

1979

347† 3p H.M.S. *Discovery* (Cook) 25 15

1980

359† 8p *Ship's boat, 1880* 35 30

362† 5p *17th-century East Indiaman* 20 20

1982

396† 29p H.M.S. *Beagle* (Darwin) 95 95

1984

433† 59p *London* (East Indiaman) (on stamp
　　No.123) 1.10 1.40

436 11p H.M.S. *Invincible* (aircraft carrier)
437 60p H.M.S. *Herald* (survey ship)
　　　　　　　　　　Set of 2 1.50 1.65

438† 10p *St. Helena* (schooner), 1814 . . . . 20 20
441† 50p *Papanui* (freighter), 1898 . . . . 1.00 1.00

1986

485† 65p *Unity* (Halley), 1676 . . . . 1.40 1.40

488 1p H.M.S. *Erebus* (Ross)
489 3p H.M.S. *Beagle* (Fitzroy)
490 5p *Nadezhda* (Von Kruenstern)
491 9p H.M.S. *Resolution* (Bligh)
492 10p *Rurik* (Von Kotzebue)
493 12p H.M.S. *Swallow* (Carteret)
494 15p *Desire* (Cavendish)
495 20p *La Boudeuse* (De Bougainville)
496 25p *Senyavin* (Lutke)
497 40p *La Coquille* (Duperry)
498 60p H.M.S. *Dolphin* (Byron)
499 £1 H.M.S. *Endeavour* (Cook)
500 £2 *L'Astrolabe* (Dumont d'Urville)
　　　　　　　　　　Set of 13 8.00 8.75

1987

501 9p H.M.S. *Repulse* (battle cruiser), 1925
502 13p H.M.S. *Vanguard* (battleship), 1941
503 38p Royal Yacht *Britannia*, 1957
504 45p H.M.S. *Herald* (survey ship), 1984
　　　　　　　　　　Set of 4 2.10 2.10

1988

519 9p *Defence* (Dampier), 1691
520 13p H.M.S. *Resolution* (Cook), 1775
521 45p H.M.S. *Providence* (Bligh), 1792
522 60p H.M.S. *Beagle* (Darwin), 1836
　　　　　　　　　　Set of 4 2.40 2.50

ST. KITTS

West Indies
100 cents = 1 dollar

1980

No. 399 of St. Kitts-Nevis overprinted **St. Kitts**
34† 30c *Europa* (liner) 10 12

42 4c H.M.S. *Vanguard* (ship of the line), 1762
43 10c H.M.S. *Boreas* (frigate), 1787
44 30c H.M.S. *Druid* (frigate), 1827
45 55c H.M.S. *Winchester* (frigate), 1831
46 $1.50 *Philosopher* (full-rigged
　　merchantman), 1857
47 $2 *Contractor* (cargo liner), 1930
　　　　　　　　　　Set of 6 1.50 90

1981

75† 55c Royal Yacht *Saudadoes* 15 15
77† $2.50 Royal Yacht *Royal George* 60 60
79† $4 Royal Yacht *Britannia* 80 80

1982

92† 15c *Naval action off St. Kitts, 1782* 10 10

1983

108 55c *Stella Oceanis* (liner)
109 $2 *Queen Elizabeth 2* (liner)
　　　　　　　　　　Set of 2 70 50

1985

173 40c *Tropic Jade* (container ship)
174 $1.20 *Atlantic Clipper* (schooner)
175 $2 *Mandalay* (schooner)
176 $2 *Cunard Countess* (liner)
　　　　　　　　　　Set of 4 3.25 3.25

182† 40c *Golden Hind* (Drake) 25 30

1986

217† $1.50 *Isere* (French naval steamer), 1885 70 75

OFFICIAL STAMPS

1980
No. 34 overprinted **OFFICIAL**
O3 30c *Europa* (liner) 10 12

1983
Nos. 75, 77 and 79 overprinted **OFFICIAL** *or surcharged also*
O23† 45c on $2.50 Royal Yacht *Royal
George* 25 25
O25† 55c Royal Yacht *Saudadoes* 30 30
O27† $1.10 on $4 Royal Yacht *Britannia* 60 70

ST. KITTS-NEVIS

West Indies
1923 12 pence = 1 shilling
20 shillings = 1 pound
1951 100 cents = 1 dollar

1923

48 ½d Merchantman, 1623
49 1d Merchantman, 1623
50 1½d Merchantman, 1623
51 2d Merchantman, 1623
52 2½d Merchantman, 1623
53 3d Merchantman, 1623
54 6d Merchantman, 1623
55 1s Merchantman, 1623
56 2s Merchantman, 1623
57 2s6d Merchantman, 1623
59 5s Merchantman, 1623
58 10s Merchantman, 1623
60 £1 Merchantman, 1623
Set of 13 £1500 £2000

1949
As No. 115 of Antigua
83† 3d Paddle-steamer 35 40

1963

138† 20c Boat building 20 5

1968

188 25c *Jamaica Producer* (freighter)
189 50c *Jamaica Producer*
Set of 2 35 15

1970

207† 1c English two-decker warship, 1650 .... 8 5
210† 4c 16th-century Portuguese caravels 15 5
211† 5c Fireships, 1669 .... 20 5
212† 6c 16th-century pirate carrack 20 5
213† 10c 17th-century smugglers' ship 25 5
218† 60c 17th-century Dutch flute 2.25 70
221† $5 16th-century sea battle 3.25 4.25

1973

261† $2.50 *Concepcion* (Sir Thomas Warner),
1623 .... 1.40 1.75

No. 261 overprinted **VISIT OF H. R. H. THE PRINCE OF WALES**
1973
268† $2.50 *Concepcion* 50 65

285† 4c Schooner and launch 8 5

1978

399† 30c *Europa* (liner) 20 10

ST. LUCIA

West Indies
1938 12 pence = 1 shilling
20 shillings = 1 pound
1949 100 cents = 1 dollar

1938

137† 5s Loading banana freighter 5.00 4.00

1949
As No. 115 of Antigua
161† 6c Paddle-steamer 30 30

1960

188 8c *Santa Maria* (Columbus)
189 10c *Santa Maria* (Columbus)
190 25c *Santa Maria* (Columbus)
Set of 3 55 30

1964

204† 12c Fishing boats 15 10
207† 35c Schooners, Castries 1.25 5
208† 50c Fishing boat 1.10 10

1967
Nos. 204 and 207/8 overprinted **STATEHOOD 1st MARCH 1967**
234† 12c Fishing boats 30 10
237† 35c Schooners, Castries 80 75
238† 50c Fishing boat 80 1.00

1970

279† 5c Liner and freighter, Castries 12 5
284† 25c Yacht 40 5

1971

315† 25c 18th-century shipping 10 10

1972

335 5c Barque (on local stamp of St. Lucia
Steam Conveyance Co Ltd)
336 10c Barque (on local stamp of St. Lucia
Steam Conveyance Co Ltd)
337 35c Barque (on local stamp of St. Lucia
Steam Conveyance Co Ltd)
338 50c Barque (on local stamp of St. Lucia
Steam Conveyance Co Ltd)
Set of 4 1.40 1.00

1973

352 15c H.M.S. *St. Lucia* (brig), 1803
353 35c H.M.S. *Prince of Wales* (ship of the
line), 1765
354 50c *Oliph Blossom* (merchantman), 1605
355 $1 H.M.S. *Rose* (frigate), 1757
Set of 4 1.50 90

1976

406 ½c *Hanna* (American schooner), 1775
407 1c *Prince of Orange* (British sailing
packet), 1777
408 2c *Edward* (British sloop), 1776
409 5c *Millern* (British full-riged
merchantman), 1777
410 15c *Surprise* (American lugger), 1777
411 35c H.M.S. *Serapis* (frigate) 1779
412 50c *Randolph* (American frigate), 1777
413 $1 *Alliance* (American frigate), 1778
Set of 8 5.00 2.25

St·LUCIA

434 10c Crest of H.M.S. *Ceres*
435 20c Crest of H.M.S. *Pelican*
436 40c Crest of H.M.S. *Ganges*
437 $2 Crest of H.M.S. *Ariadne*
Set of 4   2.10   2.10

1977

St. LUCIA

452† 20c Scout sailing dinghy 20   15
454† $1 Scout motor boat 75   90
MS455† $2.50 Scout motor boat 2.25 2.50

1978

480† 50c Defence of St. Lucia, 1778 30   10

1980

540† 20c Refrigerated freighter 20   5
542† 30c Pilot boat 30   10
544† 75c *Cunard Countess* (liner) 55   50
546† $2 Cargo liner 1.25 90
548† $10 *Queen Elizabeth 2* (liner) 5.50 4.75

MS558† $5 Schooner by moonlight 1.50 1.75

No. 540 surcharged **1980 HURRICANE $1.50 RELIEF**
565† $1.50 on 20c Refrigerated freighter 30   40

1982

617† 35c Battle of the Saints, 1782 40   10

COLLECT RAILWAYS ON STAMPS

A Stanley Gibbons thematic catalogue on this popular subject. Copies available at £7.50 (p. + p. £2) from: Stanley Gibbons Publications Ltd, 5 Parkside, Christchurch Road, Ringwood, Hants BH24 3SH.

1983

634† 30c Cruising yacht 15   10

Saint Lucia

641† 10c *Cunard Countess* (liner) 5   5

1984

675† 35c Elizabethan galleon 25   25
677† 60c Battle of Trafalgar, 1805, and royal
         crest 40   40
678† 60c Battle of Trafalgar, 1805, and King
         George III 40   40
681† $2.50 Defeat of Spanish Armada, 1588 1.40 1.40
682† $2.50 Defeat of Spanish Armada, 1588,
         and Queen Elizabeth I 1.40 1.40

1986

Saint Lucia

MS885† $7 Royal Yacht *Britannia* 3.25 3.50

1987

948† 80c *Mauretania* (liner) 35   40

OFFICIAL STAMPS

1983

Nos. 540, 542, 544, 546 and 548 overprinted **OFFICIAL**
O4† 20c Refrigerated freighter 12   15
O6† 30c Pilot boat 20   25
O8† 75c *Cunard Countess* (liner) 45   50
O10† $2 Cargo liner 1.25 1.40
O12† $10 *Queen Elizabeth 2* (liner) 6.00 6.50

ST. PIERRE & MIQUELON

North Atlantic
100 centimes = 1 franc

1909

93† 1f Fishing brigantine 1.50 1.00
121† 1f10 Fishing brigantine 1.50 1.25
122† 1f50 Fishing brigantine 2.00 2.00

94† 2f Fishing brigantine 1.75 1.25
123† 3f Fishing brigantine 3.75 3.75
95† 5f Fishing brigantine 5.00 2.75

1924

Nos. 93/5, some with colours changed, surcharged in figures and bars
125† 25c on 2f Fishing brigantine 20   20
126† 25c on 5f Fishing brigantine 20   20
130† 1f25 on 1f Fishing brigantine 70   70
131† 1f50 on 1f Fishing brigantine 1.25 1.25
132† 3f on 5f Fishing brigantine 80   80
133† 10f on 5f Fishing brigantine 6.50 6.50
134† 20f on 5f Fishing brigantine 8.50 8.50

1931

As No. 109 of Cameroun
138† 1f50 Liner 80   1.00

1932

141† 4c *Jacques Coeur* (trawler) 15   10
142† 5c *Jacques Coeur* 15   10
147† 3c *Jacques Coeur* 50   35
148† 40c *Jacques Coeur* 60   45
151† 65c *Jacques Coeur* 80   60
154† 1f *Jacques Coeur* 55   45
157† 1f75 *Jacques Coeur* 1.00 85
158† 2f *Jacques Coeur* 3.50 3.50
161† 10f *Jacques Coeur* 25.00 25.00

1934

No. 157 overprinted **JACQUES CARTIER 1534 · 1934**
166† 1f75 *Jacques Coeur* (trawler) 1.50 1.75

1937

As Nos. 110/11 of Cameroun
168† 20c Liner 50   60
169† 30c Sailing ships 50   60

1941

Nos. 141/2, 148, 151, 154 and 157/8 overprinted **FRANCE LIBRE F. N. F. L.** *or surcharged also*
248† 4c *Jacques Coeur* (trawler) 18.00 18.00
249† 5c *Jacques Coeur* £400 £400
250† 40c *Jacques Coeur* 6.50 6.50
253† 65c *Jacques Coeur* 15.00 15.00
254† 1f *Jacques Coeur* £170 £170
255† 1f75 *Jacques Coeur* 4.00 4.00
256† 2f *Jacques Coeur* 4.00 4.00
258† 5f on 1f75 *Jacques Coeur* 4.00 4.00

1942

322 5c Fishing schooner
323 10c Fishing schooner
324 25c Fishing schooner
325 30c Fishing schooner
326 40c Fishing schooner
327 60c Fishing schooner
328 1f Fishing schooner
329 1f50 Fishing schooner
330 2f Fishing schooner
331 2f50 Fishing schooner
332 4f Fishing schooner
333 5f Fishing schooner
334 10f Fishing schooner
335 20f Fishing schooner
Set of 14   3.50   3.50

1945

Nos. 322, 324 and 331 surcharged
346 50c on 5c Fishing schooner
347 70c on 5c Fishing schooner
348 80c on 5c Fishing schooner
349 1f20 on 5c Fishing schooner
350 2f40 on 25c Fishing schooner
351 3f on 25c Fishing schooner
352 4f50 on 25c Fishing schooner
353 15f on 2f50 Fishing schooner
Set of 8   1.40   1.40

1947

374†	5f Colonel Pleven (trawler)	35	35
375†	6f Colonel Pleven	45	45
377†	10f Colonel Pleven	65	65
382†	50f 16th-century galleon (air)	2.00	1.50
383†	100f Fishing schooner	3.25	2.25
384†	200f Snow-bound fishing schooner	6.00	3.00

1954

As No. 264 of Cameroun

398	15f Landing craft, Normandy, 1944	2.00	2.00

1955

399†	30c Trawler	8	10
401†	50c Trawler	8	10
404†	3f Trawler	15	20
405†	4f Fishing dinghies	40	20
406†	10f Fishing dinghies	75	35
409†	40f Trawler	1.10	1.10

1956

413	15f Galantry (trawler)	85	55

1962

420	500f Surcouf (Free French submarine)	70.00	60.00

1963

426	30f Fishing schooner	1.25	85

427	200f Garonne (French warship), 1763	5.50	3.50

1966

440	100f Revanche (immigrant ship), 1816	3.25	2.25

1967

442	25f Trawlers and fishing dinghies		
443	100f Richelieu (French cruiser)		
		Set of 2 27.00	21.00

444	48f Trawler	80	70

1968

451†	6f French warship, 1791	90	55
452†	15f Cassard (survey ship), 1841	1.25	75
453†	25f Provence (French battleship)	1.50	1.00

1969

465	34f L'Estoile (French merchantman), 1690		
466	40f La Jolie (French merchantman), 1750		
467	48f La Juste (full-rigged sailing ship), 1860		
468	200f L'Esperance (expedition ship), 1600		
		Set of 4 8.25	5.25

1970

487†	48f Narrando (trawler)	1.25	80

488	25f 18th-century French warships		
489	50f Grande Hermine (Cartier), 1534		
490	60f 17th-century French galleons		
		Set of 3 5.75	2.75

1971

491	30f St. Francis of Assisi (fisheries patrol vessel), 1900		
492	35f St. Jehanne (fisheries patrol vessel), 1920		
493	40f L'Aventure (fisheries patrol frigate), 1950		
494	80f Commandant Bourdais (fisheries patrol frigate), 1970		
		Set of 4 5.25	3.25

495	22f H.M.S. Aconite (corvette) (on loan to Free French, 1941–47)		
496	25f H.M.S. Alyssum (corvette) (on loan to Free French, 1941–42 as Alysse)		
497	50f H.M.S. Mimosa (corvette) (on loan to Free French, 1941–42)		
		Set of 3 7.00	5.50

1973

513†	1f60 18th-century French warships	1.40	80
515†	4f 17th-century French warships	1.60	1.00

523	10f Freighter	8.00	5.00

1974

524	1f60 Weather ship	1.25	80

533†	20c Fishing schooner	60	60

1976

550	1f20 Croix de Lorraine (stern trawler)		
551	1f40 Geolette (stern trawler)		
		Set of 2 3.25	1.90

1986

568	2f50 Yacht and motor cruiser	65	40

1987

591 2f50 Schooner on slipway 45 35

594 3f *La Normande* (trawler) 60 50

ST. THOMAS AND PRINCE ISLANDS

In Atlantic off West Africa
1913 100 centavos = 1 escudo
1977 100 centimes = 1 dobra

1913

Surcharged **REPUBLICA S. TOME E PRINCIPE** *and new value*

(a) On Nos. 1/2, 5 and 7 of Portuguese Colonies in Africa
203† ¼c on 2½r Departure of Vasco da Gama's
  fleet 50 40
204† ¼c on 5r Vasco da Gama's fleet at
  Calicut 50 40
207† 5c on 50r *Sao Gabriel* (flagship) 50 40
209† 10c on 100r *Sao Gabriel* 50 40

(b) On Nos. 104/5, 108 and 110 of Macao
211† ¼c on ½a Departure of Vasco da Gama's
  fleet 70 50
212† ¼c on 1a Vasco da Gama's fleet at
  Calicut 70 50
215† 5c on 8a *Sao Gabriel* (flagship) 80 60
217† 10c on 16a *Sao Gabriel* 80 60

(c) On Nos. 58/9, 62 and 64 of Timor
219† ¼c on ½a Departure of Vasco da Gama's
  fleet 70 50
220† ¼c on 1a Vasco da Gama's fleet at
  Calicut 70 50
223† 5c on 8a *Sao Gabriel* (flagship) 90 70
225† 10c on 16a *Sao Gabriel* 80 60

1962

437† 2e Sailing dinghy 35 10

1967

453† 1e50 *Vasco da Gama* (19th-century
  steam corvette) 35 25

1969

458 2e50 Vasco da Gama's fleet, 1469 . . . . . . 12 10

1972

467 20e 16th-century caravel 3.50 1.00

469 2e50 *Gladiolus* (Portuguese cruiser), 1922 15 8

1975

475 1e50 Sailing canoes
476 4e Sailing canoes
477 7e50 Sailing canoes
478 20e Sailing canoes
479 50e Sailing canoes
  Set of 5 3.25 1.90

Appendix

The following stamps have either been isssued in excess of
postal needs or have not been available to the public in
reasonable quantities at face value. Miniature sheets, imperforate
stamps etc., are excluded from this section.

1979

15th and 16th-century Sailing Ships. 50c, 1, 3, 5, 8, 25d

ST. VINCENT

West Indies
100 cents = 1 dollar

1949

As No. 115 *of Antigua*
179† 6c Paddle-steamer 30 30

1965

226† 4c H.M.S. *Providence* (sloop) (Bligh),
  1791 . . . . 5 5

231† 1c Boat building (inscr "BEQUIA") 10 15
231a† 1c Boat building (inscr "BEQUIA") 10 10
239† 12c *Antilles* (liner), 1952 . . . . 30 5

1971

330† 1c Careening fishing schooner 5 5
333† 15c Careening fishing schooner 15 5

1972

349† 30c H.M.S. *Arethusa* (frigate), 1807 . . . . 40 15
350† $1 H.M.S. *Blake* (ship of the line), 1808 1.50 80

1973

355† 12c Fleet of Columbus, 1492 . . . . 45 15
357† 50c *Santa Maria* (Columbus) 1.50 1.00

1974

387 15c *Istra* (cruise liner)
388 20c *Oceanic* (cruise liner)
389 30c *Aleksandr Pushkin* (cruise liner)
390 $1 *Europa* (cruise liner)
  Set of 4 95 40

1975

450† 70c *Geest Tide* (freighter) 40 30

455† $1.25 Yachts 1.25 1.50

1980

654† $2 Yachts 55 45

1981

656	50c *Ville de Paris* (French ship of the line), 1782		
657	60c H.M.S. *Ramilles* (ship of the line), 1782		
658	$1.50 H.M.S. *Providence* (sloop) (Bligh), 1793		
659	$2 *Dee* (paddle-steamer packet), 1840		
	Set of 4	2.00	2.00

668†	60c Royal Yacht *Isabella*	15	15
670†	$2.50 *Alberta* (royal yacht tender)	55	55
672†	$4 Royal Yacht *Britannia*	75	75

1982

706	45c *Geest Port* (freighter)		
707	60c *Stella Oceanis* (cruise liner)		
708	$1.50 *Victoria* (cruise liner)		
709	$2 *Queen Elizabeth 2* (liner)		
	Set of 4	2.00	2.00

1984

760†	35c 18th-century British warship and ship's boat	20	25
762†	$1 18th-century British warship	40	50

786†	$4 Battle of Jutland, 1916, and royal arms	1.75	1.75
787†	$4 Battle of Jutland, 1916, and King George V	1.75	1.75

1985

No. 672 surcharged **$1.50 CARIBBEAN ROYAL VISIT 1985**

937	$1.50 on $4 Royal Yacht *Britannia*	2.50	2.50

1986

952†	60c *Santa Maria* (Columbus)	30	35
956†	$2.75 *Santa Maria*	1.40	1.50

1987

1115†	$10 Fishing boats (on $10 currency note)	4.50	4.75

1988

1125†	15c *Santa Maria* (Columbus)	8	10
1126†	75c *Nina* and *Pinta* (Columbus)	35	40
1128†	$1.50 *Santa Maria* (Columbus)	70	75
MS1031†	$5 *Santa Maria* (Columbus)	2.25	2.40

1132†	10c Sailboard	5	5
1136†	$5 Cruising yacht	2.25	2.40

OFFICIAL STAMPS

1982

Nos. 668, 670 and 672 overprinted **OFFICIAL**

O1†	60c Royal Yacht *Isabella*	25	30
O3†	$2.50 *Alberta* (royal yacht tender)	80	90
O5†	$4 Royal Yacht *Britannia*	1.25	1.60

SAMOA

West Pacific
1901 100 pfennig = 1 mark
1935 12 pence = 1 shilling
20 shillings = 1 pound
1967 100 sene = tale

1901

As Nos. K7/19 of Cameroun, but inscribed "SAMOA"

G7	3pf *Hohenzollern* (German Imperial yacht)	
G8	5pf *Hohenzollern*	
G9	10pf *Hohenzollern*	
G10	20pf *Hohenzollern*	
G11	25pf *Hohenzollern*	
G12	30pf *Hohenzollern*	
G13	40pf *Hohenzollern*	
G14	50pf *Hohenzollern*	
G15	80pf *Hohenzollern*	
G16	1m *Hohenzollern*	
G17	2m *Hohenzollern*	
G18	3m *Hohenzollern*	
G19	5m *Hohenzollern*	
	Set of 13 £110 £550	

1914

Nos. G7/19 surcharged **G.R.I.** *and value in British currency*

101	½d on 3pf *Hohenzollern*	
102	½d on 5pf *Hohenzollern*	
103	1d on 10pf *Hohenzollern*	
104	2½d on 20pf *Hohenzollern*	
105	3d on 25pf *Hohenzollern*	
106	4d on 30pf *Hohenzollern*	
107	5d on 40pf *Hohenzollern*	
108	6d on 50pf *Hohenzollern*	
109	9d on 80pf *Hohenzollern*	
110	1s on 1m *Hohenzollern*	
112	2s on 2m *Hohenzollern*	
113	3s on 3m *Hohenzollern*	
114	5s on 5m *Hohenzollern*	
	Set of 13 £8000 £7250	

1935

182†	2d Outrigger canoe	90	60
184†	4d Bonito-fishing canoe	50	20

1952

224†	6d Bonito-fishing canoe	30	5

1968

309†	25s *La Boudeuse* and *L'Etoile* (Bougainville), 1768	60	25

1969

328†	20s Olympic yacht	8	5

1970

341	5s Wreck of *Adler* (German steam gunboat), Apia, 1889		
342	7s U.S.S. *Nipsic* (steam gunboat), Apia, 1889		
343	10s H.M.S. *Calliope* (screw corvette), Apia, 1889		
344	20s Wrecked small craft, Apia, 1889		
	Set of 4	3.25	1.75

347†	20s Canoe	1.25	60

352†	30s H.M.S. *Endeavour* (Cook)	2.75	1.75

1971

MS364 70s Fautasi (large canoe) 1.50 2.25

1972

378† 1s *Mini Lagoon* (freighter) 5 5

386 2s *Arend, Thienhoven* and *Africaansche Galey* (Roggeveen), 1722
387 8s *Arend, Thienhoven* and *Africaansche Galey*, 1722
388 10s Two of Roggeveen's ships and outrigger canoe, 1772
389 30s Two of Roggeveen's ships and outrigger canoe, 1772
　　　　　　　　　　　　　　Set of 4 2.50 1.60

399b† $4 Game fishing launch 5.00 7.00

1974

431† 20s Cargo liner at wharf, Apia 35 15
433† 50s *Age Unlimited* (raft), 1963 .... 80 1.00

1975

444 1s *Joyita* (inter-island coaster) at Apia, 1955
445 8s *Joyita* at sea
446 20s Crew leaving *Joyita*
447 22s *Joyita* and crew in life rafts
448 50s *Joyita* drifting
　　　　　　　　　　　　　　Set of 5 1.75 1.75

1976

461† 20s Sinking of *Bonhomme Richard* (American frigate), 1779 .... 60 35

466† 12s Fishing canoe 15 10
467† 22s Fishing canoe 30 10

1977

479† 12s Royal Yacht *Britannia* at Apia 20 5
481† 32s Royal Yacht *Britannia* 55 35

491† 50s *Energy* (schooner), 1877 .... 80 1.00

1978

514† 26s Collier, Whitby, 1766 .... 70 35
515† 50s H.M.S. *Resolution* (Cook) 1.25 1.50

1979

540 12s *Charles W. Morgan* (19th-century whaling ship)
541 14s *Lagoda* (19th-century whaling ship)
542 24s *James T. Arnold* (19th-century whaling ship)
543 50s *Splendid* (19th-century whaling ship)
　　　　　　　　　　　　　　Set of 4 1.75 1.10

COLLECT BIRDS ON STAMPS
Second revised edition of this Stanley Gibbons thematic catalogue – now available at £8.50 (p. + p. £2) from: Stanley Gibbons Publications Ltd, 5 Parkside, Christchurch Road, Ringwood, Hants BH24 3SH.

1980

561 12s *William Hamilton* (19th-century whaling ship)
562 14s *California* (19th-century whaling ship)
563 24s *Liverpool II* (19th-century whaling ship)
564 50s *Two Brothers* (19th-century whaling ship)
　　　　　　　　　　　　　　Set of 4 1.50 1.10

MS571 $1 *Fautasi* (large canoe) 1.00 1.50

1981

584 12s *Ocean* (19th-century whaling ship)
585 18s *Horatio* (19th-century whaling ship)
586 27s H.M.S. *Calliope* (screw corvette), 1884
587 32s H.M.S. *Calypso* (screw corvette), 1883
　　　　　　　　　　　　　　Set of 4 1.25 90

591† 32s H.M.S. *Alisma* (corvette) and convoy 1941 .... 40 30

MS606 $2 Game fishing launch 1.75 2.00

1982

616† 18s *Forum Samoa* (container ship) 20 20

1984

673 32s Liner at wharf, Apia
674 48s H.M.S. *Calliope* (screw corvette), 1889
675 60s *Forum Samoa* (container ship)
676 $1 *Matua* (cargo liner)
　　　　　　　　　　　　　　Set of 4 1.75 1.75

1986

731† 48s U.S.S. *Vincennes* (sail frigate) 30 35
733† 60s U.S.S. *Swan* (patrol boat) 35 40

1987

746† 60s Local longboat race 30 35

767† 80s Canoe 45 50

SAN MARINO

Southern Europe
100 centisimi = 1 lira

1942

243† 1li25 Galleon, Arbe 5 5
244† 1li75 Galleon, Arbe 5 5
245† 2li75 Galleon, Arbe 8 8
246† 5li Galleon, Arbe 2.00 3.50

1952

426† 2li Fleet of Columbus 5 5
433† 25li Fleet of Columbus 1.25 50

As No. 426, but colours changed, overprinted **FIERA DI TRIESTE**
1952
439† 2li Fleet of Columbus 5 5

1955

490 100li Yacht 3.00 1.50

1956
As No. 490, but additionally inscribed "1956"
518 100li Yacht 1.75 1.25

1959

592† 200li Fishing boats, Palermo 75 50

1960

623 30li Fishing boat, Riccione
624 125li Fishing boat, Riccione (air)
Set of 2 1.25 1.10

1961

629† 4li 16th-century wildfowl punt 5 5

1962

686† 70li Modern wildfowl punt 10 10

1963

690 1li Egyptian merchant ship, 2000 B.C.
691 2li 5th-century B.C. Greek trier
692 3li 1st-century B.C. Roman trireme
693 4li 10th-century Viking longship
694 5li *Santa Maria* (Columbus)
695 10li Carrack, *c.* 1550
696 30li Galley, *c.* 1600
697 60li *Sovereign of the Seas* (English galleon), 1637
698 70li Danish ship of the line, *c.* 1750
699 115li *Duncan Dunbar* (full-rigged merchantman), 1850
Set of 10 2.75 1.60

1970

891 230li 16th-century naval battle, Bay of Naples 20 15

1971

907 20li Gondolas, Venice
908 180li Gondolas, Venice
909 200li Gondolas, Venice
Set of 3 35 25

1973

960† 200li 17th-century shipping, New York .. 20 20

1980

1144 200li Tugs, London, 1850
1145 400li H.M.S. *President* (drillship), London
Set of 2 35 40

1983

1211† 500li Piccard's bathyscaphe, 1948 .... 50 45

1215† 400li Fishing boats, Rio de Janeiro, 1845 .... 35 25

SARAWAK

South-east Asia
100 cents = 1 dollar

1949
As No. 115 of Antigua
168† 15c Paddle-steamer 1.25 2.00

1955

194† 12c Barong panau (sailing prau) 1.50 20

SAUDI ARABIA

Arabia
1945 110 guerche = 10 riyals
1961 5 halalahs = 1 guerche (piastre)
20 guerche = 1 riyal
1976 100 halalas = 1 riyal

1945

352	½g *Fakhr el Bihar* (Egyptian royal yacht)		
353	3g *Fakhr el Bihar*		
354	5g *Fakhr el Bihar*		
355	10g *Fakhr el Bihar*		
	Set of 4	65.00	35.00

1961

446	3p Freighter at wharf, Dammam		
447	6p Freighter at wharf, Dammam		
448	8p Freighter at wharf, Dammam		
	Set of 3	5.50	1.00

1976

Size 36 × 26 mm

1167	5h Oil rig		
1168	10h Oil rig		
1169a	15h Oil rig		
1170	20h Oil rig		
1171	25h Oil rig		
1172	30h Oil rig		
1173	35h Oil rig		
1174	40h Oil rig		
1175	45h Oil rig		
1176b	50h Oil rig		
1177	55h Oil rig		
1179	65h Oil rig		
1180	1r Oil rig		
1181	2r Oil rig		
	Set of 14	25.00	4.00

1982

As Nos. 1167/80 *but smaller,* 25 × 20 mm

1306	5h Oil rig		
1307c	10h Oil rig		
1308c	15h Oil rig		
1309c	20h Oil rig		
1310	25h Oil rig		
1315c	50h Oil rig		
1318c	65h Oil rig		
1325c	1r Oil rig		
	Set of 8	2.75	1.40

1983

1355	20h *Bar'zan* (container ship)		
1356	65h *Al Drieya* (container ship)		
	Set of 2	90	50

COLLECT RAILWAYS ON STAMPS

A Stanley Gibbons thematic catalogue on this popular subject. Copies available at £7.50 (p. + p. £2) from: Stanley Gibbons Publications Ltd, 5 Parkside, Christchurch Road, Ringwood, Hants BH24 3SH.

SELANGOR

South-east Asia
100 cents = 1 dollar

1949

As No. 115 *of Antigua*

112†	15c Paddle-steamer	45	45

1957

123†	20c Malay fishing prau	25	5

1961

135†	20c Malay fishing prau	20	5

SENEGAL

West Africa
100 centimes = 1 franc

1931

As No. 109 *of Cameroun*

138†	1f50 Liner	1.00	1.00

1935

139†	1c Canoe, Dakar	5	5
140†	2c Canoe, Dakar	5	5
141†	3c Canoe, Dakar	5	5
142†	4c Canoe, Dakar	5	5
143†	5c Canoe, Dakar	5	5
144†	10c Canoe, Dakar	5	5
145†	15c Canoe, Dakar	5	5
146†	20c Canoe, Dakar	5	5
147†	25c Canoe, Dakar	5	5
148†	30c Canoe, Dakar	8	8
150†	40c Canoe, Dakar	8	8
151†	45c Canoe, Dakar	8	8

1937

As Nos. 110/11 *of Cameroun*

194†	20c Liner	25	25
195†	30c Sailing ships	25	25

1944

Nos. 140 and 145 *surcharged*

219†	1f50 on 15c Canoe, Dakar	8	8
221†	4f50 on 15c Canoe, Dakar	20	20
222†	5f50 on 2c Canoe, Dakar	65	65
224†	10f on 15c Canoe, Dakar	85	75

1961

241†	1f Pirogue racing	5	5

1964

276†	5f Titanium sand dredger	8	8
281†	85f Bulk carrier at wharf, Dakar	1.10	90

1965

301†	60f *Alsace* (cable ship)	60	40

306	10f Goree sailing pirogue		
307	20f Large pirogue, Soumbedioun		
308	30f Pirogue, Fadiouth Island		
309	45f Pirogue, River Senegal		
	Set of 4	1.60	90

1966

344†	25f *France* (liner), Dakar	30	15

1969

418†	45f Pirogues, Fadiouth Island	75	20

1970

424	500f Sailing pirogue	5.00	2.75

432†	75f Japanese sampan	55	30

1972

484	50f Gondolas, Venice		
485	100f Gondolas, Venice		
	Set of 2	1.75	1.00

506	40f Freighter	....	40	15

1974

559	100f Packet steamer	....	1.10	70

1976

582	140f Game fishing launch		
583	200f Yachts		
	Set of 2	2.10	1.40

1977

625†	5f Fishing pirogue	
627†	15f Fishing pirogue	

631†	80f River steamer	....	45	35

1978

652†	30f Racing canoes, Soumbedioun	......	15	12
653†	65f Racing canoes, Soumbedioun	......	35	25

1985

838†	150f Fishing canoe on beach	....	65	60

1987

890†	145f Canoe, Dakar (on stamp No. 148)		55	50

SERBIA

100 paras = 1 dinar

GERMAN OCCUPATION

1941

G46†	50p + 1d Paddle-steamer, Smederovo		15	55
G49†	2d + 4d Paddle-steamer, Smederovo		40	1.75

SEYCHELLES

Indian Ocean
100 cents = 1 rupee

1938

137†	6c Fishing pirogue (orange)	....	75	95
137b†	6c Fishing pirogue (green)	....	25	15
140†	20c Fishing pirogue (blue)	....	14.00	5.00
140a†	20c Fishing pirogue (yellow)	....	30	15
143†	45c Fishing pirogue	....	50	25
146†	1r Fishing pirogue (green)	....	75.00	48.00
146a†	1r Fishing pirogue (black)	....	35	40
149†	5r Fishing pirogue	....	2.00	2.50

1949

As No. 115 of Antigua

155†	50c Paddle-steamer	....	50	50

1952

Design as Nos. 137/49, but full face portrait

161†	15c Fishing pirogue	....	30	40
163†	20c Fishing pirogue	....	50	60
166†	45c Fishing pirogue	....	50	40

1954

Design as Nos. 161, 163, 166 and new value but with portrait of Queen Elizabeth II

177†	15c Fishing pirogue	....	15	15
179†	20c Fishing pirogue	....	20	20
182†	45c Fishing pirogue	....	25	20
183a†	70c Fishing pirogue	....	90	1.25

1957

No. 182 surcharged 5 cents

191	5c on 45c Fishing pirogue	....	10	5

1962

203†	45c Fishing pirogue	....	2.50	1.50

1967

No. 203 overprinted UNIVERSAL ADULT SUFFRAGE 1967

239†	45c Fishing pirogue	....	5	5

1968

No. 203 surcharged 60 CENTS

247†	60c on 45c Fishing pirogue	....	10	10

253†	20c Ship's longboat, 1768	....	10	5
254†	50c French warships, 1768	....	15	15
256†	2r25 French warships, 1768	....	50	60

1969

262†	5c French warship, 1742	....	8	5
264†	15c *Konigsberg* (German cruiser) (design shows the second cruiser of this name, instead of the first)	....	25	10
265†	20c H.M.S. *Belfast* (cruiser), H.M.S. *Rapid* (destroyer) and H.M.S. *Reward* (tug), 1945	....	25	10
270†	60c 18th-century merchantman under attack	....	1.00	1.50
271†	65c 18th-century merchantman under attack	....	1.75	2.50
275†	1r50 H.M.S. *Sybille* (frigate) and *Chiffone* (French frigate), 1801	....	1.75	2.00

1970

280†	20c French warship, 1770	....	15	10
281†	50c French warship, 1770	....	20	10

1971

No. 270 surcharged 65c

304†	65c on 60c 18th-century merchantman, under attack	....	45	75

1972

No. 265 overprinted ROYAL VISIT 1972

306†	20c H.M.S. *Belfast* (cruiser), H.M.S. *Rapid* (destroyer) and H.M.S *Reward* (tug), 1945	....	15	20

316†	15c Pirogue racing	....	5	5

1975

Nos. 265 and 275 overprinted VISIT OF Q.E. II and silhouette of liner

334†	20c H.M.S. *Belfast* (cruiser), H.M.S. *Rapid* (destroyer) and H.M.S. *Reward* (tug), 1945	....	12	15
337†	1r50 H.M.S. *Sybille* (frigate) and *Chiffone* (French frigate), 1801	....	45	70

Nos. 265 and 271 overprinted **INTERNAL SELF-GOVERNMENT OCTOBER 1975**

338†	20c H.M.S. *Belfast* (cruiser), H.M.S. *Rapid* (destroyer) and H.M.S. *Reward* (tug), 1945	12	15
339†	65c 18th-century merchantman under attack	25	30

1976

355†	20c English merchantman, 1609	10	8
357†	40c French warship, 1770	15	12

Nos. 265 and 271 overprinted **Independence 1976** *or surcharged also*

374†	20c H.M.S. *Belfast* (cruiser), H.M.S. *Rapid* (destroyer) and H.M.S. *Reward* (tug), 1945	15	30
382†	25r on 65c 18th-century merchantman under attack	11.00	15.00

1977

402	1r50 *Aurora* (Russian cruiser), 1917	30	20

1980

476†	5r Olympic yachts	40	40

480†	3r Cruise liner and pirogue	50	50
481†	5r *La Belle Coralline* (tourist launch)	70	75

485†	5r Fishing pirogue	55	55

1981

495	40c *Sao Gabriel* (Vasco da Gama), 1497		
496	2r25 *Caravel* (Mascarenhas), 1505		
497	3r50 H.M.S. *Beagle* (Darwin), 1831		
498	5r *Queen Elizabeth 2* (liner), 1968		
	Set of 4	2.50	2.75

505†	1r50 Royal Yacht *Victoria and Albert I*	20	25
507†	5r Royal Yacht *Cleveland*	75	75
509†	10r Royal Yacht *Britannia*	1.50	1.75

1983

Nos. 505, 507 and 509 surcharged

573†	50c on 1r50 Royal Yacht *Victoria and Albert I*	10	12
575†	2r25 on 5r Royal Yacht *Cleveland*	45	50
577†	3r75 on 10r Royal Yacht *Britannia*	75	80

1984

582†	10r Model pirogue	2.00	2.50

584†	2r Cargo liner, 1930's	45	55
585†	3r *Sun Viking* (cruise liner)	70	80
586†	10r R.F.A *Ennerdale II*	2.25	2.75

599†	3r Yacht	60	75

1985

611†	3r Sailboards	65	70

622†	10r Sailboards	2.25	2.40

1986

644†	50c Inter-island sailing ferry	10	12

1987

680†	2r Trawler	45	50

1988

683†	1r Sailboard	20	25
684†	2r Speedboat and yachts	45	50
685†	3r Yacht	70	75

SHARJAH

Arabia
1964 100 naye paise = 1 rupee
1966 100 dirhams = 1 riyal

1964

81†	20np Oil rig	12	8

1965

115†	5np Medieval ship	5	5
116†	5np *Savannah* (nuclear-powered freighter)	5	5

SHARJAH

166† 1np *Monarch* (cable ship) 5 5
170† 5np *Monarch* 10 5

Appendix

The following stamps have either been issued in excess of postal needs or have not been available to the public in reasonable quantities at face value. Miniature sheets, imperforate stamps etc., are excluded from this section.

1967

Famous Paintings. 5d 18th-century sea battle

1969

"Apollo 8" Moon Mission. Postage 5d; Air 4r American aircraft carrier

Post Day. Famous Sailing Ships. Postage 5d × 8; Air 90d × 8

"Apollo 12" Moon Mission. Overprinted on Post Day. Famous Sailing Ships issue. 5d × 8

1970

5th Anniversary of Ruler's Accession. Postage 5d; Air 35, 40, 60d Freighter at wharf

1971

Safe Return of "Apollo 13". Overprinted on 1969 *"Apollo 8"* issue. 4r American aircraft carrier

1972

Olympic Games, Munich. 15d Yacht
Munich Olympic Medal Winners. 5r Yacht
13th World Jamboree. Postage 2d; Air 35d Chinese junk

SIERRA LEONE

West Africa
1933 12 pence = 1 shilling
20 shillings = 1 pound
1964 100 cents = 1 leone

1933

174† 5d Bullom sailing canoe 6.50 18.00
175† 6d Dugout canoe 7.00 11.00

1949

As No. 115 *of Antigua*
206† 3d Paddle-steamer 50 50

1956

217† 1s Bullom sailing canoe 50 5

1961

239† 1s3d Royal Yacht *Britannia* 50 10

1963

No. 239 *overprinted* **1853–1959–1963 Oldest Postage Stamp Newest G.P.O. in West Africa AIRMAIL**
280† 1s3d Royal Yacht *Britannia* 20 15

1969

479 1c Ore carrier
480 2c Ore carrier
481 3½c Ore carrier
482 10c Ore carrier
483 18½c Ore carrier
484 50c Ore carrier

485 7½c Ore carrier (air)
486 9½c Ore carrier
487 15c Ore carrier
488 25c Ore carrier
489 1le Ore carrier
490 2le Ore carrier
Set of 12 6.00 6.50

1980

640 6c *Maria* (packet schooner), 1884
641 31c *Tarquah* (steam packet), 1902
642 50c *Aureol* (liner), 1951
643 1le *Africa Palm* (container ship), 1974
Set of 4 1.50 1.40

654† 50c Speedboat 40 40

1981

667† 1le Navy patrol boat 1.25 95

1983

751† 10c Mail canoe, River Mano 5 8
753† 1le British sailing packet, c. 1805 . . . . . . 55 65

1984

820 2c Portuguese caravel
821 5c *Merlin* (British galleon)
822 10c *Golden Hind* (Drake)
823 15c *Mordaunt* (British galleon)
824 25c *Atlantic* (sail transport)
825 25c H.M.S. *Lapwing* (frigate), 1785
826 30c *Traveller* (brig)

827 40c *Amistad* (schooner)
828 50c H.M.S. *Teazer* (gun vessel), 1868
829 70c *Scotia* (cable ship)
830 1le H.M.S. *Alecto* (paddle-steamer), 1882
831 2le H.M.S. *Blonde* (cruiser), 1889
832 5le H.M.S. *Fox* (cruiser), 1893
833 10le *Accra* (liner)
833c 15le H.M.S. *Favourite* (sloop), 1829
833d 25le H.M.S. *Euryalus* (screw frigate), 1883
Set of 16 15.00 13.00

835† 2le H.M.S. *Euryalus* (screw frigate), 1855 65 65

1985

863† 1le25 Langley's aircraft-launching barge, 1903 . . . . 45 45

1986

960† 1le Large cargo canoe 5 5
963† 10le Fishing canoe 40 45

Nos. 820, 826/7 *and* 829 *surcharged*
964 30le on 2c Portuguese caravel
965 40le on 30c *Traveller* (brig)
966 45le on 40c *Amistad* (schooner)
967 50le on 70c *Scotia* (cable ship)
Set of 4 7.75 8.25

1987

MS1000 60le Early 19th-century British warship, Freetown 2.40 2.50

1011 1le *U.S.A.* (yacht), 1987
1012 1le50 *New Zealand* (yacht), 1987
1013 2le50 *French Kiss* (yacht), 1987
1014 10le *Stars and Stripes* (yacht), 1987
1015 15le *Australia II* (yacht), 1983
1016 25le *Freedom* (yacht), 1980
1017 30le *Kookaburra III* (yacht), 1987
Set of 7 3.00 3.50
MS1018 50le *Constellation* (yacht), 1964 . . . . . . 2.00 2.25

SIERRA LEONE Le 5

Ducats   Santa Maria   Issac Abravanel 1437-1508 Fundraiser

Christopher Columbus 1451 - 1506

1077†	5le *Santa Maria* (Columbus)	20	25
1078†	10le *Pinta* (Columbus)	40	45
1079†	45le *Nina* (Columbus)	1.75	1.90

SIERRA LEONE   LE 15

1092†	15le Scout sailing dinghy	60	65

1988

Nos 1016 *and* 1079 *overprinted* **INDEPENDENCE 40** (*No.* 1131) *or* **Praga 88** (*No.* 1133), *each with Exhibition symbol*

1131†	25le *Freedom* (yacht), 1980	1.00	1.10
1133†	45le *Nina* (Columbus)	1.75	1.90

SINGAPORE

South-east Asia
100 cents = 1 dollar

1949

As No. 115 of Antigua

34†	15c Paddle-steamer	3.25	1.40

1955

1 CENT

SINGAPORE MALAYA

38†	1c Chinese sampan	8	25
39†	2c Malay fishing kolek	60	50
40†	4c Twa-kow lighter	35	5
41†	5c Lombok sloop	35	10
42†	6c Trengganu pinas	35	10
43†	8c Palari (schooner)	55	55
44†	10c Timber tongkong	1.50	5
45†	12c Hainan junk	1.25	1.50
46†	20c Cocos-Keeling schooner	70	5
48†	30c Tanker	1.50	5
49†	50c *Chusan III* (liner)	1.25	5

1970

15¢

NATIONAL LINE SINGAPORE

143	15c *Neptune Aquamarine* (freighter)		
144	30c Container ship		
145	75c Tanker under construction		
	Set of 3	8.50	9.25

1971

20c

SINGAPORE

151†	20c Sampans and houseboats	55	35
153†	50c Freighters, tugs and sampans	2.75	3.50

STAMP MONTHLY

— finest and most informative magazine for all collectors. Obtainable from your newsagent or by postal subscription — details on request.

SINGAPORE 10¢

Scene of Singapore River & Fort Canning in 1843-7

165†	10c Sampans, 1843	1.00	60
167†	20c Junks, 1848	2.25	1.60
170†	$1 Shipping off Singapore, 1861	10.00	12.00

1972

NEPTUNE RUBY

SINGAPORE   15¢

185	15c *Neptune Ruby* (container ship)		
186	75c *Maria Rickmers* (full-rigged sailing ship)		
187	$1 Chinese junk		
	Set of 3	8.50	8.50

1973

SINGAPORE $1

196†	$1 Sampan and houseboats	3.00	3.50

1975

SINGAPORE 20¢

247†	20c Houseboats	60	40
248†	$1 Fishing sampans	2.75	4.50

SINGAPORE 50¢

251†	50c Tanker	1.25	1.40
252†	$1 Container ship	2.00	3.00

1976

Queen Elizabeth Walk, circa 1905 - 10

SINGAPORE 10¢

279†	10c Junk and sampans, c. 1905	30	10

1977

SINGAPORE 10¢

302†	10c Freighter	15	5

1978

Neptune Spinel   SINGAPORE 10¢

10TH ANNIVERSARY OF NEPTUNE ORIENT LINES

335	10c *Neptune Spinel* (bulk carrier)		
336	35c *Neptune Aries* (tanker)		
337	50c *Anro Temasek* (container ship)		
338	75c *Neptune Pearl* (container ship)		
	Set of 4	1.60	1.75

1980

SINGAPORE   1¢

Hainan junk

364	1c Hainan junk	
365	5c Full-rigged clipper ship	
366	10c Fujian junk	
367	15c Golekkan (sailing craft)	
368	20c Palari (sailing craft)	
369	25c East Indiaman	
370	35c Galleon	
371	50c Caravel	
372	75c Jiangsu trading junk	
373	$1 *Kedah* (coaster)	
374	$2 *Murex* (tanker)	
375	$5 *Chusan* (screw steamer)	
376	$10 *Braganza* (paddle-steamer)	

Set of 13	12.00	10.00

1982

10TH ANNIVERSARY CONTAINER TERMINAL 1972-1982   PSA

SINGAPORE 10¢

431	10c Container ship at berth		
432	35c Container ship at berth		
433	50c Container ship at berth		
434	75c Container ship at berth		
	Set of 4	90	1.00

1983

singapore $1   WORLD COMMUNICATIONS YEAR

Sea Communications

466†	$1 Freighter	50	55

1986

South East Asia - Middle East - Western Europe Submarine Cable System

10¢ Singapore

535	10c *Vercors* (cable ship)		
536	35c *Vercors*		
537	50c *Vercors*		
538	75c *Vercors*		
	Set of 4	1.25	1.25

1987

SINGAPORE 10¢

554†	10c Patrol boat	5	8
MS557†	35c Patrol boat (sheet contains four other designs)	95	1.00

558†	10c Dragon boats	5	8
559†	50c Fishing punt	25	30

SLOVAKIA

Central Europe
100 haleru = 1 koruna

1939

No. 362 of Czechoslovakia optd **Slovensky stat 1939**

22†	10k River tug and barge, Bratislava	80.00	70.00

SLOVENIA

South-east Europe
100 centesimi = 1 lira

1945

119†	10c Punt, Lake Zirknitz	20	75

SOLOMON ISLANDS

West Pacific
1907 12 pence = 1 shilling
20 shillings = 1 pound
1966 100 cents = 1 dollar

1907

1	½d War canoe
2	1d War canoe
3	2d War canoe
4	2½d War canoe
5	5d War canoe
6	6d War canoe
7	1s War canoe

	Set of 7	£225	£275

1908

8	½d War canoe
9	1d War canoe
10	2d War canoe
11	2½d War canoe
11a	4d War canoe
12	5d War canoe
13	6d War canoe
14	1s War canoe
15	2s War canoe
16	2s6d War canoe
17	5s War canoe

	Set of 11	£150	£225

1939

62†	1½d Malaita canoes	35	70
63†	2d Canoe and canoe house	20	55
64†	2½s Roviana canoe	70	55
65†	3d Roviana canoes	25	60
71†	5s Malaita canoe	13.00	8.50

1949

As No. 115 of Antigua

78†	3d Paddle-steamer	1.50	75

1956

82†	½d Ysabel canoe	12	25
83†	1d Roviana canoes	15	10
84†	1½d Malaita canoes	15	20
85†	2d Canoe and canoe house1	20	15
86†	2½d Roviana canoe prow	25	40
87†	3d Malaita canoe	25	15
89†	6d *Miena* (trading schooner)	50	25
91†	1s H.M.S. *Swallow* (Carteret), 1767	50	45
94†	5s *Todos los Santos* (Mendana), 1568	8.00	3.25

1965

126†	£1 Western canoe figurehead	11.00	7.00

1966

No. 126 surcharged

152†	$2 on £1 Western canoe figurehead	4.75	3.75

1968

162†	3c *Todos los Santos* (Mendana), 1568	15	10
164†	35c "King George V" class battleship, 1939–45	35	10
165†	$1 H.M.S. *Curacoa* (corvette), 1893	60	60

167†	2c Fishing canoe	10	5
172†	12c Boat building	65	30
179†	$1 *Kylix* (tanker) and *Hollybank* (freighter)	3.00	2.25

1970

192†	14c War canoe (on stamp No. 3)	30	15
193†	18c War canoe (on stamp No. 17)	35	20

1971

201†	3c *La Boussole* (La Perouse), 1787	65	20
203†	12c *Heemskerk* (Tasman), 1643	1.75	65
204†	35c Te Puki outrigger canoe, Santa Cruz	3.50	1.50

206†	4c Missionary schooner, 1871	5	5
208†	45c Canoe	25	15

1972

215†	4c *La Boudeuse* (Bougainville), 1776	30	10
217†	15c H.M.S. *Swallow* (Carteret), 1707	85	35
218†	45c Malaita canoe	3.75	2.50

1973

236†	4c *Recherche* (D'Entrecasteaux), 1791	30	15
238†	15c H.M.S. *Alexander* (Shortland), 1788	90	50
239†	35c Tomoko (war canoe)	3.75	3.00

1974

254†	4c *Titus* (freighter)	25	10
256†	15c "Blackbirder" brig (illegal labour ship)	70	25
257†	45c U.S.S. *PT 109* (motor torpedo-boat), 1943	3.00	2.00

1975

272	4c *Walande* (coaster)
273	9c *Melanesian* (coaster)
274	15c *Marsina* (container ship)
275	45c *Himalaya* (liner)

	Set of 4	2.75	2.25

1976

304†	45c Nguzu-nguzu canoe prow	30	25

322†	20c *Amagiri* (Japanese cruiser) ramming U.S.S. *PT 109* (motor torpedo-boat), 1943	75	40

1978

371†	45c Scout canoe	65	70

1979

372† 8c H.M.S. *Discovery* (Cook) 20 10

384† 8c War canoe (on stamp No. 13) 15 10

1980

409 8c H.M.S. *Curacao* (frigate), 1839, and
crest
410 20c H.M.S. *Herald* (survey ship), 1854,
and crest
411 35c H.M.S. *Royalist* (screw corvette),
1889, and crest
412 45c H.M.S. *Beagle* (survey schooner),
1878, and crest
Set of 4 1.25 1.00

413 8c Steel fishery training ship
414 20c *Solomon Hunter* (fishery training
vessel)
415 45c *Ufi Na Tasi* (refrigerated fish
transport)
416 80c Fishery research vessel
Set of 4 1.10 1.25

417† 45c *Comliebank* (cargo liner) 50 55
420† 45c *Corabank* (container ship) 50 55

1981

430 8c H.M.S. *Mounts Bay* (frigate), 1959, and
crest
431 20c H.M.S. *Charbydis* (frigate), 1970, and
crest
432 45c H.M.S. *Hydra* (survey ship), 1972,
and crest
433 $1 Royal Yacht *Britannia*, 1974, and crest
Set of 4 1.90 1.40

436† 45c *La Princesa* (Maurelle), 1781 ...... 60 65

450† 45c Outrigger canoe 30 30

1982

MS475 $1 Royal Yacht *Britannia* (sheet also
contains two other designs) 1.25 1.40

1983

510† 25c War canoe (on stamp No. 11) 35 30
511† $1 War canoe (on stamp No. 13) 1.25 1.40

1984

519 12c *Olivebank* (barque), 1892
520 15c *Tinhow* (freighter), 1906
521 18c *Oriana* (liner)
522 $1 *Silwyn Range* (container ship)
Set of 4 1.75 1.75

1985

MS542 $1.50 Gondola, Venice 1.40 1.50

545† 45c *Soltai No 7* (trawler) 45 45

547† 12c Outrigger canoe, Titiana 15 12
548† 35c Motorised canoe, Langa 30 30

550† 12c Brownie canoe 15 12

561† $1 *Sir Walter Raleigh* (support ship) and
Zebu (brigantine) 75 80

1986

570a 18c *America*, 1851; *Magic*, 1870;
Puritan, 1885; *Mayflower*, 1886;
Columbia, 1899; *Columbia*, 1901;
Rainbow, 1934; *Ranger*, 1937;
Intrepid, 1967; *Intrepid*, 1970;
Mischief, 1861; *Madeleine*, 1876;
Vigilant, 1893; *Defender*, 1895;
Resolute, 1920; *Enterprise*, 1930;
Weatherley, 1962; *Constellation*, 1964;
Courageous, 1977; *Freedom*, 1980;
30c *Columbia*, 1871; *Volunteer*, 1887;
Reliance, 1903, *Columbia*, 1958;
Courageous, 1974; *Australia II*, 1983;
$1 *America II*, 1987; *South Australia*,
1987; *KA-14*, 1987; *Kookaburra*, 1987;
Eagle, 1987; *Secret Cove*, 1987;
Courageous III, 1987; *Crusader*, 1987;
Sail America, 1987; *French Kiss*, 1987;
Heart of America, 1987; *St. Francis IX*,
1987; *New Zealand II*, 1987; *Italia*,
1987; *True North*, 1987; *Azzurra*, 1987;
France, 1987, *Australia III*, 1987 (all
yachts, sheet also contains six other
stamps) 25.00

1987

MS575 $5 *Stars and Stripes* (yacht), 1987 .... 2.75 3.00

1988

617† $1 Canoe 55 60

618† 22c Building fishing boat 12 15
619† 80c War canoe 45 50

622† 22c *Todos los Santos* (Mendana), 1568 12 15

626 35c *Papuan Chief* (container ship)
627 60c *Nimos* (container ship)
628 70c *Malaita* (freighter)
629 $1.30 *Makambo* (freighter)
Set of 4 1.50 1.90

SOMALIA

East Africa
1924 100 besa = 1 rupia
1950 100 centesimi = 1 somalo

1924

No. 157 of Italy surcharged **SOMALIA ITALIANA besa 13**
56† 13b on 30c Ferry boat 25 2.00

1950

244† 30c Pirogue 15 12
245† 45c Pirogue 15 15
246† 65c Pirogue 20 15
247† 70c Pirogue 20 15
248† 90c Pirogue 25 20
249† 1s Pirogue 30 10
250† 1s35 Pirogue 35 30
251† 1s50 Pirogue 45 30
252† 3s Pirogue 3.50 1.00
253† 5s Pirogue 4.00 1.50
254† 10s Pirogue 4.75 1.00

1959

342† 1s20 Ancient Egyptian ships 20 20
343† 2s Freighter, Mogadishu 25 25

COLLECT RAILWAYS ON STAMPS

A Stanley Gibbons thematic catalogue on this popular subject. Copies available at £7.50 (p. + p. £2) from: Stanley Gibbons Publications Ltd, 5 Parkside, Christchurch Road, Ringwood, Hants BH24 3SH.

1979

632 75c Fishing punt
633 80c Felucca
634 2s30 Motor fishing boats
635 2s50 Trawler
Set of 4 1.40 1.00

1983

707† 3s20 Modern warship 25 20

SOMALILAND PROTECTORATE

East Africa
12 pies = 1 anna
16 annas = 1 rupee

1949

As No. 115 *of Antigua*
122† 3a on 30c Paddle-steamer 30 25

SOUTH AFRICA

Southern Africa
1926 12 pence = 1 shilling
20 shillings = 1 pound
1961 100 cents = 1 rand

PRICES. Nos. 115, 106, 127 and O366 were issued inscribed in English or Afrikaans. The prices quoted are for one of each version in a horizontal pair.

1926

115† 1d *Dromedaris* (Van Riebeeck), 1652
(black & red) 35 15

1943

As No. 115 *but redrawn with plain background to centre oval*
106† 1d *Dromedaris* (red) 65 85

1949

127 1½d *Wanderer* (emigrant ship), 1849 ...... 15 15

1952

138† 2d Van Riebeeck's fleet, 1652 .... 20 5

No. 138 *overprinted* **SADIPU**
142† 2d Van Riebeeck's fleet, 1652 .... 15 15

1961

324† 50c Freighter 4.00 1.00

1962

222 2½c *Chapman* (emigrant ship), 1820
223 12½c *Chapman*
Set of 2 2.75 2.25

1971

305† 2c Ship's boat, 1820 .... 15 10

1973

333† 5c Shipwreck of *De Jong Thomas* (Dutch East Indiaman), 1773 .... 40 10
334† 15c Shipwreck of *De Jong Thomas* 5.00 3.50

1975

379† 5c Dutch East Indiaman, Table Bay 20 8

1976

409 10c Steam packet, 1876 .... 60 85

1978

439 15c Brig, Walvis Bay, 1878 .... 50 50

1980

481† 5c 17th-century Dutch yacht 10 5

1982

506	8c *Maria van Riejbeck* (submarine)			
507	15c Missile patrol vessel			
508	20c Minesweeper			
509	25c Harbour patrol boats			
		Set of 4	70	1.00

1983

547†	25c Yacht		30	35

1988

633†	40c Caravels (Dias), 1488		20	25

OFFICIAL STAMPS

No. 115 overprinted **OFFICIAL OFFISIEEL**

O36b†	1d *Dromedaris* (Van Riebeeck), 1652		90	1.50

SOUTH GEORGIA

South Atlantic
1963 12 pence = 1 shilling
20 shillings = 1 pound
1971 100 pence = 1 pound

1963

6†	4d *R-1* (whale-catcher)		1.25	35
9†	9d *R-2* (whale-catcher)		1.75	55

1971

Nos. 6 and 9 surcharged in decimal currency

59†	4p on 4d *R-1*		12.00	10.00
26†	6p on 9d *R-2*		1.50	90

1972

32	1½p *Endurance* (Shackleton), 1915			
33	5p *James Caird* (longboat), 1915			
34	10p *James Caird*			
35	20p *Quest* (Shackleton), 1921			
		Set of 4	6.00	6.00

1974

41†	25p H.M.S. *Belfast* (cruiser)		1.75	1.00

1975

44†	8p H.M.S. *Resolution* (Cook)		2.25	2.25

1976

46†	2p *Discovery* (Scott), 1901		85	55
47†	8p *William Scoresby* (Antarctic supply vessel)		1.10	70
48†	11p *Discovery II* (Antarctic supply vessel)		1.40	80

1977

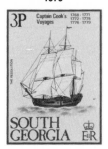

50†	6p Royal Yacht *Britannia*, 1957		80	50

1979

70†	3p H.M.S. *Resolution* (Cook)		1.10	75
71†	6p H.M.S. *Resolution*		90	65

SOUTH KOREA

See under Korea

SOUTH VIETNAM

See under Vietnam

SOUTH WEST AFRICA

Southern Africa
1900 100 pfennig = 1 mark
1926 12 pence = 1 shilling
20 shillings = 1 pound
1961 100 cents = 1 rand

1900

As Nos. K7/19 *of Cameroun, but inscribed* "DEUTSCH-SUDWESTAFRIKA"

24	3pf *Hohenzollern* (German Imperial yacht)			
25	5pf *Hohenzollern*			
26	10pf *Hohenzollern*			
27	20pf *Hohenzollern*			
15	25pf *Hohenzollern*			
16	30pf *Hohenzollern*			
17	40pf *Hohenzollern*			
18	50pf *Hohenzollern*			
19	80pf *Hohenzollern*			
29	1m *Hohenzollern*			
30	2m *Hohenzollern*			
22	3m *Hohenzollern*			
32	5m *Hohenzollern*			
		Set of 13	70.00	£200

1926

No. 115 *of South Africa overprinted* **South West Africa.** *or* **Suidwes Africa.** *alternately*

46†	1d *Dromedaris* (Van Riebeeck), 1652		1.60	2.75

The prices quoted are for a horizontal pair, containing one of each overprint

1927

No. 115 *of South Africa overprinted* **S. W .A.**

59†	1d *Dromedaris* (Van Riebeeck), 1652		1.50	3.25

No. 59 exists with the basic stamp inscribed in either English or Afrikaans. The prices quoted are for one of each in a horizontal pair.

1931

75†	1d Portuguese galleon, Cape Cross		70	1.25

No. 75 exists inscribed in either English or Afrikaans. The prices quoted are for one of each in a horizontal pair.

1937

96	1½d *Capetown Castle* (liner)		3.50	1.40

No. 96 exists inscribed in either English or Afrikaans. The prices quoted are for one of each in a horizontal pair.

1952

No. 138 *of South Africa overprinted* **SWA**

146†	2d Van Riebeeck's fleet, 1652		40	5

1961

177†	3½c Trawler		70	15

1971

As No. 305 *of South Africa, but inscribed* "SWA"

232†	2c Ship's boat, 1820		2.50	60

1975

279†	15c Freighter at wharf		70	55
280†	15c Trawler and tug, Walvis Bay		70	55

1982

396†	25c Dias's caravel, 1488		35	35
397†	30c Dias's caravel, 1488		35	40

1983

420†	20c Lobster boat and dinghies	25	30
421†	25c Lobster dinghy	30	35

1984

434†	45c *Elizabeth* and *Leipzig* (German steam corvettes), 1884	60	55

1986

457†	25c Diogo Cao's caravel, 1486	25	20

467†	14c Pirogue, Lake Liumbezi	15	12

1987

483	16c Wreck of *Hope* (whaling schooner), 1804	
484	30c Wreck of *Tilly*, 1885	
485	40c Wreck of *Eduard Bohlen*, 1909	
486	50c Wreck of *Dunedin Star*, 1942	
	Set of 4	65	80

1988

488†	30c Caravel (Dias), 1488	15	20

OFFICIAL STAMPS

1927

No. 46 overprinted **OFFICIAL** *or* **OFFISIEEL** *alternately*

O2†	1d *Dromedaris* (Van Riebeeck), 1652	65.00	95.00

The price quoted is for a horizontal pair containing one of each overprint.

1929

No. 59 overprinted **OFFICIAL** *or* **OFFISIEEL** *alternately*

O10†	1d *Dromedaris* (Van Riebeeck), 1652	75	6.00

The prices quoted are for a horizontal pair containing one of each overprint.

1938

Nos. 75 and 96 overprinted **OFFICIAL** *or* **OFFISIEEL** *alternately*

O24†	1d Portuguese galleon, Cape Cross	1.00	6.00
O20†	1½d *Capetown Castle* (liner)	7.00	12.00

The prices quoted are for horizontal pairs containing one of each overprint.

SOUTHERN CAMEROONS

West Africa
12 pence = 1 shilling
20 shillings = 1 pound

1960

Nos. 69 and 80 of Nigeria overprinted **CAMEROONS U.K.T.T.**

1†	½d 19th-century brigantine and canoes	5	20
12†	£1 Shipping at Lagos in 19th and 20th centuries	6.50	15.00

SOUTHERN RHODESIA

Central Africa
12 pence = 1 shilling
20 shillings = 1 pound

1949

As No. 115 of Antigua

68†	2d Paddle-steamer	65	25

SPAIN

South-west Europe
100 centimos = 1 peseta

1929

502†	1c Caravel	20	20
506†	15c Caravel	30	25
508†	25c Caravel	40	35

1930

593†	1c *Santa Maria* (Columbus)	15	10
594†	2c *Santa Maria* (bow view)	15	10
595†	2c *Santa Maria* (stern view)	15	10
596†	5c *Santa Maria* (bow view)	15	10
597†	5c *Santa Maria* (stern view)	15	10
598†	10c *Santa Maria*	40	50
599†	15c *Santa Maria*	40	50
600†	20c *Santa Maria*	55	45
601†	25c *Santa Maria, Pinta* and *Nina*	55	45
602†	30c Ship's boat, 1492	3.00	2.75
603†	40c *Santa Maria, Pinta* and *Nina*	2.40	1.60
604†	50c Ship's boat, 1492	3.00	2.75
605†	1p *Santa Maria, Pinta* and *Nina*	3.00	2.75

651†	4p *Santa Maria* (Columbus)	1.40	1.25

1938

857a	1p *Isaac Peral* (submarine)	
857b	2p *Narcisco Monturiol* (submarine)	
857c	4p *B-2* (submarine)	
857d	6p *Narcisco Monturiol*	
857e	10p *B-2*	
857f	15p *Isaac Peral*	
	Set of 6	£250	£225

MS924	2c, 5c each x 2 *Almirante Cervera* (cruiser) (sheet contains 16 other stamps)	25.00	22.00

MS939	50c Battle of Lepanto, 1571	£275	£300

1940

997†	50c + 5c 15th-century caravel	25	20
1002†	1p40 + 40c 15th-century caravel	25	30

1949

1130†	5c Galleon	8	8
1131†	10c Galleon	8	8
1132†	50c + 10c Galleon	40	30

1955

1234	20c 15th-century caravel	
1235	25c 15th-century caravel	
1236	50c 15th-century caravel	
1237	1p 15th-century caravel	
1238	1p10 15th-century caravel	
1239	1p40 15th-century caravel	
1240	3p 15th-century caravel	
1241	4p80 15th-century caravel	
1242	5p 15th-century caravel	
1243	7p 15th-century caravel	
1244	10p 15th-century caravel	
	Set of 11	2.75	1.00

1956

1254	3p *Ciudad de Toledo* (cargo liner)	5.50	1.75

1961

1420†	2p50 Shipbuilding	30	30

1963

1575† 80c Fleet of Columbus 12   5

1964

1660	15c	Medieval ship		
1661	25c	Carrack		
1662	40c	*Santa Maria* (Columbus)		
1663	50c	Galley		
1664	70c	Galleon		
1665	80c	Xebec		
1666	1p	*Santissima Trinidad* (ship of the line), 1769		
1667	1p50	*Atrevida* (corvette), 1794		
1668	2p	*Isabel II* (steam frigate)		
1669	2p50	*Numancia* (steam frigate)		
1670	3p	*Destructor* (destroyer)		
1671	5p	Isaac Peral's submarine		
1672	6p	*Baleares* (cruiser)		
1673	10p	*Juan Sebastian D'Elcano* (cadet schooner)		
		Set of 14	3.00	1.50

1965

1709† 1p Fishing boats, Cudillero 8   5

1967

1847 1p⁵⁰ Fishing boats, Palma 8   5

1876 1p50 16th-century caravel 8   5

1880† 1p20 *Princessa* (sail warship), Nutka 8   5
1884† 6p 18th-century warships and Indian canoe, Alaska 20   5

1968

1946 6p Olympic yacht 15   8

1971

2114† 5p Battle of Lepanto, 1571 40   8

1972

2138† 4p Fishing boats 20   8

2167† 5p Galleon and fishing boats, San Juan, 1625 45   8

1973

2202 2p Trawler 10   8

1974

2240† 15p 18th-century shipyard 40   10

1975

2288† 8p Sailing packet of the West Indian service 60   10

COLLECT BIRDS ON STAMPS
Second revised edition of this Stanley Gibbons thematic catalogue – now available at £8.50 (p. + p. £2) from: Stanley Gibbons Publications Ltd, 5 Parkside, Christchurch Road, Ringwood, Hants BH24 3SH.

1976

2353† 7p 18th-century ship of the line 1.40   15
2355† 50p *Victoria* (Del Cano) 80   15

2374† 1p Freighter 20   5

2434 12p *Santa Maria* (Columbus) 30   10

1977

2486 15p West Indies sailing packet 50   50

1978

2520† 12p Freighter and oil rig 15   8

2527† 12p 16th-century shipping, Las Palmas 20   8

1979

2573 5p *Roger de Lauria* (destroyer) 10   5

2584 5p English fleet, Tenerife, 1797 10   5

1980

2610† 8p Tankers 10 5

1981

2649 7p 16th-century galleon
2650 12p 16th-century galleon

Set of 2 25 10

1985

2803† 18p *Santissima Trinidad* (ship of the
line), 1785 .... 20 5

1987

2900 19p 18th-century warship 20 5

1987

2928 20p *Ictineo* (early submarine) 20 5

MS2930† 12p 14th-century shipping in Coruna
harbour, 20p 18th-century sailing packet,
Havona, 50p 18th-century sailing packets
(sheet contains one other design) 1.75 1.75

EXPRESS LETTER STAMPS

1930

As No. 600, but colour changed, overprinted **URGENTE**
E608 20c *Santa Maria* (Columbus) 75 60

STANLEY GIBBONS STAMP COLLECTING SERIES

Introductory booklets on *How to Start, How to Identify Stamps* and *Collecting by Theme.* A series of well illustrated guides at a low price.
Write for details.

SPANISH GUINEA

West Africa
100 centimos = 1 peseta

1925

209	5c Nipa canoe		
210	10c Nipa canoe		
211	15c Nipa canoe		
212	20c Nipa canoe		
213	25c Nipa canoe		
214	30c Nipa canoe		
215	40c Nipa canoe		
216	50c Nipa canoe		
217	60c Nipa canoe		
218	1p Nipa canoe		
219	4p Nipa canoe		
220	10p Nipa canoe		

Set of 12 13.50 5.75

1929

Nos. 506 and 508 of Spain overprinted **GUINEA**
235† 15c Caravel 8 8
237† 25c Caravel 8 8

1949

329 4p Pirogue 1.50 50

330 5p *Catalina* (ship of the line) 1.50 50

331†	2c Canoe, San Carlos Bay	20	5
333†	10c Sailing canoe, Fernando Poo	20	5
334†	15c Canoe, River Benito	20	5
335†	25c Canoe, San Carlos Bay	20	5
337†	40c Canoe, Fernando Poo	20	5
338†	45c Canoe, River Benito	20	5
339†	50c Canoe, San Carlos Bay	20	5
341†	90c Sailing canoe, Fernando Poo	20	5
342†	1p Canoe, River Benito	1.25	20
343†	1p35 Canoe, San Carlos Bay	4.75	85
345†	5p Sailing canoe, Fernando Poo	17.00	3.50
346†	10p Canoe, San Carlos Bay	65.00	15.00

1951

353† 1p *Dominie* (liner) 5 5
356† 5p *Dominie* 4.50 1.40

SPANISH MOROCCO

North Africa
100 centimos -1 peseta

II. SPANISH PROTECTORATE

1929

Nos. 502, 506 and 508 of Spain overprinted **PROTECTORADO MARRUECOS**
138† 1c Caravel 5 5
142† 15c Caravel 5 5
144† 25c Caravel 5 5

1948

317† 10p *Arango* (freighter) at quay 1.50 70

1950

361† 10p *Carabo* (fishing boat) 1.75 35

1951

367† 1p + 5p *Hernan Cortes* (brig) 4.00 2.75

1953

394† 35c *Carabo* (fishing boat) 15 5

III. INTERNATIONAL ZONE OF TANGIER

1929

Nos. 506 and 508 of Spain overprinted **TANGER**
29† 15c Caravel 8 5
31† 25c Caravel 8 5

SPANISH SAHARA

West Africa
100 centimos = 1 peseta

1929

Nos. 506 and 508 of Spain overprinted **SAHARA**
27† 15c Caravel 8 8
29† 25c Caravel 8 8

1955

117	10c + 5c Fishing boat		
118	25c + 10c Felucca		
119	50c Fishing boat		

Set of 3 20 15

1966

248† 1p50 *Fuerta Ventura* (freighter) 10 5

SRI LANKA

Indian Ocean
100 cents = 1 rupee

1983

796†	50c *Lanka Athula* (container ship)	5	8
798†	5r *Lanka Kalyani* (freighter)	25	35
799†	20r *Tammanna* (tanker)	1.10	1.75

SUDAN

North-east Africa
1000 milliemes = 100 piastres = 1 pound

1950

115†	2p Nile felucca	1.50	10
120†	4½p *Gordon Pasha* (Nile mail boat)	2.00	2.50

1951

131†	3p Ambatch reed canoe	25	5

1962

195†	10p Nile felucca	30	20

1988

420†	25p Fishing boat	8	5

POSTAGE DUE STAMPS

1901

D5	2m *Zafir* (Nile gunboat)		
D10	4m *Zafir*		
D11	10m *Zafir*		
D8	20m *Zafir*		
	Set of 4	4.75	6.00

1948

Arabic inscription at foot differs from Nos. D5/8

D12	2m *Zafir* (Nile gunboat)		
D13	4m *Zafir*		
D394	10m *Zafir*		
D395	20m *Zafir*		
	Set of 4	2.75	10.00

OFFICIAL STAMPS

1950

Nos. 115 and 120 overprinted **S.G.**

O59†	2p Nile felucca	2.50	90
O64†	4½p *Gordon Pasha* (Nile mail boat)	2.50	4.25

1951

No. 131 overprinted **S.G.**

O75†	3p Ambatch reed canoe	40	5

1962

No. 195 overprinted **S.G.** *in Arabic*

O222†	10p Nile felucca	80	20

SURINAM

South America
100 cents = 1 gulden

1936

236†	½c *Johannes van Walbeeck* (Dutch galleon), 1634	15	20
237†	1c *Johannes van Walbeeck*	25	10
238†	1½c *Johannes van Walbeeck*	40	30
239†	2c *Johannes van Walbeeck*	45	20
240†	2½c *Johannes van Walbeeck*	8	10
241†	3c *Johannes van Walbeeck*	40	30
242†	4c *Johannes van Walbeeck*	50	65
243†	5c *Johannes van Walbeeck*	45	15
244†	6c *Johannes van Walbeeck*	1.75	1.40
245†	7½c *Johannes van Walbeeck*	10	10

1942

Nos. 239, 240 and 245 surcharged with red cross and value

289†	2c + 2c *Johannes van Walbeeck* (Dutch galleon), 1634	1.00	1.50
291†	2½c + 2c *Johannes van Walbeeck*	1.00	1.50
292†	7½ + 5c *Johannes van Walbeeck*	1.00	1.50

1945

Nos. 237 and 245 surcharged

298†	½c on 1c *Johannes van Walbeeck* (Dutch galleon), 1634	8	20
299†	1½c on 7½c *Johannes van Walbeeck*	8	20
300†	2½c on 7½c *Johannes van Walbeeck*	1.50	2.00

314†	1½c Canoes	90	95
317†	3c Canoe, River Surinam	90	40

1953

410†	6c Log raft	1.10	90
416†	20c Pirogue	35	5

1962

510†	10c Trading canoe	30	30

1965

553†	20c Canoe	20	5
557†	40c *Surinam* (coaster)	35	15

1966

604†	20c Coaster, 1916	15	10

1967

617	10c Dutch galleons, Paramaribo, *c.* 1670	
618	20c Dutch galleon, New York, *c.* 1660	
619	25c Dutch river boats, Breda, *c.* 1667	
	Set of 3	50 50

1971

711†	20c Canoe, Albina, 1846	30	30

1977

884†	5c *Curacao* (paddle-steamer), 1827	5	5
885†	15c Steamship in dock, Hellevoetsluis, 1827	20	15
889†	95c *Stuyvesant* (liner)	1.25	1.25

1986

1290†	110c *Saramacca* (container ship)	90	90

SWAZILAND

Southern Africa
1949 12 pence = 1 shilling
20 shillings = 1 pound
1975 100 cents = 1 lilangeni

1949

As No. 115 of Antigua

49†	3d Paddle-steamer	40	20

1981

373†	15c Sailing dinghies	15	10

SWEDEN

Northern Europe
100 ore = 1 krona

1936

191†	20ore *Hiorten* (sailing packet), 1692 (blue)	8.00	2.50
192†	25ore *Constitutionen* (paddle-steamer), 1824 (ultramarine)	6.00	40
198†	60ore *Gripsholm* (liner) (purple)	28.00	50

1938

204†	15ore *Calmare Nyckel* and *Fagel Grip* (emigrant ships), 1638 (brown)	70	5

1944

273†	10ore *Smalands Lejon* (ship of the line), 1634 (violet)	20	10
275†	30ore *Kung Karl* (ship of the line), 1693 (blue)	55	50
277†	90ore *Gustav V* (cruiser), 1918	9.00	1.25

1953

338†	25ore Shipping, Stockholm, 1650	20	5

1957

381a	30ore Shipwrecked trawler		
382	1k40 Shipwrecked trawler		
	Set of 2	5.75	1.25

1958

395†	15ore Galleon and *Gripsholm II* (liner)	20	10
397†	40ore Galleon and *Gripsholm II* (liner)	4.00	1.50

1966

As Nos. 273, 204, 191/2 and 275, but colours changed and dated "1966" at foot

517†	10ore *Smalands Lejon* (ship of the line) (red)	10	20
518†	15ore *Calmare Nyckel* and *Fagel Grip* (emigrant ships), 1638 (red)	10	20
519†	20ore *Hiorten* (sailing packet), 1692 (green)	10	20
520†	25ore *Constitutionen* (paddle-steamer), 1824 (blue)	10	12
521†	30ore *Kung Karl* (ship of the line), 1693 (red)	10	20

1967

539†	10ore Swedish warship, 1650	5	5
541†	40ore Canal steamer, Dalsland Canal	10	5

1969

592†	55ore *Wasa* (ship of the line), 1628	30	20

595	30ore *Cyklop* (lightship)		
596	55ore *Cyklop*		
	Set of 2	60	25

1970

616†	45ore Lapp boat	30	40

622†	70ore Freighters in port	4.00	3.50

1971

638†	80ore *Storskar* (ferry), 1908	25	5

647†	55ore Container ship in berth	25	10

1972

689†	55ore *Meta* (barque)	45	45
692†	55ore *Falken* (cadet schooner)	45	45

COLLECT BIRDS ON STAMPS

Second revised edition of this Stanley Gibbons thematic catalogue – now available at £8.50 (p. + p. £2) from: Stanley Gibbons Publications Ltd, 5 Parkside, Christchurch Road, Ringwood, Hants BH24 3SH.

As No. 198, but colour changed and dated "1972" at foot

704†	60ore *Gripsholm* (liner) (blue)	30	30

707†	75ore Figurehead of *Amphion*, 1800	25	20

1973

730†	65ore Dalecarlia longboats	30	25

735†	10ore Viking longship from Larbro Stone	5	5

746†	1k Tahitian outrigger canoe	80	80
747†	1k *Vega* (Nordenskjold), 1878	80	80

1974

803†	65ore Yachts	30	30

823	1k *Bill* (tanker)		
824	1k *Snow Storm* (liner)		
825	1k *Tor* and *Atle* (ice-breakers)		
826	1k *Skanes* (train ferry)		
827	1k *Bill, Bull* and *Starkodder* (tugs)		
	Set of 5	2.75	2.75

1975

860†	90ore Shipwreck of *Merkur* (tanker)	40	20

864†	90ore Scout canoes	80	20

1976

890† 85ore Tug towing timber 20 20

898† 1k30 Battle of Hampton Roads, 1862 .... 50 45

1977

930† 95ore Fishing punt 20 20

939† 1k10 *Djurgarden 6* (ferry) 50 40

1979

995† 1k30 Sledge-boat, Aland 30 5

1002† 1k15 *Juno* (tourist launch), Gota Canal 45 45
1003† 1k15 Yachts in lock, Gota Canal 45 45
1006† 1k15 Motor barge, Gota Canal 45 45

1020† 1k70 *Argos* (fishery research ship) 35 40

1980

1046† 1k15 Yachts, Sunds Canal 30 30

**STANLEY GIBBONS
STAMP COLLECTING SERIES**

Introductory booklets on *How to Start, How to Identify Stamps* and *Collecting by Theme.* A series of well illustrated guides at a low price.
Write for details.

1981

1079 1k65 Sailing boat, Bohuslan
1080 1k65 Sailing boat, Blekinge
1081 1k65 Sailing boat, Norrbotten
1082 1k65 Sailing boat, Halsingland
1083 1k65 Sailing boat, Gotland
1084 1k65 Sailing boat, Skane
　　　　　　　　　　　　Set of 6　2.25　1.10

1090† 2k40 Tugs and gas rig 50 40

1982

1119 1k65 Yacht
1120 1k65 *Sally* (ferry)
1121 1k65 Racing yachts
1122 1k65 Buoying ship
1123 1k65 Pilot boat
　　　　　　　　　　　　Set of 5　1.60　65

1983

1151† 2k40 Yachts 50 20

1984

1205† 1k90 17th-century fishing boats, Gavle 40 30

1985

1257† 2k *Af Chapman* (youth hostel), Stockholm 45 15

1988

1374 3k10 Fishing skiff, Lake Hjalmaren
1375 3k10 Market boat, Lake Vattern
1376 3k10 Logging boat, River Byske
1377 3k10 Rowing boat, Lake Asnon
1378 3k10 Ice boat, Lake Vanern
1379 3k10 Church longboat, Lake Lockne
　　　　　　　　　　　　Set of 6　3.25　1.60

1380† 3k60 *Calmare Nyckel* and *Fagel Grip* (emigrant ships), 1638 .... 70 35

1390† 2k Garlanded longboat 40 15
1394† 2k *Norrskar* (tourist launch) 40 15

SWITZERLAND

Central Europe
100 centimes = 1 franc

1942

428† 10c + 10c Medieval fishing boat, Lake Geneva 15 30

1945

MS446a 3f + 7f Lifeboat £190 £190

1949

518† 40c Rhine barge, Basel 3.00 5

1959

597† 5c Rhine ferry 25 10

1978

MS952 20c *La Suisse* (lake steamer), 1900; 20c *Il Verbano* (lake paddle-steamer), 1826; 40c *Gotthard* (lake steamer), 1970; 40c *Ville de Neuchatel* (lake steamer), 1972; 40c *Romanshorn* (lake steamer), 1958; 40c *Le Winkelied* (lake paddle-steamer), 1871; 70c *Loetschberg* (lake paddle-steamer), 1914; 80c *Waedenswil* (lake steamer), 1895 .... 9.00 9.00

1986

1108† 45c Paddle-steamer, *c.* 1830 .... 40 15

PRO JUVENTUTE CHARITY STAMPS

1929

J48† 5c Fishing boat, Lake Lugano 15 40

OFFICIAL STAMPS

1950

No. 518 overprinted **Officiel**

O529 40c Rhine barge, Basel 4.50 2.50

SYRIA

Middle East
100 centimes = 1 piastre

1925

177† 0p50 Ancient Phoenician ships 15 15
180† 1p25 Fishing boats, Latakia 60 30

1926

Nos. 177 and 180 surcharged **Secours aux Refugies Afft,** *in English and Arabic, and new value*

197† 0p25 on 0p50 Ancient Phoenician ships 1.00 1.00
200† 0p50 on 1p25 Fishing boats, Latakia 1.00 1.00

No. 180 surcharged in English and Arabic figures

223† 2p on 1p25 Fishing boats, Latakia 20 10
218† 12p on 1p25 Fishing boats, Latakia 20 10
220† 20p on 1p25 Fishing boats, Latakia 30 15

1929

Nos. 177 and 180 overprinted with airplane or surcharged also in English and Arabic figures

225† 0p50 Ancient Phoenician ships 20 20
227† 2p on 1p25 Fishing boats, Latakia 50 50

No. 177 overprinted **EXPOSITION INDUSTRIELLE DAMAS 1929** *in English and Arabic. No. 237 is additionally overprinted with airplane*

230† 0p50 Ancient Phoenician ships 1.40 1.40
237† 0p50 Ancient Phoenician ships (air) 1.00 1.00

1956

599† 35p Phoenician galley 55 55

1957

623† 25p Freighter at quay 25 15
627† 70p Freighter at quay 90 50

628 12½p Freighter
629 17½p Freighter (air)
630 40p Freighter

Set of 3 1.25 70

1980

1484 50p Frigate 50 20

1987

1669† 330p Phoenician galley 95 50

TANGANYIKA

East Africa
1901 64 pesa = 100 heller = 1 rupee
1905 100 heller = 1 rupee

1901

As Nos. K7/19 of Cameroun, but inscribed "DEUTSCH-OSTAFRIKA". Face values in pesa and rupees

15 2p *Hohenzollern* (German Imperial yacht)
16 3p *Hohenzollern*
17 5p *Hohenzollern*
18 10p *Hohenzollern*
19 15p *Hohenzollern*
20 20p *Hohenzollern*
21 25p *Hohenzollern*
22 40p *Hohenzollern*
23 1r *Hohenzollern*
24 2r *Hohenzollern*
25 3r *Hohenzollern*

Set of 11 £100 £275

1905

As Nos. 15/25, but face values in heller

34 2½h *Hohenzollern* (German Imperial yacht)
35 4h *Hohenzollern*
36 7½h *Hohenzollern*
37 15h *Hohenzollern*
38t 20h *Hohenzollern*
39 30h *Hohenzollern*
40 45h *Hohenzollern*
33 60h *Hohenzollern*

Set of 8 24.00 £130

TANZANIA

East Africa
100 cents = 1 shilling

1965

136† 1s *Ouwerkerk* (freighter), Dar-es-Salaam 40 5
138† 2s50 Fishing boat, Mafia Island 2.25 90

1978

247† 10s Canoes, Mafia Island 1.25 1.60

1984

MS399 15s *Mapinduzi* (ferry) 1.50 2.50

TETE

East Africa
100 centavos = 1 escudo

1913

Surcharged **REPUBLICA TETE** *and value*

(a) On Nos. 1/2, 5 and 7 of Portuguese Colonies in Africa

1† ¼c on 2½r Departure of Vasco da Gama's fleet 70 60
2† ¼c on 5r Vasco da Gama's fleet at Calicut 70 60
5† 5c on 50r *Sao Gabriel* (flagship) 70 60
7† 10c on 100r *Sao Gabriel* 75 65

(b) On Nos. 104/5, 108 and 110 of Macao

9† ¼c on ½a Departure of Vasco da Gama's fleet 80 60
10† ¼c on 1a Vasco da Gama's fleet at Calicut 80 65
13† 5c on 8a *Sao Gabriel* (flagship) 80 65
15† 10c on 16a *Sao Gabriel* 70 65

(c) On Nos. 58/9, 62 and 64 of Timor

17† ¼c on ½a Departure of Vasco da Gama's fleet 80 60
18† ¼c on 1a Vasco da Gama's fleet at Calicut 80 65
21† 5c on 8a *Sao Gabriel* (flagship) 80 65
23† 10c on 16a *Sao Gabriel* 70 65

THAILAND

South-east Asia
100 satangs = 1 baht

1967

582 2b *Sri Suphanahong* (royal barge) 50 15

1971

679 4b Market boats, Wat Sai 50 15

1975

868 75s *Sukrip Khrong Maung* (ceremonial barge)
869 1b *Anekchat Phulbong* (royal barge)
870 2b *Anantana Karot* (royal barge)
871 2b75 *Krabi Ram Ron Rap* (ceremonial barge)
872 3b *Asura Wayuphak* (ceremonial barge)
873 4b *Asura Paksi* (ceremonial barge)
874 5b *Sri Suphanahong* (royal barge)
875 6b *Phali Rang Thamip* (ceremonial barge)

Set of 8 4.50 2.00

1976

901†	4b Post canoe, 1950	40	25

1979

1002	2b *Makutrajakumarn* (frigate)		
1003	3b *Tapi* (frigate)		
1004	5b *Prabparapak* (missile craft)		
1005	6b *T 91* (patrol boat)		
	Set of 4	1.40	65

1983

1147†	1b25 Cable ship	15	5

1987

1278	2b Container ship	8	5

1298	2b *Sri Suphanahong* (royal barge)	8	5

TIMOR
Australasia
1898 100 avos = 1 pataca
1960 100 centavos = 1 escudo

1898
Designs as Nos. 378/9, 382 and 384 of Portugal, but inscribed "TIMOR" and with face values in avos

58†	½a Departure of Vasco da Gama's fleet	90	60
59†	1a Vasco da Gama's fleet at Calicut	90	60
62†	8a *Sao Gabriel* (flagship)	1.25	75
64†	16a *Sao Gabriel*	1.75	1.50

1913
Nos. 58/9, 62 and 64 overprinted **REPUBLICA**

169†	½a Departure of Vasco da Gama's fleet	30	20
170†	1a Vasco da Gama's fleet at Calicut	30	20
173†	8a *Sao Gabriel* (flagship)	50	30
175†	16a *Sao Gabriel*	60	50

1935

232	½a Portuguese galeasse	
233	1a Portuguese galeasse	
234	2a Portuguese galeasse	
235	3a Portuguese galeasse	
236	4a Portuguese galeasse	
237	5a Portuguese galeasse	
238	6a Portuguese galeasse	
239	7a Portuguese galeasse	
240	8a Portuguese galeasse	
241	10a Portuguese galeasse	
242	12a Portuguese galeasse	
243	14a Portuguese galeasse	
244	15a Portuguese galeasse	
245	20a Portuguese galeasse	
246	30a Portuguese galeasse	
247	40a Portuguese galeasse	
248	50a Portuguese galeasse	
249	1p Portuguese galeasse	
250	2p Portuguese galeasse	
251	3p Portuguese galeasse	
252	5p Portuguese galeasse	
	Set of 21	41.00	17.00

1961

369†	50c Model of outrigger canoe	10	8

1967

387†	10c *Patria* (gunboat)	10	8

1969

399	4e50 *Admiral Gago Coutinho* (frigate)	1.40	70

1972

415	1e Portuguese galleon, 1572	15	10

COLLECT MAMMALS ON STAMPS
A Stanley Gibbons thematic catalogue on this popular subject. Copies available at £7.50 (p. + p. £2) from: Stanley Gibbons Publications Ltd, 5 Parkside, Christchurch Road, Ringwood, Hants BH24 3SH.

TOGO
West Africa
1900 100 p fennig = 1 mark
1914 12 pence = 1 shilling
20 shillings = 1 pound
1914 100 centimes = 1 franc

GERMAN COLONY

1900
As Nos. K7/19 of Cameroon, but inscribed "TOGO"

G7	3pf *Hohenzollern* (German Imperial yacht)	
G21	5pf *Hohenzollern*	
G9	10pf *Hohenzollern*	
G10	20pf *Hohenzollern*	
G11	25pf *Hohenzollern*	
G12	30pf *Hohenzollern*	
G13	40pf *Hohenzollern*	
G14	50pf *Hohenzollern*	
G15	80pf *Hohenzollern*	
G16	1m *Hohenzollern*	
G17	2m *Hohenzollern*	
G18	3m *Hohenzollern*	
G19	5m *Hohenzollern*	
	Set of 13	£130	£550

ANGLO-FRENCH OCCUPATION

1914
Nos. G7/19 overprinted **TOGO Anglo-French Occupation**

H1	3pf *Hohenzollern* (German Imperial yacht)	£110	85.00
H2	5pf *Hohenzollern*	£100	85.00
H3	10pf *Hohenzollern*	£120	£100
H4	20pf *Hohenzollern*	28.00	19.00
H5	25pf *Hohenzollern*	28.00	23.00
H6	30pf *Hohenzollern*	28.00	25.00
H7	40pf *Hohenzollern*	£250	£200
H8	50pf *Hohenzollern*	£9000	£7000
H9	80pf *Hohenzollern*	£275	£225
H10	1m *Hohenzollern*	£5000	£3000
H11	2m *Hohenzollern*	£7500	£5500
H25	3m *Hohenzollern*	—	£20000
H26	5m *Hohenzollern*	—	£20000

Nos. H1/2 surcharged in words

H27	½d on 3pf *Hohenzollern* (German Imperial yacht)		
H28	1d on 5pf *Hohenzollern*		
	Set of 2	30.00	28.00

Nos. G7, G21, G10/13 and G15 overprinted **TOGO Occupation franco-anglaise** *or surcharged also in figures*

1	05 on 3pf *Hohenzollern* (German Imperial yacht)	
2	10 on 5pf *Hohenzollern*	
3	20pf *Hohenzollern*	
4	25pf *Hohenzollern*	
5	30pf *Hohenzollern*	
6	40pf *Hohenzollern*	
7	80pf *Hohenzollern*	
	Set of 7	£650	£500

FRENCH ADMINISTRATION

1931
As No. 109 of Cameroun

102†	1f50 Liner	1.75	2.00

1937
As Nos. 110/11 of Cameroun

103†	20c Liner	50	50
104†	30c Sailing ships	50	50

1940

131†	20c Fishing canoes	10	5
132†	25c Fishing canoes	10	5
133†	30c Fishing canoes	10	5
134†	40c Fishing canoes	10	5
135†	45c Fishing canoes	10	5
136†	50c Fishing canoes	10	10
137†	60c Fishing canoes	10	10

1941
No. 136 surcharged **SECOURS + 1 fr. NATIONAL**

151†	1f on 50c Fishing canoe	40	50

1954
As No. 264 of Cameroun

188	15f Landing craft, Normandy, 1944	1.50	1.40

INDEPENDENT REPUBLIC

1961

287† 20f Motor launch 20 12

1963

320† 50c Paddle-steamer and *Hohenzollern*
(German Imperial yacht) (on stamp
Nos. G9 and G18) 5 5

1964

376† 85f *Panama Maru* (bulk carrier) loading
phosphate 90 5

1967

493 5f Fishing boat
494 10f Fishing boat
495 15f Fishing boat
496 25f Galleon
497 30f Fishing boat
498 45f Fishing boat (air)
499 90f Fishing boat
Set of 7 2.75 1.50

553† 5f *Hohenzollern* (German Imperial yacht)
(on stamp No. G9) 12 5
559† 90f *Hohenzollern* (on stamp No. G9) (air) 90 50

1968

588 5f Viking longship and Portuguese galleon
589 10f *Clermont* (paddle-steamer) and
Athlone Castle (liner)
590 20f Freighters, Lome
591 30f Viking longship and Portuguese
galleon
592 45f *Clermont* and *Athlone Castle*
593 90f *Savannah* (nuclear-powered freighter)
Set of 6 2.25 1.00

1969

635 50f Paddle-steamer and *Hohenzollern*
(German Imperial yacht) (on stamp No.
G16) 80 80

1973

940† 100f Scout canoe 50 25

963† 90f Early steam packet and modern liner 95 45

1974

998† 30f Freighter 25 15
1000† 90f Fishing canoe 55 35
1001† 100f Sailing canoe 70 35

1008† 30f Fishing canoe 25 15
1009† 40f Fishing canoe 25 20

1047† 30f *Loch Fada* (frigate) 25 12
1049† 100f *Loch Fada* (air) 70 40

1975

No. 940 overprinted **14eme JAMBOREE MONDIAL DES ECLAIREURS**

1107† 100f Scout canoe 55 30

1976

1119† 35f H.M.S. *Phoenix*, H.M.S. *Roebuck*
and H.M.S. *Tartar* (frigates) in
Hudson, 1776 . . . . 30 20

1126† 25f Cable ship 20 15

1147† 70f Olympic yachts 40 25

1977

No. 1147 overprinted **CHAMPIONS OLYMPIQUES YACHTING– FLYING DUTCHMAN REPUBLIQUE FEDERALE ALLEMAGNE**
1176† 70f Olympic yachts 40 30

1242 60f French warships, 1824 . . . . 35 20

1245 50f *Aurora* (Russian cruiser), 1917 . . . . . . 30 20

1978

1276† 25f Trawlers, Lome 15 8
1277† 60f Tankers under construction, Lome
(air) 35 20
1278† 100f Freighters, Lome 55 30

1324† 60f *Slieve Roe* (full-rigged ship) 35 20

1979

1335† 25f H.M.S. *Endeavour* (Cook) 20 8
1336† 50f H.M.S. *Endeavour* careened 35 20
1337† 60f *Freelove* (Whitby collier) (Cook) (air) 40 20
1338† 70f H.M.S. *Resolution* (Cook) 50 25
1340† 200f H.M.S. *Endeavour* (sail plan) 1.10 55

1382† 30f Olympic yachts 15 12

1980

1444†   40f Market canoes 12   12

1982

1579†   130f Scout canoe 65   50

1593†   90f *Hohenzollern* (German Imperial
          yacht) (on stamp No. G19) 40   40

1984

1671†   35f Pirogue, Baguida, 1884 12   10
1678†   45f *Hohenzollern* (German Imperial
          yacht) (on stamp No. G19) 15   12
1683†   45f *Hohenzollern* (on stamp No. G9) 15   12
1684†   70f *Hohenzollern* (on stamp Nos. G10
          and G17) 25   20
1698†   120f *Hohenzollern* (on stamp No. G21) 40   35
1700†   270f *Mowe* (German gunboat), 1884 .. 95   90
1701†   270f *Sophie* (German sail corvette),
          1884 95   90

TOKELAU

South Pacific
1970 100 cents = 1 dollar
1982 100 sene or cents = 1 tola or dollar

1970

22   5c H.M.S. *Dolphin* (frigate) (Byron), 1765
23   10c H.M.S. *Pandora* (frigate), 1791
24   25c *General Jackson* (American full-rigged
      ship), 1835
                                Set of 3   7.00   2.25

COLLECT RAILWAYS ON STAMPS

A Stanley Gibbons thematic catalogue on this popular
subject. Copies available at £7.50 (p. + p. £2) from:
Stanley Gibbons Publications Ltd, 5 Parkside, Christchurch Road, Ringwood, Hants BH24 3SH.

1971

31†   20c Outrigger canoe 2.00   2.00

1976

49†   1c Canoe building 10   15

1978

65   8c Canoe racing
66   12c Canoe racing
67   15c Canoe racing
68   30c Canoe racing
                                Set of 4   1.90   1.90

1980

75†   30c Canoe 20   25
76†   50c Canoe 30   35

1982

85   5s Fishing canoe
86   18s Fishing canoe
87   23s Fishing canoe
88   34s Fishing canoe
89   63s Fishing canoe
90   75s Fishing canoe
                                Set of 6   1.90   1.90

1983

91†   5s Outrigger canoe 5   8
92†   18s Wooden whaleboat 12   15
93†   23s Aluminium motor whaleboat 15   20
94†   34s *Alia* (fishing catamaran) 25   30
95†   63s *Frysna* (freighter) 45   50

1984

107†   48s Freighter and motorised whaleboat
          loading copra 40   45

1988

154   50c Small boat flotilla, Sydney Harbour
155   50c Liners and *Juan Sebastian De Elcano*
          (Spanish cadet schooner) at
          re-enactment of First Fleet, 1988
156   50c Small boats and Sydney Opera
          House
157   50c Small boats and Harbour Bridge
158   50c Small boats and Sydney waterfront
                                Set of 5   2.00   2.25

TONGA

South Pacific
1897 12 pence = 1 shilling
20 shillings = 1 pound
1967 100 seniti = 1 pa'anga

1897

51†   2s Yacht, Haapai 18.00   20.00

1923

No. 51 surcharged **TWO PENCE PENI-E-UA**
68†   2d on 2s Yacht, Haapai 3.00   5.00

1949

As No. 115 *of Antigua*
89†   3d Paddle-steamer 45   45

1951

98†   3d H.M.N.Z.S. *Bellona* (cruiser) 25   25

1953

103†   2d *Hifofua* and *Aoniu* (ketches) 20   5
104†   3d Outrigger canoe 20   5
106†   4d Freighter at wharf 35   5
109†   8d *Matua* (freighter) 30   5
111†   2s Outrigger canoe 45   60
112†   5s H.M.S. *Bounty* and launch (Bligh) 5.50   2.75

1961

116†   2d Whaling ship and whaleboat 20   5
118†   5d *Aoniu II* (inter-island freighter) 25   5

1962

Nos. 104, 109 *and* 112 *overprinted* **1862 TAU'ATAINA
EMANCIPATION 1962** *or surcharged also*
124†   8d *Matua* (freighter) 30   30
126†   2s on 3d Outrigger canoe 50   55
127†   5s H.M.S. *Bounty* and launch 75   85

1966

Nos. 116 and 118 surcharged **1866–1966 TUPOU COLLEGE & SECONDARY EDUCATION** and value, with Nos. 168, 171/2 additionally overprinted **AIRMAIL** and **CENTENARY**

164†	6d on 2d Whaling ship and whaleboat ..	10	5
165†	1s2d on 2d Whaling ship and whaleboat	12	12
166†	2s on 2d Whaling ship and whaleboat ..	15	15
167†	3s on 2d Whaling ship and whaleboat ..	20	20
168†	5d Aoniu II (inter-island freighter) (air) ..	5	5
171†	2s9d on 2d Whaling ship and whaleboat	20	20
172†	3s6d on 5d Aoniu II	20	20

1967

Nos. 103/4, 106, 109, 111/12 and 167 surcharged in new currency

186†	2s on 4d Freighter at wharf	5	5
230†	3s on 3d Outrigger canoe	5	5
232†	5s on 2d Hifofua and Aoniu (ketches)	5	5
190†	6s on 8d Matua (freighter)	10	10
235†	8s on 8d Matua (freighter)	10	10
193†	9s on 3d Outrigger canoe	15	15
238†	20s on 5s H.M.S. Bounty and launch	40	40
196†	21s on 3s on 3d Whaling ship and whaleboat	35	35
198†	30s on 2s Outrigger canoe (surch **Seniti**)	1.75	1.75
199†	30s on 2s Outrigger canoe (surch **SENITI**)	2.00	2.00
201†	60s on 2d Hifofua and Aoniu (ketches)	1.75	1.75
239†	2p on 2s Outrigger canoe	2.00	2.00

As Nos. 103/4, 106, 111/12, but imperforate, surcharged **The Friendly Islands welcome the United States Peace Corps S**

217†	2s on 2d Hifofua and Aoniu (ketches)	5	5
218†	3s on 3d Outrigger canoe	5	5
219†	4s on 4d Freighter at wharf	5	5
222†	20s on 2s Outrigger canoe	20	20
223†	50s on 5s H.M.S. Bounty and launch	35	35

As Nos. 103/4, 106, 109 and 111/12, but imperforate, surcharged **Friendly Islands Field and Track Trials South Pacific Games Port Moresby 1969** and value

259†	15s on 2s Outrigger canoe	15	15
260†	25s on 2d Hifofua and Aoniu (ketches)	20	20
264†	7s on 4d Freighter at wharf (air)	10	10
265†	8s on 8d Matua (freighter)	10	10
267†	11s on 3d Outrigger canoe	10	10
269†	38s on 5s H.M.S. Bounty and launch	30	30

1969

As No. 109, but imperforate, 165/6 and 171/2 surcharged in new currency

271†	1s on 1s2d on 2d Whaling ship and whaleboat	40	40
272†	1s on 2s on 2d Whaling ship and whaleboat	40	40
276†	4s on 8d Matua (freighter)	35	35
277†	1s on 2s9d on 2d Whaling ship and whaleboat (air)	40	40
278†	1s on 3s6d on 5d Aoniu II (inter-island freighter)	40	40

1971

As Nos. 106, 109 and 111, but imperforate, surcharged **PHILATOKYO '71**, emblem and value (Nos. 355/6, 359, 361) or **HONOURING JAPANESE POSTAL CENTENARY 1871–1971 T$1·00 AIRMAIL** (No. 364)

355†	3s on 8d Matua (freighter)	5	5
356†	7s on 4d Freighter at wharf	10	10
359†	75s on 2s Outrigger canoe	85	85
361†	10s on 4d Freighter at wharf (air)	10	10
364†	1p on 2s Outrigger canoe	1.25	1.25

1972

393	2s Olovaha (inter-island freighter)
394	10s Olovaha
395	17s Olovaha
396	21s Olovaha
397	60s Olovaha

398	9s Niuvakai (inter-island freighter) (air)
399	12s Niuvakai
400	14s Niuvakai
401	75s Niuvakai
402	90s Niuvakai

	Set of 10	8.00	4.25

No. 398 surcharged **7S NOVEMBER 1972 INAUGURAL Internal Airmail Nuku'alofa — Vava'u**

428	7s on 9s Niuvakai (inter-island freighter)	1.50	1.50

1973

449†	5s Scout outrigger canoe	20	10
450†	7s Scout outrigger canoe	30	12
451†	15s Scout outrigger canoe	85	40
452†	21s Scout outrigger canoe	1.00	50
453†	50s Scout outrigger canoe	3.75	1.75

464†	9s H.M.S. Resolution (Cook)	30	20
465†	14s H.M.S. Resolution	55	40
466†	29s H.M.S. Resolution	2.25	1.50
467†	38s H.M.S. Resolution	2.50	1.75
468†	75s H.M.S. Resolution	5.00	3.50

1974

508	5s H.M.S. Resolution (Cook)
509	10s H.M.S. Resolution
510	25s H.M.S. Resolution
511	50s H.M.S. Resolution
512	75s H.M.S. Resolution
513	9s James Cook (bulk carrier) (air)
514	14s James Cook
515	17s James Cook
516	60s James Cook
517	90s James Cook

	Set of 10	13.00	7.50

COLLECT BIRDS ON STAMPS

Second revised edition of this Stanley Gibbons thematic catalogue – now available at £8.50 (p. + p. £2) from: Stanley Gibbons Publications Ltd, 5 Parkside, Christchurch Road, Ringwood, Hants BH24 3SH.

1976

583†	9s Triton (missionary brigantine)	25	25
584†	12s Triton	30	30
585†	14s Triton	35	35
586†	17s Triton	40	40
587†	38s Triton	1.00	1.00

1977

618†	10s H.M.S. Resolution (Cook)	1.00	60
619†	17s H.M.S. Resolution	1.50	95
620†	25s H.M.S. Resolution	2.50	1.75
621†	30s H.M.S. Resolution	2.75	2.00
622†	40s H.M.S. Resolution	3.25	2.50

1978

No. 583 surcharged **17s**

646†	17s on 9s Triton (missionary brigantine)	80	85

1980

746†	15s L'Aventure (French warship), 1855	20	25
747†	17s L'Aventure	25	30
748†	22s L'Aventure	35	40
749†	31s L'Aventure	40	45
750†	39s L'Aventure	55	60

Nos. 584/5 surcharged in figures only

774†	29s on 14s Triton (missionary brigantine)	35	40
779†	47s on 12s Triton	55	60

1981

793†	9s La Princesa (Maurelle), 1781	25	20
795†	47s La Princesa	1.75	1.25
796†	1p La Princesa	4.00	3.00

802† 1p *Port au Prince* (full-rigged ship), 1806   85   75

1982

813† 9s *Olovaha II* (inter-island freighter)   10   10
814† 13s *Olovaha II*   15   15

817† 13s Mail canoe, Niuafo'ou   15   15
818† 32s Mail canoe and freighter   40   45
819† 47s Mail canoe and freighter   55   60

Nos. 817/19 overprinted **Christmas Greetings 1982**
831† 13s Mail canoe, Niuafo'ou
832† 32s Mail canoe and freighter
833† 47s Mail canoe and freighter
          Set of 3   1.00   1.10

1983

834† 29s H.M.S *Resolution* (Cook) and
       Canberra (liner)   35   40
835† 32s H.M.S *Resolution* and *Canberra*   40   45
MS838† 2p50 *Canberra* 3.00   3.25

841† 47s Trawler   50   50

857 29s Yacht, Vava'u
858 32s Yacht in cave
859 1p50 Yacht at sunset
860 2p50 Yacht at sea
          Set of 4   3.50   4.00

1984

861 32s *Zeehan* (Tasman)
862 47s H.M.S. *Dolphin* (frigate) (Wallis), 1767
863 90s H.M.S. *Bounty* (Bligh)
864 1p50 H.M.S. *Resolution* (Cook)
          Set of 4   3.75   4.00

1985

896 32s *Eendracht* (Le Maire), 1616
897 47s *Hoorn* (Le Maire), 1616
898 90s H.M.S. *Bounty* (Bligh)
899 1p50 *La Princesa* (Maurelle), 1781
          Set of 4   2.75   3.00

905 29s *Port au Prince* (full-rigged ship), 1806
906 32s *Port au Prince* under attack
907 47s 19th-century Tongan double canoe
908 1p50 Outrigger canoe
909 2p50 *Cuffnells* (full-rigged ship), 1810
          Set of 5   4.25   4.50

1986

MS955 50s H.M.S. *Resolution* (Cook) (on
     stamp No. 464); 50s *Olovaha II* (inter-island
     freighter) (on stamp No. 814) (sheet also
     contains six other designs) 3.50   3.75

959† 2p Outrigger canoe 1.75   1.90

1987

962† 32s *L'Astrolabe* (D'Urville), 1837   30   35
964† 1p *L'Astrolabe*   90   95
965† 2p50 *L'Astrolabe* aground 2.10   2.25

MS971 32s, 42s, 57s, 1p50 Racing canoes 2.10   2.50
The component stamps of No. **MS**971 were also available separately.

1988

482† 57s Outrigger canoe   45   50

OFFICIAL STAMPS

1962
Nos. 112, 116 and 118 overprinted **OFFICIAL AIR MAIL 1862 TAU'ATAINA EMANCIPATION 1962**
O11† 2d Whaling ship 11.00   6.00
O12† 5d *Aoniu II* (inter-island freighter) 12.00   6.50
O14† 5s H.M.S. *Bounty* and launch (Bligh) 90.00   55.00

1967
No. 112 surcharged **OFFICIAL AIRMAIL ONE PA'ANGA**
O21 1p on 5s H.M.S. *Bounty* and launch
       (Bligh) 2.25   2.25

1970
As No. 112, but imperforate, surcharged **OFFICIAL Commonwealth Member JUNE 1970 AIRMAIL** *and value*
O42 50s on 5s H.M.S. *Bounty* and launch
       (Bligh)
O43 90s on 5s H.M.S. *Bounty* and launch
O44 1p50 on 5s H.M.S. *Bounty* and launch
          Set of 3   2.50   2.50

As No. 112, but imperforate, surcharged **Centenary British Red Cross 1870–1970 OFFICIAL AIRMAIL**, *red cross and value*
O56† 80s on 5s H.M.S. *Bounty* and launch
       (Bligh) 2.25   2.25
O57† 90s on 5s H.M.S. *Bounty* and launch 2.25   2.25

1972

O76 20s *Aoniu* (inter-island freighter)
O77 50s *Aoniu*
O78 1p20 *Aoniu*
          Set of 3   5.00   2.25

1973
No. 396 surcharged **TONGA 1973 ESTABLISHMENT BANK OF TONGA OFFICIAL AIRMAIL** *and value*
O100 40s on 21s *Olovaha* (inter-island
       freighter)
O101 85s on 21s *Olovaha*
O102 1p25 on 21s *Olovaha*
          Set of 3   3.75   2.25

O106 25s *James Cook* (bulk carrier)
O107 80s *James Cook*
O108 1p30 *James Cook*
          Set of 3   12.00   9.00

1983
Nos. 834/5 overprinted **OFFICIAL**
O217† 29s H.M.S. *Resolution* (Cook) and
       Canberra (liner) 2.50   2.50
O218† 32s H.M.S. *Resolution* and *Canberra* ..   3.25   3.25

TRANSKEI

Southern Africa
100 cents = 1 rand

1986

181†	20c *Umzimvubu* (coaster)	12	15

1988

221†	16c *Grosvenor* (East Indiaman), 1782 . .	8	8

TRENGGANU

South-east Asia
100 cents = 1 dollar

1949
As No. 115 *of Antigua*

64†	15c Paddle-steamer	70	1.60

1957

95†	20c Malay fishing prau	20	15

TRIESTE

Southern Europe

Zone A. Allied Military Government

100 centesimi = 1 lira

1952
No. 820 *of Italy overprinted* **AMG FTT**

239	25li Fishing boat, Trieste	25	15

No. 827 *of Italy overprinted* **AMG FTT**

246†	60li Motor torpedo boat	25	30

Zone B. Yugoslav Military Government

100 paras = 1 dinar

1952

B58†	28d Yachts	15	10

1954
No. 675 *of Yugoslavia, with colour changed, overprinted* **STT VUJNA**

B108†	1d River steamer	5	5

COLLECT MAMMALS ON STAMPS

A Stanley Gibbons thematic catalogue on this popular subject. Copies available at £7.50 (p. + p. £2) from: Stanley Gibbons Publications Ltd, 5 Parkside, Christchurch Road, Ringwood, Hants BH24 3SH.

TRINIDAD AND TOBAGO

West Indies
100 cents = 1 dollar

1949
As No. 115 *of Antigua*

262†	6c Paddle-steamer	35	25

1966

314†	8c Royal Yacht *Britannia*	80	60

1970

385†	40c Brigantine, San Fernando, 1860	35	10

1972

413	5c *Lady McLeod* (paddle-steamer), 1847, and on local stamp		
414	10c *Lady McLeod*, 1847, (on local stamp)		
415	30c *Lady McLeod*, 1847, (on local stamp)		
	Set of 3	80	55

1974

454	40c *Hummingbird I* (ketch), 1960		
455	50c *Hummingbird II* (ketch), 1969		
	Set of 2	65	40

1976

479†	5c Fleet of Columbus, 1498	15	5
488†	35c Longboat on beach	30	10

1979

541†	45c Oil rig	25	25

1980

558†	$1.50 H.M.S. *Bacchante* (screw corvette), 1880	70	1.10

No. 479 *overprinted* **1844—1980 POPULATION CENSUS 12th MAY 1980**

560†	5c Fleet of Columbus, 1498	10	15

1982

607†	$1 Yacht and speedboat	55	55

1984

658†	$1.50 Yachts	80	1.00

661†	35c Slave schooner	45	20

1985

676	30c *Lady Nelson* (cargo liner), 1928		
677	95c *Lady Drake* (cargo liner), 1928		
678	$1.50 *Federal Palm* (freighter), 1961		
679	$2 *Federal Maple* (freighter), 1961		
	Set of 4	3.00	2.75

1988

735†	$1.50 Naval patrol boat	45	50

TRIPOLITANIA

North Africa
100 centisimi = 1 lira

ITALIAN COLONY

1927

36†	20c + 05c Freighter, Tripoli	45	80
37†	25c + 05c Freighter, Tripoli	45	80

BRITISH ADMINISTRATION

1951
Nos. 509/10 *of Great Britain surcharged* **B.A. TRIPOLITANIA** *and value in* **M.A.L.**

T32†	60li on 2s6d H.M.S. *Victory* (Nelson)	3.50	12.00
T33†	120li on 5s Yacht and Thames sailing barge, Dover	7.50	16.00

TRISTAN DA CUNHA

South Atlantic
1952 12 pence = 1 shilling
20 shillings = 1 pound
1971 100 pence = 1 pound

1952

Nos. 131, 135a/40 and 149/51 of St. Helena overprinted **TRISTAN DA CUNHA**

1	½d *London* (East Indiaman), 1659		
2	1d *London*, 1659		
3	1½d *London*, 1659		
4	2d *London*, 1659		
5	3d *London*, 1659		
6	4d *London*, 1659		
7	6d *London*, 1659		
8	8d *London*, 1659		
9	1s *London*, 1659		
10	2s6d *London*, 1659		
11	5s *London*, 1659		
12	10s *London*, 1659		
	Set of 12	90.00	£120

1954

19†	3d *Tristan longboat*	80	25

1965

72†	1d *Tristao da Cunha's caravel*, 1506	25	15
73†	1½d *Heemstede* (Dutch East Indiaman), 1643	25	15
74†	2d 19th-century New England whaling ship	25	15
75†	3d *Shenandoah* (Confederate warship), 1862	30	15
75a†	4d H.M.S. *Challenger* (steam survey ship), 1873	3.50	3.50
76†	4½d H.M.S. *Galatea* (screw frigate), 1867	30	15
77†	6d H.M.S. *Cilicia* (transport), 1942	30	15
78†	7d Royal Yacht *Britannia*	30	15
79†	10d H.M.S. *Leopard* (frigate)	30	15
80†	1s *Tjisadane* (liner)	30	15
81†	1s6d *Tristania* (crayfish trawler)	2.50	1.25
82†	2s6d *Boissevain* (liner)	3.25	1.75
83†	5s *Bornholm* (liner)	6.50	3.25
84a†	10s *R.S.A.* (research vessel)	22.00	12.00

1966

93	3d H.M.S. *Falmouth* (frigate), 1816		
94	6d H.M.S. *Falmouth*		
95	1s6d H.M.S. *Falmouth*		
96	2s6d H.M.S. *Falmouth*		
	Set of 4	1.00	45

1967

No. 76 surcharged **4d**

108	4d on 4½d H.M.S. *Galatea* (screw frigate), 1867	5	5

1969

121	4d 18th-century frigate		
122	1s Full-rigged sailing ship		
123	1s6d Barque		
124	2s6d Full-rigged clipper		
	Set of 4	2.25	70

125†	4d 19th-century full-rigged ship	15	10

1970

133†	4d Tristan longboat	30	15
135†	1s6d Tristan longboat	60	30

1971

Nos. 72/4, 75a, 77/83 and 84a surcharged in decimal currency

137	½p on 1d Tristao da Cunha's caravel, 1506		
138	1p on 2d 19th-century New England whaling ship		
139	1½p on 4d H.M.S. *Challenger* (steam survey ship), 1873		
140	2½p on 6d H.M.S. *Cilicia* (transport), 1942		
141	3p on 7d Royal Yacht *Britannia*		
142	4p on 10d H.M.S. *Leopard* (frigate)		
143	5p on 1s *Tjisadane* (liner)		
144	7½p on 1s6d *Tristania* (crayfish trawler)		
145	12½p on 2s6d *Boissevain* (liner)		
146	15p on 1½d *Heemstede* (Dutch East Indiaman), 1643		
147	25p on 5s *Bornholm* (liner)		
148	50p on 10s *R.S.A.* (research vessel)		
	Set of 12	16.00	22.00

149†	1½p *Quest* (Shackleton, 1921	1.00	40
152†	12½p Tristan longboat	1.50	65

153	1½p H.M.S. *Victory* (Nelson) at Trafalgar, 1805		
154	2½p *Emily of Stonington* (American schooner), 1836		
155	4p *Italia* (Italian brig), 1892		
156	7½p H.M.S. *Falmouth* (frigate), 1816		
157	12½p 19th-century American whaling ship		
	Set of 5	2.50	3.50

1972

170†	2½p Tristan longboat	20	15
173†	12½p Longboat under sail	40	25

1973

178†	5p H.M.S. *Challenger* (survey ship), 1873	35	30
179†	7½p H.M.S. *Challenger's* steam pinnace, 1873	40	40

1976

204†	5p *London* (East Indiaman) (on stamp No. 1)	15	20
206†	25p *Tristania II* (crayfish trawler)	40	50

1977

212†	10p Royal Yacht *Britannia*	30	40

215	5p H.M.S. *Eskimo* (frigate), 1970		
216	10p H.M.S. *Naiad* (frigate), 1968		
217	15p H.M.S. *Jaguar* (frigate), 1964		
218	20p H.M.S. *London* (destroyer), 1964		
	Set of 4	1.25	90

1978

235	10p Tristan longboats	20	25

250	5p R.F.A. *Orangeleaf* (tanker)		
251	10p R.F.A. *Tarbatness* (store carrier)		
252	20p R.F.A. *Tidereach* (tanker)		
253	25p R.F.A. *Reliant* (store carrier)		
	Set of 4	1.10	85

1979

259	5p Tristan longboat		
260	10p *Queen Mary* (liner)		
261	15p *Queen Elizabeth* (liner)		
262	20p *Queen Elizabeth 2* (liner)		
	Set of 4	1.25	1.50
MS263	25p *Queen Elizabeth 2* (liner)	1.50	3.25

264†	5p *London* (East Indiaman) (on stamp No. 12)	20	20

COLLECT BIRDS ON STAMPS

Second revised edition of this Stanley Gibbons thematic catalogue – now available at £8.50 (p. + p. £2) from: Stanley Gibbons Publications Ltd, 5 Parkside, Christchurch Road, Ringwood, Hants BH24 3SH.

1980

277†	5p *Tristania II* (crayfish trawler)	15	15
278†	10p Tristan longboat	15	15

283†	5p *Golden Hind* (Drake)	20	15

1982

323	5p *Marcella* (barque)		
324	15p *Eliza Adams* (full-rigged ship)		
325	30p *Corinthian* (American whaling ship)		
326	50p *Samuel and Thomas* (American whaling ship)		
	Set of 4	2.00	2.00

1983

341	5p *Islander* (barque)		
342	20p *Roscoe* (full-rigged ship)		
343	35p *Columbia* (whaling ship)		
344	50p *Emeline* (schooner)		
	Set of 4	1.90	1.90

350†	3p Tristao da Cunha's caravel, 1506	5	8
351†	4p *Heemstede* (Dutch East Indiaman), 1643	8	10
353†	10p H.M.S. *Falmouth* (frigate), 1816	20	25
357†	25p *John and Elizabeth* (American whaling ship)	45	50
359†	£1 Tristan longboat	1.75	2.00
360†	£2 H.M.S. *Leopard* (frigate), 1961	3.50	3.75

1984

365	10p *London* (East Indiaman) (on stamp No. 7)		
366	15p *London* (on stamp No. 9)		
367	25p *London* (on stamp No. 10)		
368	60p *London* (on stamp No. 12)		
	Set of 4	1.90	1.90

1985

386†	10p Shipwreck of H.M.S. *Julia* (sloop), 1817	25	25
388†	35p Shipwreck of *Glenhuntley* (barque), 1898	80	80

397†	25p H.M.S. *Falmouth* (frigate), 1816	50	55

399†	10p Lifeboat and *West Riding* (barque), 1885	25	25

1986

405†	50p H.M.S. *Paramour* (pink), 1694	1.10	1.10

411†	9p Ship's boat and wreck of *Allanshaw* (barque), 1893	25	25
413†	40p Figurehead	85	85

1987

427†	17p Wreck of *Henry A. Paull* (barquentine), 1879	45	45

437†	50p *Thorshammer* (whale factory ship)	1.00	1.10

1988

451†	50 Model longboat	1.00	1.10

455†	50p 19th-century whaling ships	1.00	1.10

TRUCIAL STATES

Arabian peninsula
100 naye paise = 1 rupee

1961

8†	1r Dhow	2.50	25
9†	2r Dhow	3.00	3.50
10†	5r Dhow	4.50	8.50
11†	10r Dhow	12.00	18.00

TUNISIA

North Africa
1906 100 centimes = 1 franc
1959 1000 milliemes = 1 dinar

1906

41†	1f Carthaginian galley (brown & red)	30	10
111†	1f Carthaginian galley (blue)	10	10
42†	2f Carthaginian galley (green & brown)	1.50	60
112†	2f Carthaginian galley (red & green on red)	20	10
43†	5f Carthaginian galley (blue & violet)	4.00	2.25
113†	5f Carthaginian galley (green & lilac)	35	30

1916

As Nos. 41 *etc, but colours changed, surcharged* **10c** *and red cross*

57†	10c on 1f Carthaginian galley (green & red)	1.00	1.00
58†	10c on 2f Carthaginian galley (blue & brown)	35.00	35.00
59†	10c on 5f Carthaginian galley (red & violet)	55.00	]55.00

1918

As Nos. 41, *etc, but colours changed, surcharged* **15c.** *and red cross*

66†	15c on 1f Carthaginian galley (violet & red)	8.00	8.00
67†	15c on 2f Carthaginian galley (red & brown)	30.00	30.00
68†	15c on 5f Carthaginian galley (black & violet)	70.00	70.00

1923

As Nos. 41, *etc, but colours changed, surcharged* **AFFt 25c** *below medal*

97†	25c on 1f Carthaginian galley (mauve & lake)	2.00	2.00
98†	25c on 2f Carthaginian galley (red & blue)	7.50	7.50
99†	25c on 5f Carthaginian galley (brown & green)	30.00	30.00

1927

Nos. 111/13 overprinted **Poste Aerienne** and aeroplane or surcharged also

148†	1f Carthaginian galley (blue)	30	30
150†	1f75 on 5f Carthaginian galley (green & lilac)	1.25	1.10
151†	2f Carthaginian galley (red & green on red)	1.10	1.00

1947

No. 965 of France surcharged **TUNISIE 10 + 15**

300	10f + 15f on 2f + 3f Emile Bertin (cruiser) and Lorraine (battleship)	35	40

1959

503†	200m Fishing boats, Sfax	3.50	1.90

1983

1040	80m French frigate, 1963	30	15

1986

1108†	160m Phoenician ship, 800 B.C.	25	20

TURKEY

South-east Europe and Asia Minor
1914 40 paras = 1 piastre or grush
1929 40 paras = 1 kurus
100 kurus = 1 lira

1914

508†	2pi Hamidiye (cruiser)	60	8

No. 508 overprinted

530†	2pi Hamidiye (cruiser)	3.00	75

1940

1272†	10k Early paddle-steamer and modern mail launch	1.50	65

1941

1274	30p Etrusk (freighter), Izmir	10	5
1281†	3k Barbarossa's corsair fleet, c. 1540	20	10
1282†	6k Barbarossa's corsair fleet, c. 1540	35	20
1283†	10k Barbarossa's corsair fleet, c. 1540	45	25
1284†	12k Barbarossa's corsair fleet, c. 1540	1.00	30

1946

1353	9k U.S.S. Missouri (battleship)		
1354	10k U.S.S. Missouri		
1355	27½k U.S.S. Missouri		
	Set of 3	1.25	55

1949

1409†	5k Galley	25	5
1410†	10k Mahmudiye (ship of the line)	40	8
1411†	15k Hamidiye (cruiser)	45	12
1412†	20k Sakarya (submarine)	50	20
1413†	30k Yavuz (battle cruiser)	90	40

1951

1457†	15k Providence (liner) and Hora (tug)	40	15
1458†	20k Iskendrun (liner)	40	15
1464†	60k Halas (ferry)	1.40	70

1953

1506†	10k 15th-century naval battle between Turks and Byzantines	10	5
1507†	12k 15th-century galleys	15	10

1955

1558†	30k Nusret (minelayer), 1915	35	20

1958

1753†	5k Freighters and fishing boats, Trabzon	10	5

1959

1854†	5k Karadeniz (liner)	20	5

1965

2128	50k Savarona (naval training ship)		
2129	60k Piri Reis (submarine)		
2130	100k Alpaslan (destroyer)		
2131	130k Gelibolu (destroyer)		
2132	220k Gemlik (destroyer)		
	Set of 5	3.75	1.90

1968

2244	50k Kismet (ketch)	35	20

1969

2280†	60k Bandirma (cargo liner), 1919	40	20

1970

2350†	250k Fishing boats	60	50

1971

2388†	110k Train ferry, Lake Van	60	20

1973

2451	5k *Nusret II* (minelayer), 1971		
2452	25k *Istanbul* (destroyer)		
2453	100k *Simsek* (motor torpedo-boat)		
2454	250k *Nurud-i-Futuh* (cadet brig)		
		Set of 4	2.00	80

1977

2573	400k *Hora* (oil exploration ship)	65	25

2929	20li *Abdulhamit* (submarine)	5	5

OBLIGATORY TAX STAMPS

1944

T1349	2½k Hospital ship	25	8

TURKS AND CAICOS ISLANDS

West Indies
1900 12 pence = 1 shilling
20 shillings = 1 pound
1969 100 cents = 1 dollar

1900

110	½d 19th-century full-rigged ship		
102	1d 19th-century full-rigged ship		
103	2d 19th-century full-rigged ship		
104a	2½d 19th-century full-rigged ship		
112	3d 19th-century full-rigged ship		
105	4d 19th-century full-rigged ship		
106	6d 19th-century full-rigged ship		
107	1s 19th-century full-rigged ship		
108	2s 19th-century full-rigged ship		
109	3s 19th-century full-rigged ship		
		Set of 10	85.00	£120

1948

210†	½d 19th-century full-rigged ship	15	15
211†	2d 19th-century full-rigged ship	30	15
212†	3d Freighter	35	15

1949

As No. 115 of Antigua

218†	3d Paddle-steamer	30	30

1950

223†	1½d Caicos sloop	20	50
225†	2½d Caicos sloop	20	50
232†	5s Caicos sloop	5.00	5.50
233†	10s 19th-century full-rigged ship	12.00	14.00

1955

235†	5d *Kirksons* (coaster)	30	20

1957

244†	6d Caicos sloop	25	12
248†	2s *Uakon* (Caicos sloop)	1.75	2.25
250†	£1 19th-century full-rigged ship	5.50	9.00

1966

268†	1d British frigate, 1766	5	5
269†	8d Merchant ships, 1766	5	5

1967

275†	1½d Boat building	5	5
278†	4d Caicos sloop	10	5
285†	5s Caicos sloops and trawler	1.00	1.50

1969

Nos. 275, 278 and 285 surcharged in decimal currency

301†	4c on 4d Caicos sloop	8	5
304†	8c on 1½d Boat building	12	5
309†	50c on 5s Caicos sloops and trawler	1.00	45

1971

As Nos. 275, 278 and 285, but face values in decimal currency

336†	4c Caicos sloop	20	5
339†	8c Boat building	30	5
344†	80c Caicos sloops and trawler	1.75	2.00

351†	2c Pirate sloop	10	10

1972

368	½c Fleet of Columbus, 1492		
369	8c *Revenge* (English galleon), 1591		
370	10c 17th-century English merchantman		
371	30c Spanish caravel		
		Set of 4	1.10	75

1973

396	2c Bermuda sloop		
397	5c H.M.S. *Blanche* (screw sloop), 1867		
398	8c *Grand Turk* (American privateer) and *Hinchinbrooke* (British sailing packet), 1778		
399	10c H.M.S. *Endymion* (frigate), 1790		
400	15c *Medina* (paddle-steamer)		
401	20c H.M.S. *Daring* (brig), 1804		
		Set of 6	1.10	1.75

1974

427†	12c Caicos sloop	20	15

1976

446	6c American schooner, 1776		
447	20c British ship of the line, 1776		
448	25c *Grand Turk* (American privateer), 1778		
449	55c British ketch, 1776		
		Set of 4	3.25	1.50

1978

490†	20c Caicos sloop	35	40
491†	25c Motor cruiser	40	45
492†	55c *Jamaica Planter* (freighter)	85	1.00

1979

545†	6c *Medina* (paddle-steamer)	5	5
547†	45c *Orinoco* (paddle-steamer)	30	30
548†	75c *Shannon* (screw steamer)	50	50
549†	$1 *Trent* (paddle-steamer)	65	65
550†	$2 19th-century full-rigged ship (on stamp No. 102)	1.10	1.10

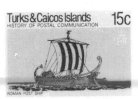

557†	15c Roman galley	20	20
560†	25c Paddle-steamer	30	30

1980

612†	$1 Lobster trawler	80	80

1981

630	6c Yachts	
631	15c Yachts and trimaran	
632	35c Speedboats	
633	$1 Caicos sloops	
	Set of 4 1.25	1.00

1983

738†	65c Yacht	85	90

769	4c Arawak dug-out canoe	
770	5c *Santa Maria* (Columbus)	
771	8c 18th-century Spanish galleon and British warship	
772	10c Bermuda sloop	
773	20c *Grand Turk* (American privateer)	
774	25c H.M.S. *Boreas* (frigate), 1784	
775	30c H.M.S. *Endymion* (frigate), 1790	
776	35c *Caesar* (barque)	
777	50c *Grapeshot* (American schooner)	
778	65c H.M.S. *Invincible* (battle cruiser), 1907	
779	95c H.M.S. *Magicienne* (cruiser), 1888	
780	$1.10 H.M.S. *Durban* (cruiser), 1919	
781	$2 *Sentinel* (cable ship)	
782	$3 H.M.S. *Minerva* (frigate), 1964	
783	$5 Caicos sloop	
	Set of 15 14.00	15.00

1985

841†	65c *Isere* (French full-rigged ship), 1885	1.25	1.25

844	20c H.M.S. *Royal George* (ship of the line), 1782	
845	30c H.M.S. *Victoy* (ship of the line), 1805	
846	65c H.M.S. *Albion* (ship of the line), 1802	
847	95c H.M.S. *Indefatigable* (battle cruiser), 1916	
	Set of 4 3.75	3.75

850†	35c *Grand Turk* (Mississippi river steamer)	55	55

1987

902	8c H.M.S. *Victoria* (ship of the line), 1855	
903	35c *Victoria* (paddle-steamer)	
904	55c Royal Yacht *Victoria and Albert I*, 1843	
905	95c Royal Yacht *Victoria and Albert II*, 1854	
	Set of 4 2.10	2.25
MS906	$2 *Victoria* (barque)	2.40	2.50

1988

912	4c *Santa Maria* (Columbus)	
913	25c Ship's boat	
914	70c *Santa Maria*	
915	95c *Santa Maria*	
	Set of 4 2.25	2.40
MS916	$2 *Santa Maria*, *Pinta* and *Nina*	2.40	2.50

918†	35c *Santa Maria* (Columbus)	40	45

Nos 772, 774 *and* 781 *overprinted* **40TH WEDDING ANNIVERSARY H.M.S. QUEEN ELIZABETH II H.R.H. THE DUKE OF EDINBURGH**

922	10c Bermuda sloop	
923	25c H.M.S. *Boreas* (frigate), 1784	
924	$2 *Sentinel* (cable ship)	
	Set of 3 2.50	2.75

COLLECT RAILWAYS ON STAMPS

A Stanley Gibbons thematic catalogue on this popular subject. Copies available at £7.50 (p. + p. £2) from: Stanley Gibbons Publications Ltd, 5 Parkside, Christchurch Road, Ringwood, Hants BH24 3SH.

TUVALU

Pacific Ocean
100 cents = 1 dollar

1976

3†	35c Canoes of Gilbert and Ellice Islands	1.25	1.75

Nos. 174, 177 *and* 184 *of Gilbert and Ellice Islands overprinted*
TUVALU

20†	2c Fishing canoe	65	30
5†	5c Gilbertese canoe	1.00	60
25†	35c Fishing canoes at night	3.00	2.25

41†	50c Fishing canoe	1.00	40
69†	$5 *Nivanga* (inter-island coaster)	10.00	6.00

1977

51†	35c Ceremonial canoe	1.75	80

74†	20c Scout canoe	60	50

80†	35c H.M.S. *Beagle* (Darwin), 1831	60	40

1978

85	8c *Laweduna* (inter-island coaster)	
86	20c *Wallacia* (tug)	
87	30c *Cenpac Rounder* (freighter)	
88	40c *Pacific Explorer* (freighter)	
	Set of 4 1.10	95

1979

123†	8c H.M.S. *Resolution* (Cook), 1779	30	20
124†	30c H.M.S. *Resolution* (Cook), 1779	40	25
126†	$1 H.M.S. *Resolution* (Cook), 1779	50	35

133† $1 Canoes of Gilbert and Ellice Islands
(on stamp No. 3) 50 40

1981

162 10c *Elizabeth* (brig), 1809
163 25c *Rebecca* (brigantine), 1919
164 35c *Independence II* (whaling ship), 1821
165 40c H.M.S. *Basilisk* (paddle-sloop), 1872
166 45c H.M.S. *Royalist* (corvette), 1890
167 50c *Olivebank* (barque), 1920
　　　　　　　　　　　　　Set of 6 1.75 1.75

168† 10c Royal Yacht *Carolina* 10 12
170† 45c Royal Yacht *Victoria and Albert III* .. 35 35
172† $2 Royal Yacht *Britannia* 1.00 1.00

1982

181† 25c Motor launch 25 25
182† 35c Motor launch 35 35
183† 45c Freighter 40 40

No. 170 *surcharged* **TONGA CYCLONE RELIEF 1982** +20c
187† 45c + 20c Royal Yacht *Victoria and
　　　Albert III* 40 50

1983

213† 20c *Te Tautai* (trawler) 20 20
216† 50c *Morning Star* (container ship) 50 50

222† 35c Outrigger canoe 40 45

1984

235 10c *Titus* (freighter), 1897
236 20c *Malaita* (freighter), 1905
237 25c *Aymeric* (freighter), 1906
238 35c *Anshun* (freighter), 1965
239 45c *Beaverbank* (freighter), 1970
240 50c *Benjamin Bowring* (freighter), 1981
　　　　　　　　　　　　　Set of 6 1.60 1.60

1986

377 15c *Messenger of Peace* (missionary
　　　schooner)
378 40c *John Wesley* (missionary brig)
379 50c *Duff* (missionary full-rigged ship)
380 60c *Triton* (missionary brigantine)
　　　　　　　　　　　　　Set of 4 1.40 1.40

1987

442 15c *Southern Cross IV* (missionary
　　　steamer)
443 40c *John Williams VI* (missionary steamer)
444 50c *John Williams IV* (missionary steamer)
445 60c *Southern Cross* (missionary steamer)
　　　　　　　　　　　　　Set of 4 1.75 1.75

494† $1 H.M.S. *Endeavour* (Cook) 55 60

1988

523† 20c H.M.S. *Endeavour* (Cook) 15 20
524† 40c Stern of H.M.S. *Endeavour* 35 40
525† 50c H.M.S. *Endeavour* at Tahiti 45 50
527† 80c H.M.S. *Resolution* and Hawaiian
　　　canoe 70 75
MS529† $2.50 H.M.S. *Resolution* in Antarctic 1.60 1.75

UBANGI-SHARI

Central Africa
100 centimes = 1 franc

1931

As No. 109 *of Cameroun*
106† 1f50 Liner 1.50 1.50

UGANDA

East Africa
100 cents = 1 shilling

1986

530 50s *Gloria* (Colombian cadet ship)
531 100s *Mircea* (Rumanian cadet ship)
532 140s *Sagres II* (Portuguese cadet ship)
533 2500s *Gazela Primiero* (wrongly inscribed
　　　"Primero") (American cadet ship)
　　　　　　　　　　　　　Set of 4 2.50 2.75

1987

574† 35s U.S.S. *Pennsylvania* (battleship) (first
　　　aircraft take-off and landing from ship),
　　　1911 .... 70 75

603† 35s Scout canoe, Lake Victoria 70 75

UNITED ARAB EMIRATES

Arabian peninsula
100 fils = 1 dirham

1973

10† 3d Motor barge, Ras al Khaima 3.50 1.25

1975

32† 50f Offshore oil drilling platform 85 25
34† 125f Marine oil production platform 1.90 1.40

1984

177† 1d Dhow 85 50

1986

201 2d Container ship
202 3d Container ship
　　　　　　　　　　　　　Set of 2 2.00 1.25

214† 50f Dhow 20 10
215† 1d Dhow 30 15

1987

228†	50f Oil rig	15	8
231†	2d Tanker	60	45

UNITED NATIONS
A. New York Headquarters
100 cents = 1 dollar

1964

127	5c Freighter and liner		
128	11c Freighter and liner		
	Set of 2	50	40

1975

263	10c Bulk carrier		
264	26c Bulk carrier		
	Set of 2	90	75

B. Geneva Headquarters
100 centimes = 1 franc

1975
As Nos. 263/4 but inscribed in French

G46	60c Bulk carrier		
G47	70c Bulk carrier		
	Set of 2	1.60	1.60

UNITED STATES OF AMERICA
North America
100 cents = 1 dollar

1869

119†	12c *Adriatic* (early steamship)	£500	60.00

1893

237†	3c *Santa Maria* (Columbus)	35.00	10.00
238†	4c Fleet of Columbus	50.00	4.00

1898

299†	$2 *Grey Eagle* (Mississippi paddle-steamer)	£1800	£600

1901

300†	1c *City of Alpena* (Great Lakes steamer)	13.00	2.75
304†	8c *Carrington* (freighter) in Sault Sainte Marie canal lock	£100	50.00
305†	10c *St. Paul* (liner)	£150	24.00

1909

379	2c *Clermont* (Fulton's paddle-steamer), 1807, and *Half Moon* (Hudson), 1609 ..	11.00	3.25

1920

556†	1c *Mayflower* (Pilgrim Fathers), 1620	3.75	2.00

1922

698†	20c *W. F. Babcock* (brig), San Francisco	8.00	5

1924

618†	1c *Nieu Nederland* (emigrant ship), 1642	3.25	3.00

624	2c *Restaurationen* (emigrant sloop), 1825		
625	5c *Raven* (replica Viking longship)		
	Set of 2	22.00	18.00

1934

735	3c *Ark* and *Dove* (emigrant ships), 1634	15	12

1936

786†	1c Battle of Flamborough Head, 1779 ..	8	5
787†	2c U.S.S. *United States* (frigate), 1812 ..	10	5
788†	3c U.S.S. *Hartford* (steam frigate), 1862	15	5

COLLECT BIRDS ON STAMPS
Second revised edition of this Stanley Gibbons thematic catalogue – now available at £8.50 (p. + p. £2) from: Stanley Gibbons Publications Ltd, 5 Parkside, Christchurch Road, Ringwood, Hants BH24 3SH.

1939

853	3c *Andrea F. Luckenbach* (freighter) in Panama Canal	15	5

1944

920	3c *Savannah* (paddle-steamer), 1819	10	5

1945

933	3c *Arthur Middleton* (supply ship) and U.S. Coastguard landing craft	8	5

1946

936	3c "Liberty" type freighter	8	5

944	3c Liner	8	5

1947

948	3c U.S.S. *Constitution* (frigate), 1797	8	5

1948

953	3c Sinking of *Dorchester* (liner), 1943	8	5

1950

991	3c Mississippi river steamer, 1850	8	5

994	3c Paddle-steamer, 1850	8	5

1953

1018 5c U.S.S. *Susquehanna* and U.S.S. *Mississippi* (paddle-steamers), Tokyo Bay, 1853 .... 10 5

1024 3c Dutch galleon, New York, 1653 ...... 8 5

1954

1065 3c Keel boat 8 5

1955

1071 3c *Altadoc* (Great Lakes freighter) 8 5

1957

1090 3c Freighters 8 5

1093 3c U.S.S. *Forrestal* (aircraft carrier) 8 5

1097 3c *Virginia of Sagadahock* (Maine shallop), 1607 .... 8 5

1959

1127 4c U.S.S. *Nautilus* (submarine) 8 5

1962

1196 4c Mississippi sternwheel steamer 8 5

1210 4c Yachts 10 5

1965

1252 5c *Clermont* (Fulton's paddle-steamer), 1807 .... 10 5

1967

1305 5c Canal barge 10 5

1968

1341 6c Indian canoe, 1668 .... 15 5

1969

1361 6c Rowing boat, 1869 .... 15 5

1970

1379† 6c Haida ceremonial canoe 20 5

1405 6c Keel boat, 1820 .... 15 5

1416 6c *Mayflower* (Pilgrim Fathers), 1620 .... 20 5

1971

1444† 8c *Charles W. Morgan* (whaling ship) .. 20 8

COLLECT MAMMALS ON STAMPS

A Stanley Gibbons thematic catalogue on this popular subject. Copies available at £7.50 (p. + p. £2) from: Stanley Gibbons Publications Ltd, 5 Parkside, Christchurch Road, Ringwood, Hants BH24 3SH.

1973

1501 8c English merchantman, Boston, 1773
1502 8c English merchantman, Boston, 1773
1503 8c Rowing boats, Boston, 1773
1504 8c Rowing boat, Boston, 1773
        Set of 4 55 30

1978

1710† 13c H.M.S. *Resolution* and H.M.S. *Discovery* (Cook) at Hawaii, 1778 .... 20 5

1981

1915† 18c Battle of Virginia Capes, 1781 ...... 25 5

1983

2028 20c *Concord* (emigrant ship), 1683 ...... 25 5

1984

2077 2c Eastern Polynesian canoe 25 5

2090 20c *Elizabeth* (English galleon), 1584 .... 25 5

1985

2163b† 10c Canal barge, 1880s 12 5
2169† 14c Iceboat, 1880s 20 5
2170† 15c Tug, 1900s 20 5

2202† 22c Indian canoe 30 5

1986

2224† 22c *Advance* (polar brig), 1853 .... 30 5

2235† 22c Ship's figurehead 30 5

1988

2330 22c *Charles W. Morgan* (whaling ship) 25 5

2339 22c *Clarence Crockett* (yacht) 25 5

2345 44c *Calmare Nyckel* and *Fagel Grip*
        (Swedish immigrant ships), 1638 ...... 50 10

PARCEL POST STAMPS

1912

P428† 10c *Kronprinz Wilhelm* (liner) 32.00 1.40

UPPER VOLTA

West Africa
100 centimes = 1 franc

1931

As No. 109 of Cameroun
66† 1f50 Liner 1.10 1.10

1970

299† 15f Medieval German kogge 20 15

1971

353 40f Outboard motor boat 35 20

1972

362† 150f Gondolas 1.40 85

382 40f Freighter 30 20

389 200f Olympic yacht 1.25 80

1973

No. 353 surcharged **O. M. S. 25e Anniversaire 45F**
401 45f on 40f Outboard motor boat 40 30

1976

417† 200f H.M.S. *Victory* at Battle of St.
        Vincent, 1797 .... 1.10 45

1978

487† 65f H.M.S. *Endeavour* (Cook) 45 20
490† 350f H.M.S. *Resolution* (Cook) 1.75 1.10

1983

663† 45f Canoe 20 10

673† 50f Fishing canoe 20 10

675 90f "Soling" class yacht
676 120f "Type 470" yacht
677 300f Sailboard
678 400f Sailboard
                        Set of 4 2.75 2.50

1984

710† 450f *Trieste* (Piccard's bathyscaphe) 1.60 1.40

734 20f *Maiden Queen* (full-rigged ship)
735 60f *Scawfell* (full-rigged ship)
736 120f *Harbinger* (full-rigged ship)
737 400f *True Briton* (full-rigged ship)
                        Set of 4 2.50 1.90

Appendix

The following stamps have either been issued in excess of
postal needs, or have not been available to the public in
reasonable quantities at face value. Miniature sheets, imperforate
stamps etc., are excluded from this section.

1974

Centenary of U.P.U. 40f Liner
Centenary of Berne Convention (1974). *Centenary of U.P.U. issue
optd* **100e ANNIVERSAIRE DE L'UNION POSTAL
UNIVERSELLE 9 OCTOBER 1974.** 40f Liner

1975

Birth Centenary of Sir Winston Churchill 125f Convoy
Expo'75 Exhibition, Okinawa. Modern Japanese ships. Postage
    15, 25, 45, 50, 60 f, Air 150f

1976

Olympic Games, Montreal (1st issue) Pre-olympic year (1975).
    50f Yachts
Zeppelin Airships. 40f Yachts

URUGUAY

South America
1000 milesimos = 100 centesimos = 1 peso

1895

158† 20c *Elbe* (early steamer) (black & green) 4.00 55

1897

As No. 158, but colour changed
188† 20c *Elbe* (early steamer) (black &
        mauve) 3.50 40

1908

279 1c *Montevideo* (cruiser) and *Diez-y-Ocho de Julio* (cadet ship)
280 2c *Montevideo* and *Diez-y-Ocho de Julio*
281 5c *Montevideo* and *Diez-y-Ocho de Julio*
        Set of 3 2.25 2.25

1909

282 2c *Montevideo* (cruiser)
283 5c *Montevideo*
        Set of 2 2.00 1.40

1919

349 5m Shipping, Montevideo
350 1c Shipping, Montevideo
351 2c Shipping, Montevideo
352 4c Shipping, Montevideo
353 5c Shipping, Montevideo
354 8c Shipping, Montevideo
355 20c Shipping, Montevideo
356 23c Shipping, Montevideo
357 50c Shipping, Montevideo
358 1p Shipping, Montevideo
       Set of 10 15.00 5.50

1930

647† 20c Shipping, Montevideo, 1830 . . . . 85 70
649† 50c Shipping, Montevideo, 1930 . . . . 2.75 1.75

1945

913 8c *La Eolo* (full-rigged sailing ship) 1.00 35

1963

1231† 90c *Alferez Campora* (ketch), 1960 . . . . 20 8
1232† 1p40 *Alferez Campora* 30 25

1968

1381† 12p *Suarez* (screw gunboat) 20 15
1385† 20p *Isabel* (privateer), 1818 (air) 30 12

1979

1723 10p Caravel 1.75 85

1982

1807 3p *Capitan Miranda* (cadet schooner) . . 40 15

1983

1815† 3p *Santa Maria* (Columbus) 35 15

PARCEL POST STAMPS

1974

P1558† 300p Paddle-steamer 75 50

VANUATU
South Pacific
1980 100 centimes = 1 franc
1981 Vatus

1980

295E† 50f Outrigger canoe, Shepherd Island (inscribed in English) 75 70
295F† 50f Outrigger canoe, Shepherd Island (inscribed in French) 75 70

1983

362† 20v *Oriana* (liner) and outrigger canoe 25 25

368† 25v Fishing boats off Dover, 1785 . . . . . . 35 35

1984

382† 20v *Induna* (container ship) 30 35
384† 45v *Brahman Express* (container ship) . . 65 70

390 25v *Makambo* (inter-island freighter)
391 45v *Rockton* (inter-island freighter)
392 100v *Waroonga* (inter-island freighter) ⬎
        Set of 3 2.10 2.40

1985

411† 35v *Mala* (patrol boat) 45 50
412† 45v Japanese trawlers 65 70

428† 100v Sailboard 1.10 1.25

434† 45v *President Coolidge* (liner) leaving San Francisco 55 60
435† 55v *President Coolidge* as troopship, 1942 . . . . 65 70

1988

496	20v Tambo (freighter)			
497	45v Induna (freighter)			
498	55v Morinda (freighter)			
499	65v Marsina (freighter)			
		Set of 4	2.00	2.10

As No. 428, but with additional Australian "Expo 88" symbol

MS501 100v Sailboard (sheet contains one other design) 1.75 1.90

VATICAN CITY

Southern Europe
100 centesimi = 1 lira

1972

575†	50li Galleons, Venice, 1581		5	5
576†	50li Galleons, Venice, 1581		5	5
577†	50li Galleons, Venice, 1581		5	5
578†	50li Galleons, Venice, 1581		5	5

1987

893†	4000li Pacific Islands canoe and sampans		4.00	4.00

VENEZIA GIULIA AND ISTRIA

Southern Europe
100 centesimi = 1 lira

YUGOSLAV MILITARY GOVERNMENT

1945

62	4li Istrian fishing boat (blue)		5	5
79	4li Istrian fishing boat (red)		5	5
101	6li Istrian fishing boat		15	10

VENEZUELA

South America
100 centimos = 1 bolivar

1926

394	10c Paddle-steamer		85	55

COLLECT MAMMALS ON STAMPS

A Stanley Gibbons thematic catalogue on this popular subject. Copies available at £7.50 (p. + p. £2) from: Stanley Gibbons Publications Ltd, 5 Parkside, Christchurch Road, Ringwood, Hants BH24 3SH.

1937

464†	10c Sailing barges, River Orinoco		70	25

488†	70c Liner, La Guaira		1.75	70
489†	1b80 Liner, La Guaira		3.00	1.25

No. 464 overprinted **RESELLADO 1937–1938**

492†	10c Sailing barges, River Orinoco		1.40	65

1941

No. 464 overprinted **HABILITADO 1940**

648†	10c Sailing barges, River Orinoco		1.25	35

1943

No. 464 overprinted **Resellado 1943**

659†	10c Sailing barges, River Orinoco		5.00	3.50

1948

Size 37½ × 22½ mm (Nos. 780/90) or 22½ × 37½ mm (Nos. 791/806). Inscribed "AMERICAN BANK NOTE COMPANY" at foot

780	5c Republica de Venezuela (freighter)
781	7½c Republica de Venezuela
782	10c Republica de Venezuela
783	15c Republica de Venezuela
784	20c Republica de Venezuela
785	25c Republica de Venezuela
786	30c Republica de Venezuela
787	37½c Republica de Venezuela
788	40c Republica de Venezuela
789	50c Republica de Venezuela
790	1b Republica de Venezuela
791	5c Republica de Venezuela (air)
792	10c Republica de Venezuela
793	15c Republica de Venezuela
794	20c Republica de Venezuela
795	25c Republica de Venezuela
796	30c Republica de Venezuela
797	45c Republica de Venezuela
798	50c Republica de Venezuela
799	70c Republica de Venezuela
800	75c Republica de Venezuela
801	90c Republica de Venezuela
802	1b Republica de Venezuela
803	2b Republica de Venezuela
804	3b Republica de Venezuela
805	4b Republica de Venezuela
806	5b Republica de Venezuela

Set of 27 38.00 15.00

1949

820	5c Santa Maria (Columbus)
821	10c Santa Maria
822	20c Santa Maria
823	1b Santa Maria

824	5c Santa Maria (air)
825	10c Santa Maria
826	15c Santa Maria
827	25c Santa Maria
828	30c Santa Maria
829	1b Santa Maria

Set of 10 21.00 6.50

1951

Nos. 781 and 787 surcharged **RESELLADO** and value

884	5c on 7½c Republica de Venezuela (freighter)			
885	10c on 37½c Republica de Venezuela			
		Set of 2	70	30

As Nos. 780/2 and 791/3 but size 38 × 23½ mm (Nos. 1012/14) or 23½ × 38 mm (Nos. 1015/17). Inscribed "COURVOISIER S.A." at foot

1012	5c Republica de Venezuela (freighter)
1013	10c Republica de Venezuela
1014	15c Republica de Venezuela
1015	5c Republica de Venezuela (air)
1016	10c Republica de Venezuela
1017	15c Republica de Venezuela

Set of 6 14.00 40

1963

1789†	30c Shell Charaima (tanker), Lake Maracaibo		35	15
1790†	35c Shell Charaima, Lake Maracaibo ..		40	20
1791†	80c Shell Charaima, Lake Maracaibo ..		75	40

1965

Nos. 1791, 804 and 805 surcharged **RESELLADO VALOR** and value

1852†	60c on 80c Shell Charaima (tanker), Lake Maracaibo		85	35
1860†	10c on 3b Republica de Venezuela (freighter) (air)		15	8
1861†	10c on 4b Republica de Venezuela		70	35

1966

1933	60c 19th-century sailing packet		1.00	50

1968

2039†	5b Olympic yacht		3.50	2.00

1973

2228†	1b Battle of Maracaibo, 1823		85	40
2229†	2b Battle of Maracaibo, 1823		1.75	85

1974

2278†	50c Liner and sailing packet	40	20

1980

2437†	1b50 *Mariscal Sucre* (frigate)	70	30
2438†	1b50 *Picua* (submarine)	70	30
2440†	1b50 *Simon Bolivar* (cadet barque)	70	30

1985

2561†	3b Support vessel and oil rig	35	20

1987

2672†	6b Sailing dinghy	35	15
2675†	6b50 Motor boat marina	35	15
2677†	6b50 Rowing boats	35	15

2691†	2b Bulk carrier	10	5

2704†	4b *Zulia* (freighter)	20	10
2705†	4b *Guarico* (freighter)	20	10
2706†	5b *Cerro Bolivar* (bulk carrier)	25	12

2710†	2b National Guard patrol boat	10	5
2719†	4b National Guard patrol boat	20	10

COLLECT BIRDS ON STAMPS

Second revised edition of this Stanley Gibbons thematic catalogue – now available at £8.50 (p. + p. £2) from: Stanley Gibbons Publications Ltd, 5 Parkside, Christchurch Road, Ringwood, Hants BH24 3SH.

VIETNAM

South-east Asia

South Vietnam

100 cents = 1 piastre

1955

S5	70c Refugee raft	
S6	80c Refugee raft	
S7	10p Refugee raft	
S8	20p Refugee raft	
S9	35p Refugee raft (inscribed "CHEIN-DICH-HUYNE-DE")	
S10	100p Refugee raft	
	Set of 6	30.00 20.00

1956

No. S9 with inscription obliterated by bar

S26	35p Refugee raft	4.50	3.25

1964

S229†	1p50 Junks, Phan Thiet	20	15

1968

S318†	80c Junk	10	10

1971

S383	3p Warships		
S384	40p Warships		
	Set of 2	1.25	60

1972

S397†	40 Trawler	15	10

1974

S455	5p Sampan		
S456	10p Sampan		
	Set of 2	35	20

National Front for the Liberation of South Vietnam

100 xu = 1 dong

1964

NLF8	30x Sinking of U.S.S. *Card* (destroyer)	2.00	1.50

North Vietnam

100 xu = 1 dong

1961

N187	5x Freighter loading at Haiphong	
N188	12x Freighter loading at Haiphong	
	Set of 2	4.50 2.25

1963

N265†	12x Trawler	2.75	1.10

1964

N315	12x Sampans	55	30

N327†	5x Naval longboat	45	20

N340†	12x Patrol boat and junks	55	25

1967

N491†	20x *Aurora* (Russian cruiser), 1917	50	35

N498†	12x Fast patrol boat	35	20

1969

N567†	12x Log raft	25	15
N568†	12x Tug and log rafts	25	15

Socialist Republic of Vietnam
100 xu = 1 dong

1977

183†	1d *Aurora* (Russian cruiser), 1917	50	35

338†	1d Olympic yachts	65	35

1982

511†	30x *Aurora* (Russian cruiser), 1917	20	12

1983

531	30x Sampan			
532	50x Junk			
533	1d Houseboats			
534	3d Junk			
535	5d Sampan			
536	10d Sampan			
		Set of 6	3.75	1.75

1984

714†	50x Junks	20	5
717†	50x Junks	20	5
719†	1d Junk	30	12
721†	3d Junk	80	30
722†	5d Junk	1.10	40
723†	8d Junks	1.40	55

1985

811†	5d Barge, Haiphong	8	5

856†	2d Freighter	5	5

864†	1d Oil rig	5	5

1986

984	1d Greek bireme	
985	1d Viking longship	
986	2d Medieval kogge	
987	3d Greek cargo galley	
988	3d Phoenician war galley	
989	5d Ancient Mediterranean cargo ship	
990	5d Roman trireme	

		Set of 7 35	25

WALLIS AND FUTUNA ISLANDS

South Pacific
100 centimes = 1 franc

1920

Nos. 99/101 *and additional value of New Caledonia overprinted* **ILES WALLIS et FUTUNA**

15†	1f *President Felix Faure* (barque) (blue on green)	1.25	1.25
28†	1f10 *President Felix Faure*	80	1.00
16†	2f *President Felix Faure*	1.90	1.90
17†	5f *President Felix Faure* (black on orange)	3.25	3.25

1922

As Nos. 15/17, *some with colours changed, surcharged in figures*

33†	25c on 2f *President Felix Faure*	20	20
34†	25c on 5f *President Felix Faure*	20	20
38†	1f25 on 1f *President Felix Faure* (blue)	20	20
39†	1f50 on 1f *President Felix Faure* (blue)	50	70
40†	3f on 5f *President Felix Faure* (mauve)	1.25	1.25
41†	10f on 5f *President Felix Faure* (brown on mauve)	8.50	8.50
42†	20f on 5f *President Felix Faure* (red on yellow)	12.00	12.00

1930

Nos. 137/45 *and* 161/70 *of New Caledonia overprinted* **ILES WALLIS et FUTUNA**

43†	1c Fishing boat, Pointe des Paletuviers	5	5
44†	2c Fishing boat, Pointe des Paletuviers	5	5
45†	3c Fishing boat, Pointe des Paletuviers	5	5
46†	4c Fishing boat, Pointe des Paletuviers	5	5
47†	5c Fishing boat, Pointe des Paletuviers	5	5
48†	10c Fishing boat, Pointe des Paletuviers	5	5
49†	15c Fishing boat, Pointe des Paletuviers	5	5
50†	20c Fishing boat, Pointe des Paletuviers	5	5
51†	25c Fishing boat, Pointe des Paletuviers	10	25
67†	1f *L'Astrolabe* (La Perouse) (red & brown)	1.25	1.25
68†	1f *L'Astrolabe* (red)	50	50
69†	1f *L'Astrolabe* (green & red)	15	10

70†	1f10 *L'Astrolabe*	10.00	10.00
71†	1f25 *L'Astrolabe* (green & brown)	70	70
72†	1f25 *L'Astrolabe* (red)	20	15
73†	1f40 *L'Astrolabe*	25	25
74†	1f50 *L'Astrolabe*	15	20
75†	1f60 *L'Astrolabe*	30	30
76†	1f75 *L'Astrolabe* (red & blue)	4.50	4.50
77†	1f75 *L'Astrolabe* (blue)	75	65
78†	2f *L'Astrolabe*	45	40
79†	2f25 *L'Astrolabe*	30	5
80†	2f50 *L'Astrolabe*	30	30
81†	3f *L'Astrolabe*	45	45
82†	5f *L'Astrolabe*	45	45
83†	10f *L'Astrolabe*	80	80
84†	20f *L'Astrolabe*	1.50	1.50

1931

As No. 109 *of Cameroun*

88†	1f50 Liner	1.50	1.75

1941

Nos. 43/51, 68, 71, 74, 77/8 *and* 80/4 *further overprinted* **France Libre**

96†	1c Fishing boat, Pointe des Paletuviers	25	30
97†	2c Fishing boat, Pointe des Paletuviers	25	30
97a†	3c Fishing boat, Pointe des Paletuviers	40.00	40.00
98†	4c Fishing boat, Pointe des Paletuviers	25	30
99†	5c Fishing boat, Pointe des Paletuviers	25	30
100†	10c Fishing boat, Pointe des Paletuviers	25	30
101†	15c Fishing boat, Pointe des Paletuviers	35	35
102†	20c Fishing boat, Pointe des Paletuviers	70	70
103†	25c Fishing boat, Pointe des Paletuviers	70	70
116†	1f *L'Astrolabe* (La Perouse)	70	70
117†	1f25 *L'Astrolabe*	70	70
118†	1f50 *L'Astrolabe*	45	45
119†	1f75 *L'Astrolabe*	45	45
120†	2f *L'Astrolabe*	70	70
121†	2f50 *L'Astrolabe*	70.00	70.00
122†	3f *L'Astrolabe*	45	45
123†	5f *L'Astrolabe*	2.00	2.00
124†	10f *L'Astrolabe*	22.00	22.00
125†	20f *L'Astrolabe*	35.00	35.00

1954

As No. 264 *of Cameroun*

160†	3f Landing craft, Normandy, 1944	3.00	3.00

1955

168a†	27f Freighter at wharf	2.00	1.75
169†	33f 19th-century full-rigged ship	3.75	3.25

1965

186	11f *Reine Amelia* (inter-island ferry)	3.00	3.00

1967

195	12f H.M.S. *Dolphin* (frigate) (Wallis), 1767	3.50	2.50

1969

199†	1f Outrigger canoe	25	25
203†	50f Fishing canoe	2.25	2.00

1971
No. 169 surcharged

208† 21f on 33f 19th-century full-rigged ship   2.50   2.50

1972

217†   14f Model pirogue 1.25   60
219†   18f Racing pirogue 1.50   1.00
220†   200f Racing pirogues (air) 15.00   10.00

1973

221   22f *La Boussole* (La Perouse), 1788
222   28f *H.M.S. Dolphin* (frigate) (Wallis), 1767
223   40f *L'Astrolabe* (D'Urville), 1828
224   72f *La Boudeuse* (Bougainville), 1768
           Set of 4   10.50   5.75

1976

255†   47f Battle of Virginia Capes, 1781 ......   2.00   1.75

1977
No. 255 overprinted **JAMES COOK Bicentaire de la decouverte des Iles Hawaii 1778–1978**

277†   47f Battle of Virginia Capes, 1781 ......   3.75   2.25

1978

287   150f *Triomphant* (destroyer)
288   200f *Cap des Palmes* and *Chevreuil*
      (patrol boats)
289   280f *Savorgnan de Brazza* (destroyer)
           Set of 3   20.00   15.00

1979

308†   68f *Moana* (inter-island freighter) 1.25   90

310†   10f Bonito fishing boat   30   30

COLLECT RAILWAYS ON STAMPS
A Stanley Gibbons thematic catalogue on this popular subject. Copies available at £7.50 (p. + p. £2) from: Stanley Gibbons Publications Ltd, 5 Parkside, Christchurch Road, Ringwood, Hants BH24 3SH.

317†   52f Model outrigger canoe 1.00   80

323†   70f *President Felix Faure* (on stamp No. 15) 1.25   90

332   130f *H.M.S. Resolution* (Cook), Hawaii, 1779 ....   3.75   2.75

1980
Design as No. 308

350†   3f *Moana* (inter-island freighter)   10   10

1981

380   66f Battle of Virginia Capes, 1781
381   74f Battle of Virginia Capes, 1781
           Set of 2   3.25   1.75

386   60f *La Dieppoise* (patrol boat)
387   85f *Protet* (frigate)
           Set of 2   3.25   2.10

1982

391   300f Fishing boats 4.50   30

395†   140f *L'Astrolabe* (on stamp No. 67) 2.10   1.40

1983

419   270f Sailboard 4.00   2.40

1984

437   67f *Commandant Bory* (frigate) 1.40   75

1985

471   350f Sailing canoe 4.25   2.75

473   51f *Jacques Cartier* (landing ship)   75   45

1986

488†   8f *Eendracht* (Schouten), 1616   15   5
489†   9f *Hoorn* (Lemaire), 1616   15   5

494   6f *La Lorientaise* (patrol boat)
495   7f *Commandant Blaison* (frigate)
496   120f *Balny* (frigate)
           Set of 3   2.00   1.50

1987

516	135f Piccard's bathyscaphe, 1948	1.40	1.10

526	260f French frigate, 1838	3.00	2.25

1988

530	70f *L'Astrolabe* and *La Boussole* (La Perouse), 1788	85	65

POSTAGE DUE STAMPS

1920

Nos. D102/9 of New Caledonia overprinted **ILES WALLIS et FUTUNA**

D18	5c Outrigger canoe		
D19	10c Outrigger canoe		
D20	15c Outrigger canoe		
D21	20c Outrigger canoe		
D22	30c Outrigger canoe		
D23	50c Outrigger canoe		
D24	60c Outrigger canoe		
D25	1f Outrigger canoe		
	Set of 8	3.00	3.50

1927

No. D109 of New Caledonia but colours changed, surcharged in figures

D43	2f on 1f Outrigger canoe		
D44	3f on 1f Outrigger canoe		
	Set of 2	9.00	10.00

YEMEN

Arabia
40 bogaches = 1 imadi

1952

90	30b Dhow		
91	30b Dhow (air)		
	Set of 2	15.00	18.00

1961

138	4b Freighter		
139	6b Freighter		
140	16b Freighter		
	Set of 3	3.00	2.75

REPUBLIC ISSUES

1963

Nos. 139/40 overprinted **Y. A. R. 27. 9. 1962** *in English and Arabic*

217†	6b Freighter	1.25	1.25
218†	16b Freighter	2.00	2.00

1964

267†	½b Liner and freighter, Hodeida	25	20
270†	16b Liner and freighter, Hodeida (air)	1.75	1.25

1966

Nos. 267 and 270 overprinted **1965 SANA'A** *in English and Arabic*

427†	½b Liner and freighter, Hodeida	20	12
430†	16b Liner and freighter, Hodeida (air)	2.50	2.00

444†	½b American aircraft carrier	15	15
446†	8b American aircraft carrier (air)	95	75

Nos. 444 and 446 overprinted **GEMINI IX CERNAN-STAFFORD JUNE 3-1966** *in English and Arabic*

453†	½b American aircraft carrier	15	15
455†	8b American aircraft carrier (air)	1.40	1.00

Appendix

The following stamps have either been issued in excess of postal needs, or have not been made available to the public in reasonable quantities at face value. Miniature sheets, imperforate stamps etc., are excluded from this section.

1971

Pres. Gamal Nasser of Egypt Commemoration. 2b Freighter in Suez Canal

ROYALIST ISSUES

1967

R336†	½b Fishing boats, Lake Patzcuaro, Mexico	10	5
R342†	20b Fishing boats, Lake Patzcuaro, Mexico (air)	2.00	60

Appendix

The following stamps have either been issued in excess of postal needs or have not been made available to the public in reasonable quantities at face value. Miniature sheets, imperforate stamps etc., are excluded from this section.

1967

Visit of Queen of Sheba to Solomon. 6b Galley

STAMP MONTHLY

— finest and most informative magazine for all collectors. Obtainable from your newsagent or by postal subscription — details on request.

YEMEN PEOPLE'S DEMOCRATIC REPUBLIC

Arabia
1000 fils = 1 dinar

1972

105	25f Dhow building		
106	80f Dhow at sea		
	Set of 2	1.75	1.10

1979

MS229	250f Dhow (on stamp No. 12 of Aden)	1.25	1.25

1980

237	110f *Dido* (screw steamer)		
238	180f *Anglia* (screw steamer)		
239	250f *India* (screw steamer)		
	Set of 3	2.40	1.50

1983

305	50f *Europa* (liner)		
306	100f *World Discoverer* (liner)		
	Set of 2	1.75	1.00
MS307	Two sheets. (a) 20f *Kruzenshtern* (Russian cadet barque); 40f *Grossherzogin Elisabeth* (German cadet schooner); 60f *Sedov* (Russian cadet barque); 80f *Dar Pomorza* (Polish cadet full-rigged ship); (b) 200f *Gorch Fock* (German cadet barque)		
	Set of 2 sheets	10.00	10.00

YUGOSLAVIA

South-east Europe
100 paras = 1 dinar

1939

406	50p + 50p *Jadran* (cadet barquentine)		
407	1d + 50p *King Alexander* (liner)		
408	1d50 + 1d *Triglav* (freighter)		
409	2d + 1d50 *Dubrovnik* (destroyer)		
	Set of 4	4.50	4.00

1948

582 2d Danube river steamer
583 3d Danube river steamer
584 5d Danube river steamer
585 10d Danube river steamer

Set of 4 17.00 17.00

1950

665 2d 16th-century galleon
666 3d Partisan patrol boat
667 5d Freighter
668 10d *Zagreb* (freighter)
669 12d Yachts
670 20d Destroyer

Set of 6 6.50 2.75

1951

675† 1d Paddle-steamer, River Danube 15 5

1958

892† 5d Shipbuilding (brown) 15 5
983† 5d Shipbuilding (orange) 30 5

1960

952† 55d Olympic yachts 35 12

1966

As No. 983, but value expressed as "0.05"
1194† 5p Shipbuilding 10 5

1224 30p Yachts 20 5

1969

1378 50p *Eber* (barque)
1379 1d25 *Tare* (barque)
1380 1d50 *Sela* (brigantine)
1381 2d50 16th-century galleon, Dubrovnik
1382 3d25 *Madre Mimbelli* (sail frigate)
1383 5d 16th-century caravel

Set of 6 3.00 1.50

1972

1512† 6d50 Olympic yachts 60 55

1973

1547† 2d50 18th-century shipping, Kotor 15 5
1549† 5d 19th-century fishing boats, Split 30 15

1979

1887 4d90 Rowing 30 10

1910 4d90 *Deligrad* (Danube paddle-steamer)
1911 10d *Serbia* (Danube paddle-steamer)

Set of 2 2.25 1.50

1981

2001 8d *Karlovac* (tug) pushing barges, River Danube
2002 13d Paddle-steamer towed by railway locomotive, Sip Canal

Set of 2 1.60 90

1982

2017† 15d *Splendido* (Austrian sail frigate) 60 25

2035† 8d80 Armed tug, 1942 .... 35 15
2036† 15d Missile gunboat 60 30

1983

2067 8d80 Freighters 20 12

1985

2225 8d Yacht (aerial view)
2226 10d Sailboard
2227 50d Yacht at sunset
2228 70d Yacht near coast

Set of 4 1.40 80

1986

2278† 200d Freighter 1.00 35

2307 50d "Flying Dutchman" class yachts
2308 80d "Flying Dutchman" class yachts

Set of 2 60 40
MS2309 100d "Flying Dutchman" class yachts 45 45

1987

2397† 200d Fire-fighting tug 20 8

2417 80d Tug in canal, Titov Vrbas 8 5

1988

2446† 1200d Container ship 1.00 55

ZAIRE

Central Africa
100 sengi = 1 kuba
100 kuba = 1 zaire

1980

MS1012 10z 18th-century fishing boats, Naples 5.00 5.00

1044† 75k Canoes, Stanley's expedition, 1879   35   20

1984

1180† 10k River ferry 5   5

1985

1258† 7z Kokolo (river ferry) 15   5
1260† 15z Luebo (river ferry) 30   20

1986

1267† 7z Deliverance (stern wheel paddle-steamer) (on Belgian Congo stamp No. 79) 10   5

ZAMBIA

Central Africa
1964 12 pence = 1 shilling
20 shillings = 1 pound
1968 100 ngwee = 1 kwacha

1964

101† 1s Night fishing boat, Mpulungu 15   5

1970

159† 25n Ceremonial canoe 70   1.00

1978

276† 18n Police motorised canoe 35   50

STAMP MONTHLY

— finest and most informative magazine for all collectors. Obtainable from your newsagent or by postal subscription — details on request.

1987

504† 1k25 Inflatable raft, River Zambezi 30   25

1988

543† 2k50 Fishing canoe 60   50

ZANZIBAR

Indian Ocean
1908 100 cents = 1 rupee
1936 100 cents = 1 shilling

1908

239†	10r Dhow	65.00	85.00
240†	20r Dhow	£140	£190
241†	30r Dhow	£225	£300
242†	40r Dhow	£400	
243†	50r Dhow	£350	
244†	100r Dhow	£600	
245†	200r Dhow	£900	

1913

290†	1r Sailing canoe	1.40	1.60
291†	2r Sailing canoe	2.50	3.75
292†	3r Sailing canoe	3.75	5.50
293†	4r Sailing canoe	9.50	15.00
294†	5r Sailing canoe	12.00	27.00
295†	10r Dhow	28.00	50.00
296†	20r Dhow	85.00	£125
260b†	30r Dhow	£110	£150
260c†	40r Dhow	£225	£275
260d†	50r Dhow	£200	£250
260e†	100r Dhow	£300	
260f†	200r Dhow	£600	

1936

As Nos. 290/5, but with face values in shillings

318†	1s Sailing canoe	45	5
319†	2s Sailing canoe	55	25
320†	5s Sailing canoe	2.25	3.00
321†	7s50 Sailing canoe	6.00	7.50
322†	10s Dhow	4.50	4.50

1944

327	10c Shah Alam (Sultan's dhow)	
328	20c Shah Alam	
329	50c Shah Alam	
330	1s Shah Alam	
	Set of 4	35 1.40

1949

As No. 115 of Antigua

336† 30c Paddle-steamer 80   50

1957

360†	15c Dhows	10	5
361†	20c Sultan's barge	10	5
363†	30c Dhows	15	5
368†	1s25 Dhows	55	5

1961

As Nos. 360/8, but with portrait of Sultan Seyyid Sir Abdulla bin Khalifa

375†	15c Dhows	12	5
376†	20c Sultan's barge	12	5
378†	30c Dhows	25	5
383†	1s25 Dhows	45	35

1964

Nos. 375/83 overprinted **JAMHURI 1964**

416†	15c Dhows	5	5
417†	20c Sultan's barge	5	5
419†	30c Dhows	5	5
424†	1s25 Dhows	15	10

1966

456†	20c Freighter	10	5
458†	1s30 Freighter	10	10

ZIL ELWANNYEN SESEL

Indian Ocean
100 cents = 1 rupee

1980

17† 1r50 Cinq Juin (travelling post office) 30   30

1981

23†	40c Royal Yacht Royal Escape	10	10
25†	5r Royal Yacht Victoria and Albert II	60	60
27†	10r Royal Yacht Britannia	1.25	1.40

1982

35	1r75 Cinq Juin (travelling post office)	
36	2r10 Junon (fisheries protection launch)	
37	5r Diamond M. Dragon (drilling ship)	
	Set of 3	1.25 1.25

38 40c *Paulette* (inter-island ferry)
39 1r75 *Janette* (inter-island ferry)
40 2r75 *Lady Esme* (inter-island ferry)
41 3r50 *Cinq Juin* (travelling post office)
                 Set of 4 1.40 1.10

1983
Nos. 23, 25 and 27 surcharged
73† 30c on 40c Royal Yacht *Royal Escape* 20 20
75† 2r on 5r Royal Yacht *Victoria and Albert II* 60 60
77† 3r on 10r Royal Yacht *Britannia* 75 75

1984
p5

83† 50c Game fishing launch 12 15
86† 10r Game fishing launch 2.00 2.50

93† 3r Sailing canoe 75 80

1985

125 50c Phoenician trading ship, 600 B.C.
126 2r H.M.S. *Sealark* (survey ship), 1908
127 10r *Sao Gabriel* (Vasco da Gama), 1502
                 Set of 3 3.50 3.50

Index Section

This section is arranged in two parts, indexed by ship name or by type.

I. By Individual Ship Name

A

Abdulhamit
  Turkey 2929
Abegweit
  Canada 406 O9 O28
Abtao (armed steamer)
  Chile 279/80
Abtao (submarine)
  Peru 1642
Acali
  Mexico 1331
Accommodation
  Canada 1222
Accra
  Sierra Leone 833
Achilles, H.M.N.Z.S.
  Falkland Islands 308
  New Zealand 673 886 1380
Aconite, H.M.S.
  St. Pierre et Miquelon 495
Act 6
  Pitcairn Islands 273
Active, H.M.S.
  Gibraltar 510
Adamastor
  Portugal 1910
Adler
  Samoa 341
Admella
  Central African Republic 1014 1083
Admiral Gago Coutinho
  Timor 399
Admiral Graf Spee
  Falkland Islands 309
Admiral Makarov
  Russia 4846
Admiral Saldanha
  Brazil 847 1996
Admiral Tegetthoff
  Austria 1666
Adriatic (paddle-steamer)
  Peru D32/35 D48/51 D53/56 D250 D253
    D256 D257 D262 D267 D269 D271
    D349/51 D363/4
Adriatic (early steamship)
  United States of America 119
Advance
  United States of America 2224
Adventure
  Aitutaki 267
  Cameroun 836
  Niue 476
Aegna
  Estonia 127
A.E.S.
  Falkland Islands 331
Af Chapman
  Sweden 1257
Africa
  Italy 1555
Africa Palm
  Sierra Leone 643
Africaansche Galey
  Samoa 386/7

African Glen
  Liberia 730, 751
Agamemnon, H.M.S. (sail warship)
  Anguilla 113
Agamemnon (freighter)
  Guatemala 291
Age Unlimited
  Samoa 433
Aguila
  Chile 1061
Aitape
  Papua New Guinea 410
Ajanta
  India 599
Ajax, H.M.S. (cruiser)
  Falkland Islands 310
Ajax, H.M.S. (sail warship)
  Liberia 1125
Akademik Kurchatov
  Russia 4953
Akademik Kurtschatow
  Germany (East Germany) E1418
Akademik Mstislav Keldysh
  Russia 5058
Adademik Sergei Korolev
  Russia 5056
Alabama
  Grenadines of St.Vincent 217
Aladdin
  Norfolk Island 362
Al Alwah
  Iraq 1753, 1755
Alarm, H.M.S.
  Jersey 418
Albanus
  Aland Islands 32
Albatros
  French Southern & Antarctic Territories 194
Alberta (mail packet)
  Guernsey 70
Alberta (royal yacht tender)
  St.Vincent 670, O3
Albion, H.M.S.
  Turks and Caicos Islands 846
Al Derbaran
  Korea (South Korea) 1484
Al Drieya
  Saudi Arabia 1356
Alecto
  Sierra Leone 830
Aleksandr Pushkin
  Russia 3272 4341 5759
Aleksandr Sibiryakov
  Russia 4654
Alene
  Jamaica 701
Alert
  Bermuda 514
Alexander
  Finland **MS**1107
  St. Vincent 389
Alexander, H.M.S.
  Solomon Islands 238
Alexandra
  Grenadines of St. Vincent 197 O3
Al-Faq
  Iraq 856
Alferez Campora
  Uruguay 1231/2
Alfred
  Grenadines of Grenada 181

Alia
  Tokelau 94
Aliance
  British Virgin Islands 358
  St. Lucia 413
Alisma, H.M.S.
  Samoa 591
Allanshaw
  Tristan da Cunha 411
Alligator
  Liberia 29 351 404 418 466/70 537 548 704
    707 O364 O432 O446
Almendares
  Cuba **MS**2864
Almirante Cervera
  Spain **MS**924
Almirante Grau
  Peru 1558
Almirante Guise
  Peru 1597
Almirante Irizar
  Argentine 1702
Almirante Latorre
  Chile 1110
Almirante Padilla
  Colombia 1311
Almirante Tamandare
  Brazil 969 1202
Al Mirqab
  Kuwait 1109
Al Mokattam
  Egypt 597
Al Mubarakiah
  Kuwait 1110
Al Munassir
  Oman 298
Al Nasser
  Egypt 668
Alpaslan
  Turkey 2130
Alphonse Fondere
  Congo 504 508
Al-Rashid
  Iraq 854
Al Sabahiah
  Kuwait 453/4
Alsace
  Monaco 828
  Senegal 301
Altadoc
  United States of America 1071
Al-Wajda
  Qatar 799
Al-Walid
  Iraq 853
Alyssum, H.M.S.
  St. Pierre et Miquelon 496
Amagiri
  Solomon Islands 322
Amazonas (sail warship)
  Brazil 1911
Amazonas (cadet ship)
  Peru 847/9
Amelia
  Falkland Islands 343
America (sail warship)
  Argentine 1007
America (yacht)
  Gambia 700
  Solomon Islands 570

America (gunboat)
  Peru 1598
America II (yacht)
  Belize 985
  Solomon Islands 572
Amerigo Vespucci
  Anguilla 692
  Gibraltar 207
  Italy 312 1728
Amerikanis
  Grenada 1345
Amethyst, H.M.S.
  Christmas Island 51
Amguema
  Russia 4660
Amiable
  Anguilla 112
Amistad
  Sierra Leone 827 966
Ampere
  France 1475
Amphion, H.M.S. (submarine)
  Ascension 132
Amphion (royal yacht)
  Sweden 707
Amur
  Russia 4121
Ancon (freighter, 1939)
  Canal Zone 214
Ancon (liner, 1902)
  Panama 574
Ancud
  Chile 1060
Andorinha
  Mozambique 564
Andrea F. Luckenbach
  Canal Zone 152
  United States of America 853
Andrew Doria
  Grenadines of Grenada 179
  Netherlands Antilles 626
Andria Doria
  Italy 1234
Anglia (cable ship)
  Ascension 250
  Cocos (Keeling) Islands 130
  Nauru 161 163
Anglia (merchant sailing ship)
  Yemen 238
Ango
  Gabon 312
Anna
  Isle of Man 275
Anshun
  Tuvalu 238
Anro Temasek
  Singapore 337
Antara
  Iraq 852
Antarctic
  British Antarctic Territory 72
  Falkland Islands Dependencies G39
Antares
  French Southern & Antarctic Territories 166
Antelope (merchant sailing ship)
  Ciskei 81
  Montserrat 696
  Palau 34/41
Antelope, H.M.S. (destroyer)
  Gibraltar 567

II. By Ship Type

Entries are arranged under the following headings:

ANCIENT CRAFT

Keep this Catalogue up to date month by month with

the only magazine with the Stanley Gibbons Catalogue supplement – and much much more besides?

Please send for a FREE copy and subscription details to:–

Hugh Jefferies
Gibbons Stamp Monthly
Stanley Gibbons Publications Ltd.,
5 Parkside, Christchurch Road,
Ringwood, Hampshire BH24 3SH
Telephone 042 54 2363

CATALOGUES
FOR THE THEMATIC COLLECTOR

3 Volumes

NOW IN THREE VOLUMES

For the general 'All World' and the vast majority of thematic collectors there is no practical alternative to the famous 'Stamps of the World' Simplified Catalogue.

It provides a clear straightforward listing of the ¼ million or so different stamps issued worldwide since 1840 and, with well over 60 thousand illustrations, is the perfect guide when you are hunting for that elusive theme!

From the 1990 edition, published during autumn 1989, Stamps of the World will be published in three volumes

2881 Volume 1 (Foreign Countries A – J)
2882 Volume 2 (Foreign Countries K – Z)
2883 Volume 3 (Commonwealth Countries)

Its annual re-valuation of Worldwide Stamp market prices makes it essential that you always have the current edition of Stamps of the World on your bookshelf.

STANLEY GIBBONS THEMATIC
CATALOGUES

COLLECT BIRDS ON STAMPS, the first Stanley Gibbons thematic catalogue, was first published in 1983 and proved an instant success. A completely revised second edition has now been published as well as three new titles (including this catalogue). Further catalogues in the series are already in preparation.

Each is divided into an illustrated countries section which lists, in chronological order, the relevant stamps issued by each territory with year of issue and Stanley Gibbons catalogue number.

Comprehensive indexes allow sub-themes to be easily identified and cross-referenced to the main catalogue listings.

2864 Collect Birds on Stamps
2852 Collect Mammals on Stamps
2888 Collect Railways on Stamps
2899 Collect Ships on Stamps

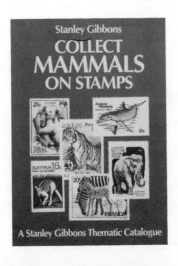

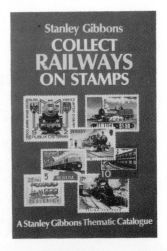

GUIDES & HANDBOOKS

STANLEY GIBBONS STAMP COLLECTING SERIES

Well illustrated handbooks packed with essential information for all collectors.

2760 Stamp Collecting: How to Start. Written especially for the beginner this handbook gives an outline of the basic essentials of the hobby.

2761 Stamp Collecting: How to Identify Stamps. An indispensable companion to any collection. Packed full with information on both normal and unfamiliar scripts.

2762 Stamp Collecting: Collecting by Theme. Sound, practical advice on how to form and develop a thematic collection – including an A—Z to collecting subjects.

2763 Stamp Collecting: How to Arrange and Write-up a Stamp Collection. How to present a collection in the best possible way.

2764 Stamp Collecting: A Guide to Modern Philately. This book – a philatelic classic – tells, the story of the post, stamp designing and printing . . . in fact everything you need to know about this fascinating hobby. Hard Bound.

2740 Stamp Collection: Philatelic Terms Illustrated new edition by James Mackay. A real dictionary of stamp collecting, fully illustrated in colour and black and white – should be on every collector's bookshelf!

HANDBOOKS

2772 Enjoy Stamp Collection by James Negus. A useful little boolet designed to give the junior collector a basic grounding in Stamp Collecting – great stocking filler at Christmas time!

2783 The Stamp Atlas by Stuart Rossiter and John Flower. The geographical, social, political and postal history of every stamp issuing nation in the World gathered together in one Volume. 336 superbly illustrated pages. Casebound.

2784 The Orbis Philatelic Atlas edited by Kenneth Chapman. A handy pocket-size volume providing an invaluable source of reference for all collectors. 352 pages, 115 full colour maps.

2776 The New Observer's Book of Stamp Collecting by Anthony New. Experienced collectors as well as beginners will benefit from the advice contained in this informative little book. Pocket sized with a great many colour illustrations. Highly recommended.

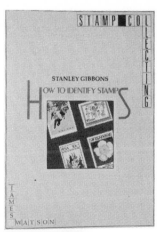

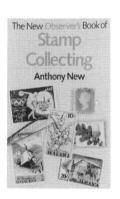

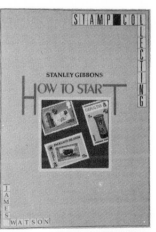

THEMATIC ALBUMS
DAVO KOSMOS

Davo Kosmos is a new range of albums conceived with the thematic collector in mind.

BINDERS are hand made using extra heavy board for maximum protection and incorporate a high-capacity four ring fitting. In a uniform shade of navy blue 'leatherette' with an appropriate motif emblazoned on the cover (or blank if you prefer), each comes with a matching slip-box.

LEAVES: All binders come with a title page and a sample of each type of leaf available – we know that there are almost as many ways of mounting a thematic collection as there are themes to choose from, so we leave the type of leaf entirely up to you. The four types are:

a) fine heavyweight white cartridge with feint grey quadrille
b) as above but with a plain border
c) Black stockleaf as illustrated – there are nine formats of stockleaf available to choose from
d) a large polypropylene 'wallet' leaf suitable for sheets and large blocks.

Item No.	Themes
5533	Blank
5534	Birds
5535	Flowers
5536	Animals
5537	Motor Vehicles
5538	Railways
5539	Religion
5540	Ships
5541	Sport

BLANK SPRINGBACK ALBUMS

These fine albums give you, the thematic collector, the freedom and flexibility you need to arrange your collection exactly as you want it.

Leaves are finely printed with a feint quadrille and most have side and centre markings to aid arrangement.

Albums and binders are now supplied with a sheet of self-adhesive, gold-blocked title panels, a selection of country titles and a run of volume numbers; allowing them to be clearly identifiable on the shelf or left blank if you prefer.

1. Tower (Item 0331) A choice of red, green, or black binder with 100 leaves of white cartridge $11\frac{1}{8} \times 9\frac{7}{8}$. Boxed.

2. Senator Medium (Item 0384) A very popular 'first, blank leaved album for many years now. 50 leaves $10\frac{3}{8}" \times 8\frac{3}{4}"$, a choice of three binder colours; black, green or red.

3. Senator Standard (Item 0386) As the Senator Medium but with 100 larger sized leaves ($11\frac{1}{8}" \times 9\frac{7}{8}"$). One of our best selling albums!

4. Simplex Medium (Item 3810) Fifty leaves of high quality cream paper with a subtle decorative border ($10\frac{3}{8}" \times 8\frac{3}{4}"$). Binder choice of green or red.

5. Simplex Standard (Item 3812) 100 larger sized leaves ($11\frac{1}{8}" \times 9\frac{7}{8}"$), otherwise the same style as the Simplex Medium. Boxed. Popular with generations of stamp collectors!

6. Utile (Item 3821) 25 white cartridge special double linen-hinged transparent faced leaves ($11\frac{1}{8}" \times 9\frac{7}{8}"$) designed to lie flat when album is opened. Attractive binder in choice of green or red.

Transparent Interleaving Fine quality glazed transparent paper in packs of 100 sheets for Tower, Senator, Simplex or similar types of loose-leaf springback albums.
Item 3310 Standard size $11" \times 9\frac{5}{8}"$.
Item 3311 Medium size $10" \times 8\frac{1}{8}"$.

For further details visit your favourite stamp shop, or, in case of difficulty, write to:
Stanley Gibbons Publications Ltd.,
5 Parkside, Christchurch Road,
Ringwood, Hampshire BH24 3SH
Telephone 0425 472363

STOCKBOOKS

We are pleased to announce that Stanley Gibbons are now offering a selected range of Lighthouse stockbooks in addition to the popular S.G. branded junior style. Fastbound with stout linen-hinged leaves, all come with glassine interleaving to ensure complete protection for your stamps and will give years of use.

1. Junior Stockbooks

With a bright full-colour, stamps design cover these stockbooks have white leaves with glassine strips and interleaving – ideal for the younger collector.

	Size (ins)	No. of Pages	No. of Strips
Item 2625	7½ × 5¼	8	48
Item 2659	8½ × 6⅝	8	48
Item 2650	11 × 8¾	8	72

2. Lighthouse Stockbooks

A variety of bright single colour covers with gold blocking on the front and spine.

	Size (ins)	No. of Pages	No. of Strips
Item 2649	7¾ × 5½	16	96
Item 2651	9 × 7	16	96
Item 2631	9 × 7	32	192

For further details visit your favourite stamp shop or, in case of difficulty, write to:

Stanley Gibbons Publications Ltd.,
5 Parkside, Christchurch Road,
Ringwood, Hampshire BH24 3SH
Telephone 0425 472363

The larger page size stockbooks feature a luxury leather look binding and have double glassine interleaving for even greater protection. NOTE the new 48-page stockbook (item 2662) has double linen hinged 'lay flat' leaves.

	Size (ins)	No. of Pages	No. of Strips
Item 2652	12 × 9	16	144
Item 2653	12 × 9	32	288
Item 2662	12 × 9	48	432

3. Two stylish stockbooks with binding as above but with black leaves and crystal clear acetate strips. Double glassine interleaving.

	Size (ins)	No. of Pages	No. of Strips
Item 2664	12 × 9	16	144
Item 2665	12 × 9	32	288

4. The 'King Size' member of the S.G. Stock-book range! Cover Specifications as above with 64 double linen-hinged leaves to ensure that the book lies absolutely flat when open. White leaves with glassine strips and double interleaving. Definitely the top of the range and a luxury stockbook any collector would be proud to own.

	Size (ins)	No. of Pages	No. of Strips
Item 2678	12 × 9	64	576

ACCESSORIES

From Stamp Hinges to Ultra Violet Lamps; from Tweezers and Magnifiers to Colour Keys and Watermark Detectors – Stanley Gibbons accessories are the answer to every collector's requirements.

The range has been completely revised with an improved selection of tweezers and the addition of a drying book and photo mounts for cover and postcard collectors.

The magnifiers have been completely revised to allow a wider variety of choice with each item having been carefully selected for its quality and value for money.

Current details of our superb range are available direct from Stanley Gibbons or your favourite supplier.

**Stanley Gibbons Publications Ltd.,
5 Parkside, Christchurch Road,
Ringwood, Hampshire BH24 3SH**

Telephone 0425 472363

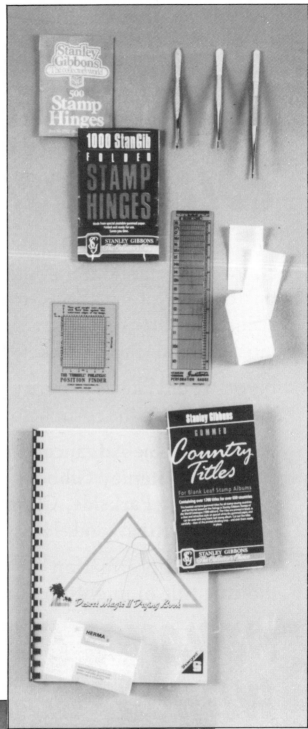

IMPORTANT MESSAGE TO THEMATIC STAMP COLLECTORS!

You know how important it is to have the very latest Stanley Gibbons Thematic Catalogues with their listings of all new issues, up to date information on earlier stamps and of course prices accurately set by experts with their finger on the pulse of the current international stamp market.

If you would like us to notify you of the next edition all you have to do is complete the form below and post it to:

The Advance Information Service,
Stanley Gibbons Publications Ltd.,
5 Parkside, Christchurch Road,
Ringwood, Hampshire BH24 3SH.

For similar information on other SG thematic catalogues please indicate title of interest on the form.

ADVANCE INFORMATION WITHOUT OBLIGATION

To: The Advance Information Service,
    Stanley Gibbons Publications Ltd.,
    5 Parkside, Christchurch Road,
    Ringwood, Hampshire BH24 3SH.

Please notify me of publication dates of new editions

of ....

Name: ....

Address: ....

....

....